LAYING the FOUNDATION

Connecting Algebra 1 to Advanced Placement* Mathematics

A Resource and Strategy Guide

*Pre-AP, AP, and Advanced Placement Program are registered trademarks of the College Entrance Examination Board, which was not involved in the production of and does not endorse this product.

Published by
Advanced Placement Strategies, Inc.
4311 Oak Lawn Avenue, Suite 620
Dallas, Texas 75219
www.apstrategies.com

Acknowledgements

Funding for the *Laying the Foundation*® series was provided through a grant from the O'Donnell Foundation.

Advanced Placement Strategies, Inc. gratefully acknowledges the tireless efforts of the following educators who were responsible for the writing and editing of the *Laying the Foundation*® series.

Brenda Bradford
Pre-Calculus Guide Editor
Dallas Independent School District
Dallas, TX

Sharon Morgan
Algebra 1 Guide Editor
J.L. Long Middle School
Dallas, TX

Tammy Brown
Geometry Guide Co-Editor
Northwest High School
Justin, TX

Scott Pass
Geometry Guide Co-Editor
Westlake High School
Austin, TX

Donna Enochs
Middle Grades Guide Co-Editor
Taylor Middle School
Taylor, TX

Dixie Ross
Series Editor
Pflugerville High School
Austin, TX

Michael Legacy
Statistics Content Editor
Greenhill School
Addison, TX

Wanda Savage
Assessment Editor
Klein Forest High School
Houston, TX

Carol Lindell
Middle Grades Guide Co-Editor
Taylor Independent School District
Taylor, TX

Debbie Trahan
Algebra 2 Guide Editor
Mayde Creek High School
Houston, TX

Stacey McMullen
Contributing Editor
Advanced Placement Strategies, Inc.
Dallas, TX

The production of the guides would not have been possible without the assistance of:

Sonya Pullen
Graphic Specialist
Advanced Placement Strategies, Inc.
Dallas, TX

Stephanie Turner
Production Assistant
Colleyville Heritage High School
Colleyville, TX

Advanced Placement Strategies, Inc. would also like to thank the following educators for their generous submissions of lessons and activities and their assistance in reviewing and editing the series.

Diane Butler
St. Stephen's Episcopal School
Austin, TX

Kathy Fritz
Plano West Senior High School
Plano, TX

Ray Cannon
Baylor University
Waco, TX

Marcia Hilsabeck
Round Rock High School
Round Rock, TX

Richard Cowles
McCallum High School
Austin, TX

Diann Resnick
Bellaire High School
Houston, TX

Dora Daniluk
Mayde Creek High School
Houston, TX

David Rogers
Taylor High School
Taylor, TX

Kathy Duren
St. Stephen's Episcopal School
Austin, TX

Candace Smalley
Advanced Placement Strategies, Inc.
Dallas, TX

Carolyn Foster
Advanced Placement Strategies, Inc.
Dallas, TX

Nancy Stephenson
Clements High School
Sugar Land, TX

Table of Contents

Assessment

Introduction to the Laying the Foundation Series

The premise of the *Laying the Foundation* series is that we can prepare more students to be more successful in Advanced Placement courses by beginning their preparation early through a well-designed and focused Pre-AP program. Each guide is designed to help you connect what you are currently teaching in your mathematics classes to the skills, concepts and assessment strategies that will help your students to be successful in Advanced Placement (AP) mathematics classes and other advanced coursework.

As the committee of math teachers came together to begin work on these guides, the theme of "CONNECTIONS" kept coming up again and again:

> We wanted to help teachers see that what they are teaching in their math classes is strongly connected to the material and skills necessary for success in AP math classes.

> We wanted to insure that math lessons are designed in such a way that the connections between multiple representations (verbal, algebraic, numerical, graphical, physical) are obvious to both students and teachers.

> We wanted to help teachers to connect with one another in order to better align their curriculum horizontally and vertically.

> We wanted to connect many more students, especially those in groups that have been traditionally underrepresented, to the opportunity to take Advanced Placement math courses.

Pre-AP is not so much a particular curriculum as it is a philosophy and way of teaching. The list of topics covered in a Pre-AP mathematics program looks much like the topics that are covered in a "normal" mathematics sequence. What differs is the sophistication of the response we ask of students, the rigor of the work we require, and the global connections that reach far beyond the boundaries of what is done in our textbooks. The greatest difference is the strong expectation that all of the students in a Pre-AP program are preparing for Advanced Placement classes in calculus and/or statistics.

We hope that you will use these guides to help you better define and refine your Pre-AP math program, both in your own classroom and in your school district. The guides can be used by individual teachers or by groups of teachers who have a common goal of preparing more students for further study in mathematics. Someone once told me, "If you don't know where you are going, you probably won't get there." This guide is meant to help you not only to clarify the destination, but to provide you with the strategies and tools that you will need, both along the way and when you arrive at your ultimate destination. The journey will still be difficult at times and not all students will choose to travel this particular path. For those teachers and students who are willing to work hard and commit to AP as their destination, we hope that this guide will be of help.

Dixie Ross

Introduction to Connecting
Algebra 1 to AP Mathematics

Algebra 1 is the Gatekeeper to Advanced Placement mathematics. In the past, Algebra I was a rite of passage that allowed some students the privilege of continuing their study of mathematics. Now, it should be considered a student's right to have an algebra class that will prepare them adequately for whatever subsequent courses they wish to take. It has been the formidable barrier which prevented students from ever considering taking an AP math course. Algebra I should be a gate swinging open to welcome and encompass as many students as possible.

Three very specific responsibilities fall on the shoulders of a Pre-AP Algebra I teacher. The first is to do everything in the teacher's power to ensure that this class is accessible to and understandable by all. The second is to teach in such a manner that a deep, rigorous understanding of algebra is engrained in the mind, heart, and soul of students. The last is to make the class a positive environment where the learning of mathematics is a joyful experience.

The purpose of this guide is to help us open wide the door to Advanced Placement by connecting Pre-AP Algebra I to both AP Statistics and AP Calculus and by providing additional strategies and tools to make those connections. What makes a class "Pre-AP" is much more than the curriculum. We make our classes "Pre-AP" by the way we teach, the level of response that we require from our students, and the way we assess what we've taught. We make our classes Pre-AP by providing multiple experiences with a topic, knowing that the more connections that a student can make, the more likely the student is to know, remember, and own that mathematics. We make our classes Pre-AP by knowing not only what mathematics our students have learned in the past, but by also knowing how they will use the math they are learning today in the AP classes they will take in the future. A Pre-AP class is marked by the frequent references to "When you take calculus you'll use this to …" or "When you take statistics…". Our classes become Pre-AP when we make the taking of AP classes an expectation and a probability, not a maybe.

This guide is not intended to provide you an algebra curriculum. It does not include many necessary lessons which are well represented in our current textbooks and curricula. It is intended to give you additional resources for topics that are specifically tied to Advanced Placement courses. Some of the lessons in this book are discovery lessons, written with the idea that the more students can figure out about mathematics by themselves, the more they will remember. Some are lessons that start with situations based on real world situations or actual data. Many are lessons that weave several topics together. Knowing that a topic should not be taught, tested, and then discarded, some of these lessons can be used as review weeks after the concept has been covered.

Algebra I should not be the point that breaks students, but the one that strengthens, inspires and conditions them for future learning. Giving students lessons where they can explore mathematics in depth and work in learning groups with their peers, builds an excitement about mathematics and a confidence in their abilities. As my own students have worked through the lessons in this guide, it has been a joy to listen to them discuss the many thought provoking questions and their varied and creative responses. The mathematics that they excitedly, sometimes even heatedly, debate together is the mathematics that they will remember.

We can help our students to develop positive attitudes about mathematics and good study skills, in addition to a firm grasp of concepts, skills, and knowledge of algebra. By doing this, those of us who teach Pre-AP Algebra I can change our role from the gatekeeper who bars the door to one who welcomes, nurtures, and dramatically increases the probability that our students will be well prepared for and eager to take an AP mathematics class.

Sharon Morgan

Introduction to Concepts
and Skills Progression Chart

Part of having a successful Pre-AP program is for teachers to have awareness of what students have done prior to a particular class and what they will be expected to do in subsequent classes. Teachers have a responsibility to build on student's knowledge and to prepare them for what will be coming next. In the *Skills and Concepts Progression Chart* that you will find on the next few pages, teachers can see how a particular concept or skill is developed over a period of years.

As you examine each category, you should note the increasing level of sophistication that is required of students. You can also see how important it is that all teachers address these topics. Leaving out one link in the chain can seriously undermine the strength of the program. If there is some topic with which you are unfamiliar, you might find it addressed in more detail in the *Connecting to AP Mathematics* section of this guide. You will also see many of these topics addressed in the lessons that make up the nucleus of this guide.

A Vertical Team Activity: Examining a Strand

Choose another skill or concept not covered in the chart and have teachers write up one or two examples of how they address it in their particular classes. Post them on the wall in order.

Discuss these questions as a group:

1. Is there agreement amongst teachers of the same level/courses as to the level of sophistication required of the student?

2. Examining the concept/skill as it progresses across the grade levels, is there an increase in the level of expectations?

3. Are we building toward some clear objective?

4. Do we effectively reinforce students' previous learning as it pertains to this topic?

Possible Skills/Concepts for discussion: solving equations, unit multipliers, inverses, volume

Connecting Algebra 1 to Advanced Placement Mathematics
A Resource and Strategy Guide

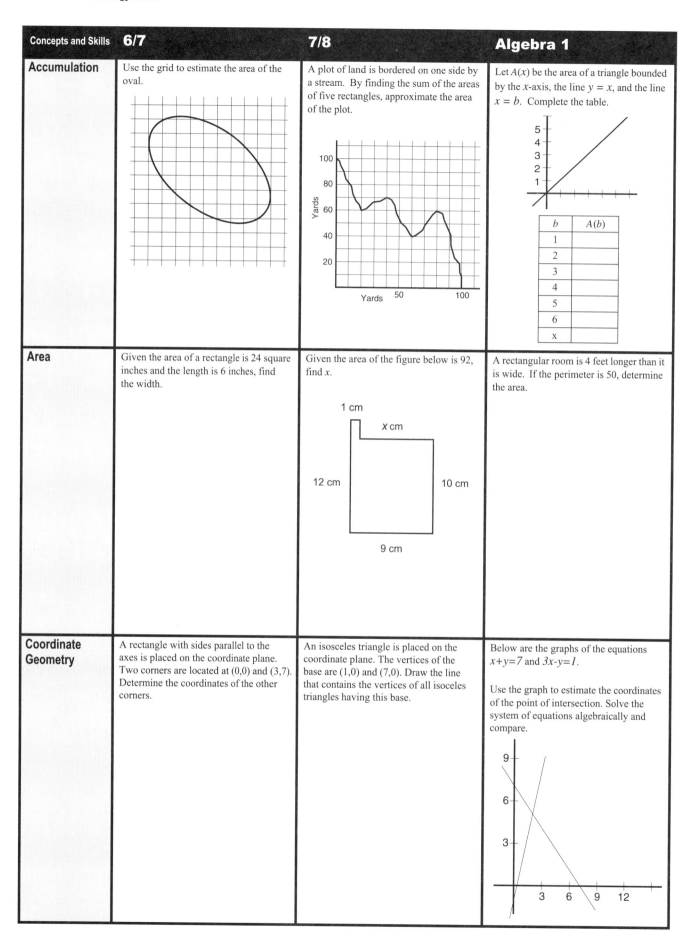

Concepts and Skills	6/7	7/8	Algebra 1
Accumulation	Use the grid to estimate the area of the oval.	A plot of land is bordered on one side by a stream. By finding the sum of the areas of five rectangles, approximate the area of the plot.	Let $A(x)$ be the area of a triangle bounded by the x-axis, the line $y = x$, and the line $x = b$. Complete the table.
Area	Given the area of a rectangle is 24 square inches and the length is 6 inches, find the width.	Given the area of the figure below is 92, find x.	A rectangular room is 4 feet longer than it is wide. If the perimeter is 50, determine the area.
Coordinate Geometry	A rectangle with sides parallel to the axes is placed on the coordinate plane. Two corners are located at (0,0) and (3,7). Determine the coordinates of the other corners.	An isosceles triangle is placed on the coordinate plane. The vertices of the base are (1,0) and (7,0). Draw the line that contains the vertices of all isoceles triangles having this base.	Below are the graphs of the equations $x+y=7$ and $3x-y=1$. Use the graph to estimate the coordinates of the point of intersection. Solve the system of equations algebraically and compare.

In the Accumulation/Algebra 1 cell, the table:

b	$A(b)$
1	
2	
3	
4	
5	
6	
x	

Geometry	Algebra 2	Pre-Calculus
Consider the region bounded by $y = \sqrt{x}$ and the x-axis between $x = 1$ and $x = 5$. Use four trapezoids to approximate the area of the region.	Consider the region bounded by the x-axis, y-axis, $y = x^2 + 1$, and $x = 4$. Using four subdivisions, approximate the area of the region using: a) inscribed rectangles b) circumscribed rectangles c) trapezoids Is there a mathematical relationship between your answers to parts a), b), and c)?	A speeding car brakes. The following chart indicates the velocity in feet per second for every 2 seconds. Find an upper and lower estimate of the distance the car traveled after braking. | Time (seconds)	0	2	4	6
---	---	---	---	---
Velocity (ft/sec)	110	90	50	0	
Determine the area, in terms of x of a rectangle inscribed in the semi-circle shown below, so that two of its vertices lie on the x-axis and the other two vertices lie on the semicircle.	A person has 340 yards of fencing for enclosing two separate fields, one of which is to be a rectangle twice as long as it is wide, and the other is to be a square. Express the total area enclosed by the two fields as a function of x, the length of a side of the square.	The base of a rectangular box is enclosed between the x-axis and $f(x) = \cos x$. Find the volume of the box in terms of x if the height is 5.
Below is a parallelogram with vertices O (0,0), A (a,b), B (?,?), and C (c,0). Determine the coordinates of B. Determine the coordinates of the midpoints of $\overline{OB}$ and $\overline{OC}$. What conclusion can you draw about diagonals of a parallelogram?	Find an expression for the distance between A (0,0) and P (x,y) and an expression for the distance between B (12,0) and P (x,y). Write an equation if the distance between A and P is twice the distance between B and P. Simplify the equation and show the points lie on a circle.	Let a triangle in the first quadrant be bounded by the x-axis, y-axis, and a line passing through the point (3,2). Express the area of the triangle in terms of x, the x-intercept of the line.

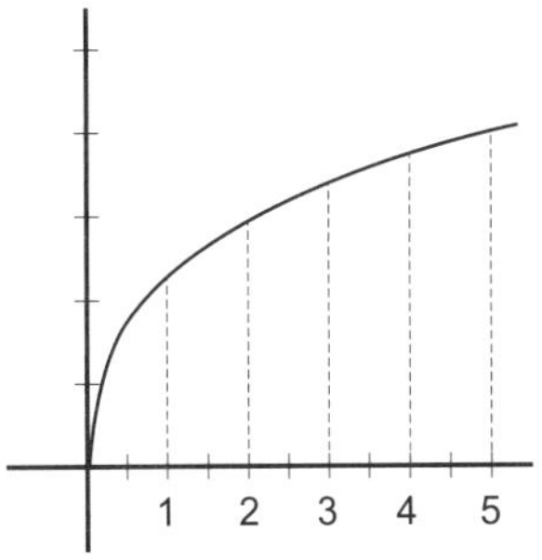

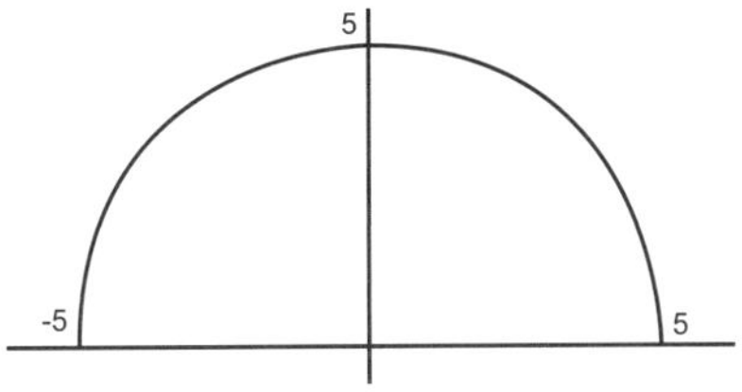

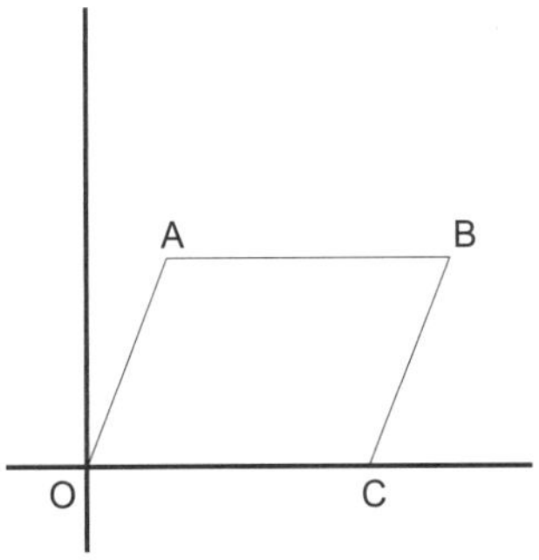

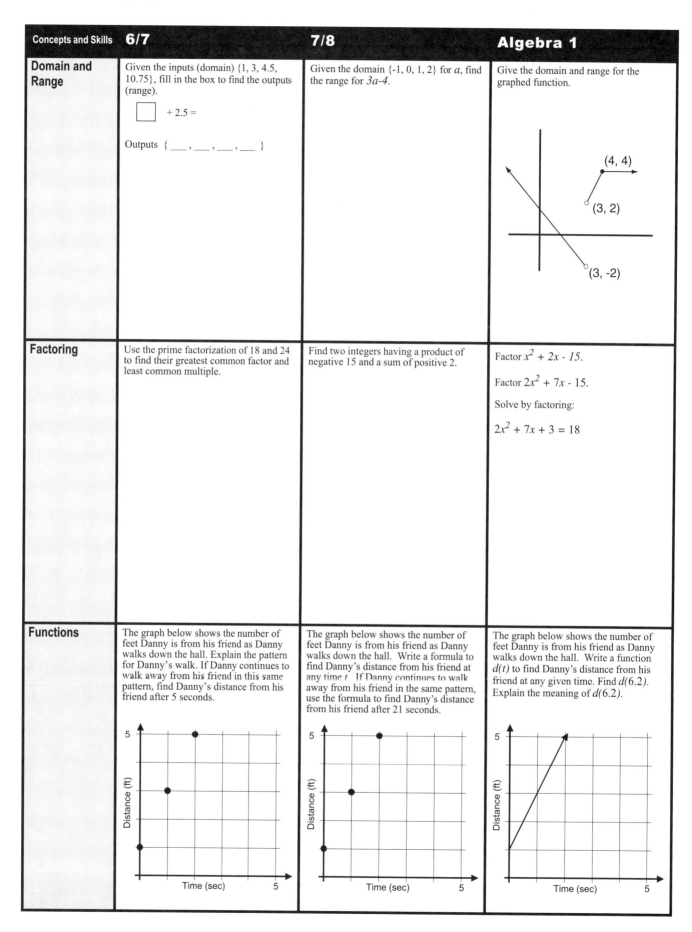

Concepts and Skills	6/7	7/8	Algebra 1
Domain and Range	Given the inputs (domain) {1, 3, 4.5, 10.75}, fill in the box to find the outputs (range). □ + 2.5 = Outputs { ___ , ___ , ___ , ___ }	Given the domain {-1, 0, 1, 2} for a, find the range for $3a-4$.	Give the domain and range for the graphed function. (4, 4) (3, 2) (3, -2)
Factoring	Use the prime factorization of 18 and 24 to find their greatest common factor and least common multiple.	Find two integers having a product of negative 15 and a sum of positive 2.	Factor $x^2 + 2x - 15$. Factor $2x^2 + 7x - 15$. Solve by factoring: $2x^2 + 7x + 3 = 18$
Functions	The graph below shows the number of feet Danny is from his friend as Danny walks down the hall. Explain the pattern for Danny's walk. If Danny continues to walk away from his friend in this same pattern, find Danny's distance from his friend after 5 seconds.	The graph below shows the number of feet Danny is from his friend as Danny walks down the hall. Write a formula to find Danny's distance from his friend at any time t. If Danny continues to walk away from his friend in the same pattern, use the formula to find Danny's distance from his friend after 21 seconds.	The graph below shows the number of feet Danny is from his friend as Danny walks down the hall. Write a function $d(t)$ to find Danny's distance from his friend at any given time. Find $d(6.2)$. Explain the meaning of $d(6.2)$.

Geometry	Algebra 2	Pre-Calculus
A piece of cardboard is to be made into a box by cutting out a square x inches wide on each corner and folding up the edges. Find the feasible domain for x. 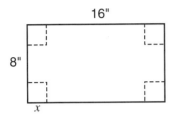	Give the domain and range for $$f(x) = \sqrt{4x^2 - 9} + 2$$	Find the domain and range for $$f(x) = \frac{\ln(2x^3 + e)}{2}$$
The area of a modern art painting is 15 square inches. Find the dimensions of the painting if the height is 7 inches more than twice the width. 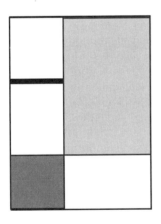	Solve by factoring: $$2e^{2x} + 7e^x + 3 = 18$$	Solve by factoring: $$2e^{2\sin x} + 7e^{\sin x} + 3 = 18$$
Write a function $f(x)$ to find the surface area of the box below in terms of x. Find the value for x if $f(x) = 362$. Explain the meaning of your answer. Be sure to include units. 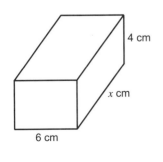	A clown throws a ball straight up into the air. The height of the ball at a given time after leaving the clown's hand is shown in the table below.	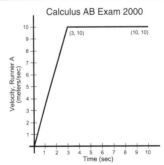

Geometry box diagram: 16", 8", x

Geometry box labels: 4 cm, x cm, 6 cm

Algebra 2 table:

Time (seconds)	Height (meters)
0.2	2.804
0.5	4.775
1.05	4.975

Write a quadratic equation $h(t)$ for the height of the ball at any given time.

Find $h(0)$ and explain the meaning of this answer in the context of this problem.

Pre-Calculus (Runner graph): Calculus AB Exam 2000, (3, 10), (10, 10), Velocity, Runner A (meters/sec), Time (sec)

Two runners (A and B) run on a straight track for $0 \le t \le 10$ seconds. The graph above shows the velocity of Runner A. The velocity, in meters/second, of Runner B is given by the function v defined by
$$v(t) = \frac{24t}{2t + 3}$$
Find the velocity of Runner A and the velocity of Runner B at time $t = 2$ seconds. Indicate units of measure.

Concepts and Skills	6/7	7/8	Algebra 1
Limits	A plant is growing in the following pattern. If the pattern of growth continues, what is the maximum height of the plant? Month | Height (ft.) 1 | 2 2 | 3 3 | 3.5 4 | 3.75 5 | 3.875 6 | 3.9375	$\frac{1}{2} + \frac{1}{4} =$ $\frac{1}{2} + \frac{1}{4} + \frac{1}{8} =$ $\frac{1}{2} + \frac{1}{4} + \frac{1}{8} + \frac{1}{16} =$ $\frac{1}{2} + \frac{1}{4} + \frac{1}{8} + \frac{1}{16} + \frac{1}{32} =$ Based on the pattern, can you predict the sum of the first 10 terms?	$f(x) = \dfrac{3x - 1}{x + 1}$ $f(10) =$ $f(100) =$ $f(1000) =$ As x gets large, $f(x)$ approaches what number?
Optimization	Given three pieces of string each 12 inches long, form a triangle, square, and circle. Which figure has the maximum area?	Given a rectangle with a perimeter of 24 inches, determine the dimensions that maximize the area.	The height of a thrown ball is given by $h(t) = -16t^2 + 48t$. At what time does the ball reach its maximum height?
Transformations	Plot the points (1,1), (4,1), (5,3) on a coordinate plane and connect the points to form a triangle. Using patty paper, translate the triangle eight units to the left. Write the coordinates of the vertices for the translated triangle.	Plot the points (1,1), (4,1), (5,3) on a coordinate plane and connect the points to form a triangle. Write a formula that will translate the point (x, y) on the triangle eight units to the left.	Translate the line, $y = 2x$ eight units to the left. Write the function for the translated line in slope-intercept form. How does the equation $y = 2(x+8)$ relate to the function you wrote and the translation you performed?

Geometry	Algebra 2	Pre-Calculus
A regular n-gon is inscribed inside a circle with a radius of 10. As n increases, the perimeter must be less than _____ ?	$f(x) = \dfrac{3x-1}{x+1}$ <table><tr><td>x</td><td>$f(x)$</td></tr><tr><td>-.5</td><td></td></tr><tr><td>-.7</td><td></td></tr><tr><td>-.9</td><td></td></tr></table> Describe what is happening to the value of the function as x gets closer to -1.	$\displaystyle\lim_{x \to -1} \frac{3x-1}{x+1}$ $\displaystyle\lim_{x \to \infty} \frac{3x-1}{x+1}$
Squares are cut from the corners of an 8.5 inch by 11 inch paper and sides are folded to make an open-topped box. How much should be cut from each corner to produce a box of maximum volume?	Given a box with a square base and a volume of 48 cubic inches, find the dimensions that minimize the surface area.	A rectangle is inscribed in an ellipse centered at the origin with axes of lengths 8 and 6. Find the maximum area of the rectangle.
Translate the circle $x^2 + y^2 = 25$ eight units to the left. Write the equation for the translated circle.	Given the graph of the function $f(x)$: Graph the transformation $f(x+8)$. Write piecewise functions for $f(x)$ and $f(x+8)$.	Write in function notation the equation for the the graph of $f(x) = e^x$ translated eight units to the left. Simplify the equation so that it is expressed in terms of $f(x)$.

Concepts and Skills	6/7	7/8	Algebra 1
Rate of Change	Which of the following are examples of rates? a) miles you have driven b) the number of elephants you capture in 3 video games c) how many people walk in a park per day d) glasses of milk you drink e) gallons of ice cream	The water level in a tank is dropping at the rate of 3 inches every 4 minutes. At what rate is the water level dropping in feet per hour?	Which function or functions have a constant rate of change?

For the Algebra 1 Rate of Change cell:

A

x	f(x)
1	1
2	3
4	5
8	7

B

x	g(x)
1	3
2	3
4	3
8	3

C

x	h(x)
3	2
6	6
12	14
21	26

D

x	j(x)
3	0
6	1
9	4
12	9

Concepts and Skills	6/7	7/8	Algebra 1
Sequences and Series	What is the sum of the missing terms? 78, 38, 18, 8, ___ , ___	What is the 7th term of the sequence? $x+6, x-5, x+4, ...$	What is the sum of the infinite series? $8 + 4 + 2 + 1 + ...$
Probability	You wish to toss two coins. List the possible outcomes in the sample space. Find the probability that two tails will occur.	Toss a die and a coin. a) Find the probability that a head and four will occur. b) Find the probability that a tail or a three will occur.	In a random sample of 100 people, 63 own computers, 38 own DVD players, and 15 own both. Represent the data in a Venn diagram. a) Find the probability that a randomly selected person owns a DVD but not a computer. b) Find the probability that a randomly selected person owns neither a DVD player nor a computer.

Geometry	Algebra 2	Pre-Calculus
Water is pouring in at the same rate in all 3 containers. In which of the containers is the water level at the dark line rising the fastest? In which of the containers is the water level at the dotted line rising fastest? 	What is the letter of the point on the graph where the rate of change is the fastest? 	For $s(t) = 3t^2 + t - 2$, find the average rate of change for $s(t)$ for [-1,3].
If the pattern below is continued, how many dots will be in the sixth figure? 	1, 3, 6, 10, 15, ..., a_n Write a formula for a_n.	$$\frac{\sin x}{x} + \frac{\sin 2x}{x} + \frac{\sin 3x}{x} + \frac{\sin 4x}{x}$$ If x is a very, very small number, what is the approximate sum of the series?
A circle is inscribed inside a square with a side length of 5 units. What is the probability that a randomly selected point will be in the square but outside of the circle?	How many different tickets are possible in the Texas Lotto if a player may select six different numbers from the 55 available? Based on your answer, what is the probability that a particular six number combination will be selected for the Lotto winner?	A team is to play five games over the next week. The probability that they win any one game is .75. Assuming that the games are independent, use the binomial theorem to determine the probability that the team will win exactly four of the five games.

Concepts and Skills	6/7	7/8	Algebra 1
Statistics and Graphical Displays of Data	The number of home runs Babe Ruth hit in his 15 years with the New York Yankees is listed below. {54, 59, 49, 46, 35, 41, 41, 34, 25, 46, 22, 47, 60, 54, 46} Use the data to construct a stem-and-leaf plot and then describe its distribution.	Each of twenty-two vanilla ice cream bars was evaluated for calorie content. The data below lists the calories for each of the twenty-two bars. 342, 377, 319, 353, 295, 234, 294, 286, 377, 182, 310, 439, 111, 201, 182, 197, 209, 147, 190, 151, 131, 151 Construct a boxplot for the data. What are the values of the upper and lower quartiles and how can you use those statistics to describe the calories in a typical ice cream bar?	The table below represents the number of hours spent on safety training (x) and the number of work-hours lost due to accidents (y) at a large company. <table><tr><th>x</th><th>y</th></tr><tr><td>10</td><td>82</td></tr><tr><td>20</td><td>66</td></tr><tr><td>30</td><td>71</td></tr><tr><td>45</td><td>53</td></tr><tr><td>50</td><td>34</td></tr><tr><td>65</td><td>12</td></tr><tr><td>80</td><td>15</td></tr></table> Draw a scatterplot and a trend line for this data. Write the equation for your trend line.
Statistics and Inferences from Data	The number of home runs Roger Maris hit in his 10 years in the American League is listed below. {8, 13, 23, 33, 61, 14, 26, 39, 16, 28} The number of home runs Babe Ruth hit in his 15 years with the New York Yankees is listed below. {54, 59, 49, 46, 35, 41, 41, 34, 25, 46, 22, 47, 60, 54, 46} Use the Roger Maris data and the Babe Ruth data to construct a back-to-back stem plot. Based on this data, who do you think was the better home run hitter? Justify your answer.	Below is data relating the age (in years) and height (in feet) of a fast-growing tree. <table><tr><th>Age</th><th>Height</th></tr><tr><td>1</td><td>4.5</td></tr><tr><td>2</td><td>5.8</td></tr><tr><td>3</td><td>8.4</td></tr><tr><td>4</td><td>10.4</td></tr><tr><td>5</td><td>12.9</td></tr><tr><td>6</td><td>15.0</td></tr></table> Draw a scatterplot of the data. Based on your scatterplot, predict the height of a 7 year-old tree and a 40 year-old tree. Which prediction would you expect to be more accurate? Support your decision.	Using the trend line found above, interpret the meaning of the slope and y-intercept in the context of this situation.

Geometry	Algebra 2	Pre-Calculus
Collect data to determine the relationship between the diameter and circumference of circular objects. Define the variables to be measured in inches. Draw a scatterplot of the data and write the equation of a trend line.	A car dealership keeps a weekly record of the number of TV ads (x) and the number of cars (y) sold each week.	A forest manager has been keeping a record of the number of acres that have been destroyed by an insect.

Algebra 2 table:

x	y
8	9
20	37
7	7
14	27
25	39
16	31
28	40
18	34
11	21
10	18

Draw the scatterplot. Define a piecewise linear function that models this data.

Pre-Calculus table:

Year	Acres
1997	56,700
1998	203,600
1999	816,000
2000	2,543,500

Determine which model (logarithmic, exponential, quadratic, power) best represents the data. Justify your answer.

Geometry: If the measurements above had been made in centimeters instead of inches (2.54 cm = 1 in), explain how the appearance of the scatterplot would change. What would be the slope of the trend line for this data? Interpret the slope in the context of the problem.

Algebra 2: At the Pizza By The Yard Restaurant, the prices for pepperoni pizza are determined by the size of the pizza.

Diameter	Price
10	5.00
12	7.25
14	10.00
18	16.00
24	28.00
28	39.00

The manager has created a new "football team" size pizza with a 36 inch diameter. He would like to charge $58.00 for this pizza. Is the manager overcharging or undercharging for this pizza? Justify your answer.

Pre-Calculus: Listed below are the lengths (in inches) and weights (in pounds) of alligators captured in Florida.

Length	Weight
94	130
147	640
86	80
63	33
69	36
128	366
82	80
88	70
74	54
90	106
68	36
114	197
78	57

Create a model to predict weight based on the alligator's length. Predict the weight of a 100 inch alligator.

Connecting to AP Mathematics

Pre-AP teachers should regularly connect the material they are teaching in their classes to the concepts and themes that underlie the study of calculus and statistics. It can be difficult to do so, however, if the teacher is unfamiliar with the content of those AP courses. In this section, we provide a brief overview of the most important concepts along with examples of how they can be introduced and developed in the Pre-AP classroom. By regularly making these connections, Pre-AP teachers will build in their students an intuitive understanding that can then be developed more formally and rigorously in the AP course.

A Vertical Team Activity:
Connecting to AP Mathematics

Choose one or two concepts from this section and have teachers read and study the examples provided. Then have teachers brainstorm other ways they can introduce and develop the concept in their own classroom. Have them share their ideas with the larger group.

	Families of Curves	Transformations	Vocabulary
Algebra 1	Linear Quadratic Exponential Piecewise	Vertical Shifts $y = f(x) + d$ $y = f(x) - d$ Reflection $y = -f(x)$ Vertical Stretch $y = a\,f(x)$ $a > 1$ $0 < a < 1$	domain and range constant identity x-intercepts (roots, zeroes) y-intercepts increasing/decreasing positive/negative maximum/minimum symmetry vertex concave up/concave down end behavior horizontal asymptote growth and decay
Algebra 2	All of the above Square Root Rational Logarithmic Conic Sections	All of the above Horizontal Shifts $y = f(x + c)$ $y = f(x - c)$	All of the above inverse function vertical asymptote slant asymptotes continuity
Pre-Calculus	All of the above Greatest Integer Function Signum Polynomial Trigonometric Inverse Trigonometric Parametric	All of the above Reflections $y = f(-x)$ $y = |f(x)|$ $y = f(|x|)$ Horizontal Stretch $y = f(bx)$ $b > 1$ $0 < b < 1$	All of the above absolute vs. relative extrema odd function even function amplitude frequency

Connecting to AP Calculus: Analysis of Functions

In AP Calculus, students use first and second derivatives to determine the intervals on which functions are increasing/decreasing and concave up/concave down, as well as to locate relative extrema, absolute extrema and points of inflection.

Students in Pre-AP mathematics courses can be introduced to some of the vocabulary used to describe the behavior of functions as they learn about the families of functions and how they are affected by various transformations. Students should be exposed to and expected to work with multiple representations of functions (verbal, physical, graphical, algebraic). The chart on the adjacent page offers a suggested sequence for the introduction of the relevant vocabulary.

Example:

The function $f(x) = x^2 - 8x + 15$ has a minimum value at the point $(4, -1)$. What transformations would relocate the minimum value to the point $(4, -5)$? Verify your answers by graphing.

Answer:

$f(x) - 4$, which would give us the new function $g(x) = x^2 - 8x + 11$ or $5 \cdot f(x)$, which would give us the new function $g(x) = 5x^2 - 40x + 55$.

Example:

The graph of the velocity $v(t)$, in ft/sec, of a car traveling on a straight road, for $0 \le t \le 50$, is shown below. A table of values for $v(t)$, at 5 second intervals of time t, is shown to the right of the graph. For what time intervals is the velocity of the car increasing?

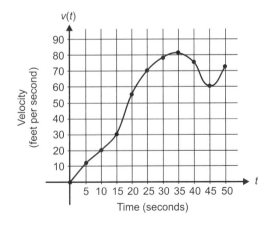

t (seconds)	$v(t)$ (feet per second)
0	0
5	12
10	20
15	30
20	55
25	70
30	78
35	81
40	75
45	60
50	72

Answer:

The velocity of the car is increasing for time intervals $0 < t < 35$ and $45 < t < 50$.

Example:

Given the function $f(x) = 2x\, e^{(2x)}$, what happens as x approaches negative infinity? What happens as x approaches positive infinity? Support your answer with both a graph and a table of values.

Answer:

As x approaches negative infinity, $f(x)$ is getting closer and closer to zero. As x approaches positive infinity, the function is increasing without bound. In other words, the values of f are approaching positive infinity.

Connecting to AP Calculus: Limits

The concept of limit underlies the definitions of both the derivative and the definite integral in AP Calculus. Students in Pre-AP mathematics courses can investigate the concept of limit by examining patterns, graphs and function behavior.

Example:

Fill in the next five terms of the sequence. Convert each fraction into a decimal value. What value are the terms of the sequence approaching?

$$\frac{1}{2}, \frac{2}{3}, \frac{3}{4}, \frac{4}{5}, \underline{\quad}, \underline{\quad}, \underline{\quad}, \underline{\quad}, \underline{\quad}, \cdots\cdots$$

Answer:

The terms of the sequence are approaching the value of one.

Example:

As the number of sides, n, of a polygon inscribed in a circle of radius 2 increases, the area of the polygon is approaching what value?

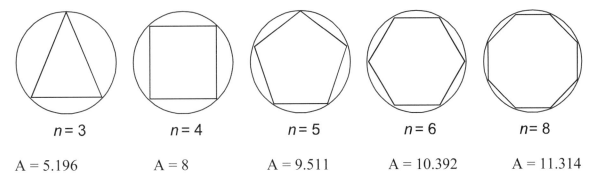

$n = 3$	$n = 4$	$n = 5$	$n = 6$	$n = 8$
A = 5.196	A = 8	A = 9.511	A = 10.392	A = 11.314

Answer:

The area of the polygon is approaching the area of the circle, which is 4π or ≈ 12.566.

Example:

Let $f(x) = \dfrac{3x - 2}{2x + 1}$

As x increases in value, $f(x)$ is approaching what number? Support your answer with both a table of values and a graph.

Answer:

$f(x)$ is approaching $\dfrac{3}{2}$.

Connecting to AP Calculus: Optimization

In AP Calculus, students use derivatives to locate maximum and minimum values of functions.

Students in Pre-AP mathematics courses can explore this concept through trial and error, tables of values, graphs, and technology.

Example:

Find the dimensions of a right circular cylinder that has a volume of $108\pi \; cm^3$ and the least possible surface area.

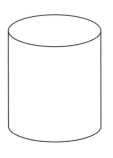

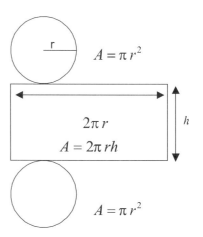

Radius (cm)	Surface Area (cm²)
.5	1358.7
1.0	684.87
1.5	466.53
2.0	364.42
2.5	310.7
3.0	282.74
3.5	270.85
4.0	270.18
4.5	278.03
5.0	292.8

$$V = \pi r^2 h$$

$$108\pi = \pi r^2 h$$

$$\frac{108\pi}{\pi r^2} = \frac{\pi r^2 h}{\pi r^2}$$

$$\frac{108}{r^2} = h$$

$$S = 2\pi rh + 2\pi r^2$$

$$S = 2\pi r\left(\frac{108}{r^2}\right) + 2\pi r^2$$

$$S = \frac{216\pi}{r} + 2\pi r^2$$

Answer:

Based upon the values in the table, the minimum surface area of $270.18\ \text{cm}^2$ occurs with radius ≈ 4.0 cm and height ≈ 6.75 cm. Based on the graph, the minimum surface area of approximately $269.296\ \text{cm}^2$ occurs with radius ≈ 3.780 cm and height ≈ 7.559 cm.

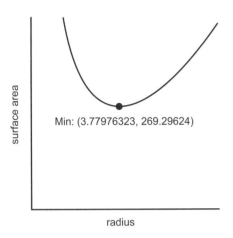

Example:

James wants to fence a rectangular pen for his puppy. He has 12 yards of fencing material. James will use the side of his garage as one side of his pen. Find the dimensions of the rectangular pen with the largest area.

w (yd)	l (yd)	Area (yd^2)
0	12	0
1	10	10
2	8	16
3	6	18
4	4	16
5	2	10
6	0	0

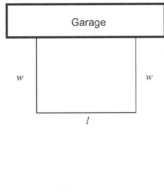

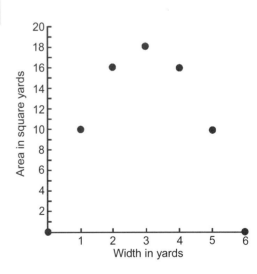

Answer:

A pen with a length of 6 yards and a width of 3 yards would have the maximum area of 18 square yards.

Connecting to AP Calculus: Rate of Change

In AP Calculus, students use the derivative to find the instantaneous rate of change of a function at a particular point. The derivative also finds the slope of a line tangent to a function at a particular point, so it is important that students understand how rate of change is connected to slope.

Students in Pre-AP mathematics courses can explore this concept by finding an average rate of change over a small interval or by approximating an instantaneous rate of change using the slopes of secant lines and tangent lines respectively.

Example:

The table below shows the population of coho salmon in Lake Michigan since their introduction into the lake in 1965.

Year	65	70	72	75	78	80	83	86	90
Population (thousands)	25	45	59	83	122	151	219	315	500

Compare the rate of population growth from 1965 to 1975 with that from 1980 to 1990.

Answer:

The rate of growth from 1965 to 1975 is an average of 5,800 salmon per year. From 1980 to 1990, the average growth rate is 34,900 salmon per year. The growth rate has increased by a factor slightly larger than six.

Example:

Eliza walked from her home to the bus stop at a constant rate of 3 miles per hour for 10 minutes. When she realized that she was late, she doubled her speed for 5 minutes. She arrived at the bus stop and realized that she had missed the bus so she had to sit there and waited for another 15 minutes. Draw a graph showing the distance Eliza has traveled as a function of time.

Answer:

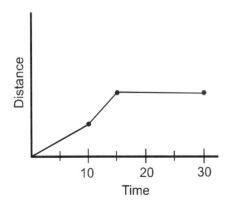

Example:

The graph below shows the amount of water in a reservoir over a 24-hour period of time. At what time (approximately) was the instantaneous rate of flow equal to the average rate of flow from $t = 0$ until $t = 12$?

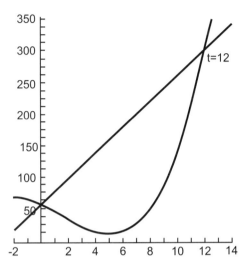

Answer:

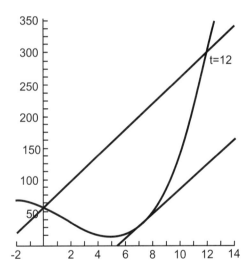

At approximately $t = 7$ hours

Connecting to AP Calculus: Position / Velocity / Acceleration

In AP Calculus, students are given a function that represents either the position, velocity, or acceleration of an object. Using derivatives and integrals, they can then find equations for the other two and answer questions regarding the object's movement, location, direction, distance traveled, etc.

Students in Pre-AP mathematics courses can explore these concepts if they are given graphs or equations for the position, velocity or acceleration of an object and are then asked to answer appropriate questions.

Example:

A bug begins to crawl up a vertical wire at time $t = 0$. The velocity v, in feet per minute, of the bug at time t, $0 < t < 8$, is given by the function whose graph is shown below.

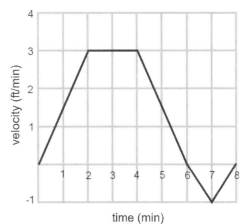

1. At what times is the bug not moving?

2. How far does the bug travel from $t = 2$ until $t = 4$?

3. At what times is the bug traveling at a constant rate?

4. At what times does the bug change directions?

5. What is the bug's acceleration for $0 < t < 2$?

Answers:

1. The bug is not moving when velocity is zero, so $t = 0$, $t = 6$, and $t = 8$.

2. The bug travels 6 feet up the wire.

3. The bug is traveling at a constant rate for $2 < t < 4$.

4. The bug is traveling down the wire when velocity is negative for $6 < t < 8$. The bug changes direction at $t = 6$. For $0 < t < 6$, the bug is moving up the wire because velocity is positive.

5. The bug's acceleration is the rate of change (or slope) of the velocity graph, so $\dfrac{3}{2} \dfrac{\text{ft/min}}{\text{min}}$.

Example:

A particle moves along the x-axis so that its position at time t, $0 \le t \le 5$, is given by $x(t) = t^3 - 6t^2 + 9t - 2$. Its velocity is given by $v(t) = 3t^2 - 12t + 9$ and its acceleration is given by $a(t) = 6t - 12$.

1. Where is the particle located at $t = 0$?

2. At $t = 0$, is the particle moving left or right? Justify your answer.

3. At $t = 0$, is the velocity of the particle increasing or decreasing? Justify your answer.

4. For what values of t, $0 < t < 5$, is the particle moving to the left?

5. What is the total distance traveled by the particle over the given time interval?

Answers:

1. The particle is located on the x-axis at x = ⁻2.

2. The particle is moving to the right because the velocity is positive, v(0)= 9.

3. The velocity of the particle is decreasing because the acceleration is negative, a(0) = ⁻12.

4. The particle is moving to the left when velocity is negative, so $1 < t < 3$.

5. The particle travels 4 units to the right from ⁻2 to 2, then travels 4 units back to ⁻2, then travels 20 units right to 18 for a total distance traveled of 28 units.

Connecting to AP Calculus: Areas and Volumes

In AP Calculus, students use definite integrals to determine the areas and volumes of irregular shapes. They also estimate areas and volumes of such shapes using numerical methods such as a right hand, left hand, trapezoidal or midpoint approximation.

Students in Pre-AP mathematics courses can be introduced to these ideas by finding the area and volumes of shapes enclosed by various equations using geometric formulas or by approximating the values using an appropriate method.

Example:

1. Find the area of the region enclosed by $y = \dfrac{-1}{2}x + 3$, the x-axis and the y-axis.

2. Find the volume of the solid formed by revolving the given region around the y-axis.

Answers:

1. The region is a right triangle with an area of 9 square units.

2. The volume is that of a right circular cone with a height of 3 units and a radius of 6 units, 36π cubic units.

Example:

The teacher should measure and record the volume of a hard boiled egg for each pair of students using the displacement of water in a large graduated cylinder. Give each pair of students an egg and an egg slicer and have them peel and slice their egg. By measuring the radius and height of each "cylindrical" slice and summing the volumes of the slices, they should be able to approximate the volume of the egg. Compare the students' measurements to those of the teacher.

Answers:

Answers will vary.

Example:

A surveyor must approximate the area of the surface of a small lake. She makes 7 measurements across the lake, each 20 feet apart as shown in the figure below. Approximate the area of the surface of the lake by finding the sums of the areas of six trapezoids and two triangles (for the end pieces.) If the lake has an average depth of 11 feet, approximate the volume of water in the lake.

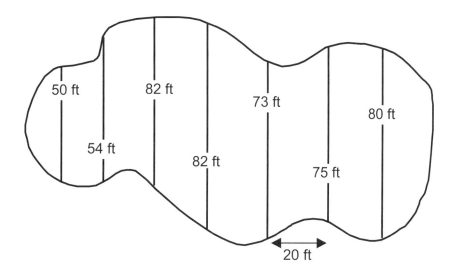

Answers:

The area of the surface of the lake is approximately 9920 square feet. It holds approximately 109,120 cubic feet of water.

$$\frac{1}{2}(50)\cdot 20 + 20\left(\frac{50+54}{2}\right) + 20\left(\frac{54+82}{2}\right) + 20\left(\frac{82+82}{2}\right) + 20\left(\frac{82+73}{2}\right) +$$

$$20\left(\frac{73+75}{2}\right) + 20\left(\frac{75+80}{2}\right) + \frac{1}{2}(80)20 = 9920$$

Connecting to AP Calculus: Accumulation

In AP Calculus, students can approximate the value of a definite integral by finding the sum of the areas of rectangles (or other geometric figures) where the height is the value of the function and the base is measured along the x-axis. In situations where the function is a rate of change, multiplying the rate times the increment of the independent variable should yield the amount of change that has taken place over that interval.

In Pre-AP mathematics classes, students can work with data or graphs and calculate accumulated change using various methods such as right hand, left hand, midpoint or trapezoidal approximations.

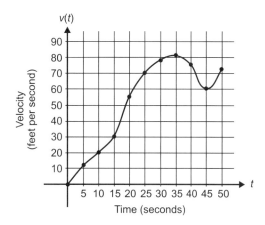

t (seconds)	$v(t)$ (feet per second)
0	0
5	12
10	20
15	30
20	55
25	70
30	78
35	81
40	75
45	60
50	72

Example:

The graph of the velocity $v(t)$, in ft/sec, of a car traveling on a straight road, for $0 \le t \le 50$, is shown above. A table of values for $v(t)$, at 5 second intervals of time t, is shown to the right of the graph.

Using five subintervals of equal length, approximate the distance traveled by the car over the 50-second interval with each of the following methods.

Notice that the velocity is measured along the y-axis and time is measured along the x-axis. Most students are familiar with the relationship distance = rate $\cdot$ time. They need to understand that the velocity is the rate at which the car is traveling. Multiplying velocity times the time interval should give the distance traveled for that particular interval.

Checking the units $\left(\dfrac{\text{feet}}{\text{sec}} \cdot \text{sec} = \text{feet} \right)$ should verify that this approach is correct.

a) right hand approximation

$$10\sec\bullet\left(\frac{20\,ft}{\sec}\right)+10\sec\left(55\,\frac{ft}{\sec}\right)+10\sec\left(78\,\frac{ft}{\sec}\right)+$$

$$10\sec\left(75\,\frac{ft}{\sec}\right)+10\sec\left(72\,\frac{ft}{\sec}\right)=$$

$$200\,ft+550\,ft+780\,ft+750\,ft+720\,ft=3000\,ft$$

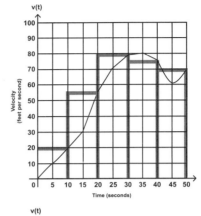

b) left hand approximation

$$10(0)+10(20)+10(55)+$$

$$10(78)+10(75)=2280\,ft$$

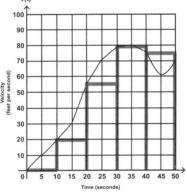

c) midpoint approximation

$$10(12)+10(30)+10(70)+$$

$$10(81)+10(60)=2530\,ft$$

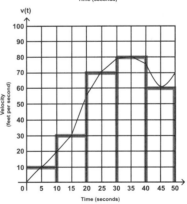

d) trapezoidal approximation

$$10\left(\frac{0+20}{2}\right)+10\left(\frac{20+55}{2}\right)+10\left(\frac{55+78}{2}\right)+$$

$$10\left(\frac{78+75}{2}\right)+10\left(\frac{75+72}{2}\right)=2640\,f$$

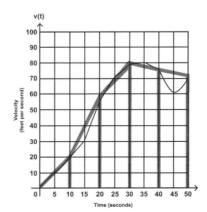

15

Connecting to AP Statistics: Data Gathering and Simulation

Some probabilities are so difficult or time-consuming to calculate that statisticians find it is easier to model the real problem by running experiments that closely resemble the real situation.

To do this, statisticians use a simulation, a procedure in which you set up a model of a chance process (picking three cards from a deck, for example) that closely copies the real situation (selecting three people at random to be part of an experiment). If a random event is simulated **n** times and the outcome of interest occurs in **x** out of those n times, then the <u>estimated</u> probability of the occurrence of that event is **x/n**.

In most cases, simulations are accomplished by using a computer or calculator. The simulation is run thousands of times and the relative frequency of occurrence of the event that is to be estimated is found from the simulation. Students in Pre-AP mathematics courses can explore the notion of simulation by using various physical devices such as coins, number cubes, cards, spinners, random number charts, and calculators. The simulations in Pre-AP classes can be run many times and as the data is pooled, the experimental probability should approach the theoretical probability.

Example:

If a student flipped a fair coin four times with results of HHHH, what is the probability that the fifth flip will result in a tail?

Answer:

The probability is 1/2, since each flip of a coin is independent.

Example:

In a bag of marbles, there are 5 red marbles, 3 blue marbles, and 2 green marbles. If you randomly draw two marbles from the bag, what is the probability that:

1. The first marble drawn is red and the second marble drawn is red if there is replacement?

2. The first marble drawn is red and the second marble drawn is red if there is no replacement?

Answer:

1. $(1/2)(1/2)=1/4$

2. $(1/2)(4/9)=4/18$

Example:

Sara is interested in knowing how likely it is that she can pass a multiple-choice quiz without doing any studying. To answer this question she wants to conduct a simulation for a ten-question quiz, which has 4 choices for each question. Describe how she should accomplish this simulation. Complete 20 trials.

Answer:

Since there are 4 choices, the probability of correctly guessing an answer is 1/4 or 0.25. Sara will use a deck of cards in her simulation. Since each suit is 1/4 of the deck of cards, hearts will represent getting an answer correct and the other suits will represent getting an answer incorrect. Each card will represent a question on the quiz. To model one run of the simulation, shuffle the deck of cards. Pick one card at a time and look to see if it is a heart. Replace the card and shuffle the deck. Pick a card again and look to see if it is a heart. Continue this process until 10 cards are drawn, making sure to replace the card between each draw. Count the number of hearts. If there were three hearts then Sara got three questions correct on the ten-question quiz. Record the results in a table. Label the left column *# of hearts* and the right column *frequency*. This completes one run of the simulation. Put the cards back into the deck, shuffle, and again start the process of picking 10 cards. Continue for the 20 runs. The average of the 20 runs or trials represents an estimate of the average number of questions she got correct by guessing on all ten of them.

Connecting to AP Statistics: Probability

In AP Statistics, the concept of probability is the foundation of all inference.

Students in Pre-AP mathematics courses can investigate probability by collecting data and conducting simulations. Students can use charts, probability trees, Venn diagrams, and formulas to aid in the calculation of probabilities.

Example:

What is the probability that a tack thrown in the air will land with the point end up?

To calculate an estimated probability, run an experiment by throwing a tack in the air multiple times and count the frequency it lands with the point end up. Convert this count to a relative frequency, that is, divide the number of times it lands with the point up by the number of times the tack was thrown.

Example:

In a survey of 100 students, 71 have a CD player, 25 have an MP3 player, and 12 have both. Draw a Venn diagram to represent this data. What is the probability that a randomly chosen student:

1. Owns only a CD player?

2. Owns a CD player or an MP3 player?

3. Owns neither a CD player nor an MP3 player?

Answer:

1. $\dfrac{59}{100}$

2. $\dfrac{84}{100}$

3. $\dfrac{16}{100}$

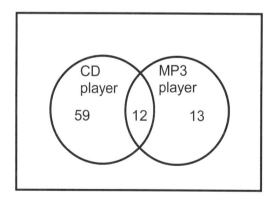

Example:

In the school cafeteria, 35% of the students select chocolate milk with their lunch. What is the probability that, out of the next five students that are randomly selected, exactly three of them will select chocolate milk?

Answer:

$$\Pr(x=3) = {}_5C_3(.35)^3(.65)^2 = 0.1811$$

Example:

A circle with radius two is inscribed in a square. What is the probability that a randomly selected point inside the square lies in the shaded region?

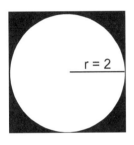

Answer:

$$\frac{16-4\pi}{16}$$

Connecting to AP Statistics: Graphical Displays

In AP Statistics, graphical displays provide a method of organizing and presenting data. In addition, these displays may be used to assess the conditions necessary for inference.

Given a set of data, students in Pre-AP mathematics courses should be able to construct a stem-plot, a dot plot, a histogram, and a box-and-whisker plot.

Example:

Biologists have identified approximately fifty species of oak tress that grow in the United States. In a study of the size of acorns produced by these trees, twenty-eight species from the Atlantic (A) region and 11 from California (C) region were studied. The size of each species' acorns (in cubic centimeters) and the corresponding height of the tree (in meters) from which the acorn came were recorded. To help determine if a difference in the size of the acorns exists between the Atlantic and California regions, graphical displays of the data will be used.

Region	Size	Height
A	1.4	27
A	3.4	21
C	7.1	18
A	9.1	25
A	1.6	3
A	10.5	24
C	0.4	1
C	17.1	15
A	2.5	17
A	0.9	15
C	1.0	21
A	1.8	24
A	0.3	11
C	6.0	26
C	2.6	23
A	0.9	15
A	0.8	23
A	2.0	24
C	5.9	30
A	2.0	24

Region	Size	Height
A	0.6	13
A	1.8	30
A	4.8	9
A	1.1	27
C	5.5	20
A	3.6	9
A	1.1	24
C	2.4	17
C	1.6	6
C	4.1	18
A	1.1	23
A	3.6	27
A	8.1	24
A	3.6	23
A	1.8	18
A	0.4	9
A	1.1	9
A	1.2	4
A	1.1	3

1. Draw a back-to-back stemplot of the data to compare the acorn sizes from the Atlantic and California regions. Identify what the stem and leaves represent.

2. Using the same scale, draw parallel boxplots for the size of acorns from the Atlantic and California regions.

3. The data collected also included for each acorn the corresponding height of the tree from which it came. Draw a scatterplot that could be used to predict the size of the acorn from the height of the tree. Use the data from the California region.

The above data as well as additional data sets may be found at the Data And Story Library. (http://lib.stat.cmu.edu/DASL/Datafiles)

Answers:

1. Stem-and-Leaf Plot for Acorn Sizes

California Region		Atlantic Region
4	0	346899
60	1	11111246888
64	2	005
	3	4666
1	4	8
95	5	
0	6	
1	7	
	8	1
	9	1
	10	5
	11	
	12	
	13	
	14	
	15	
	16	
1	17	

Stem = units
Leaf = tenths
8|1 = 8.1

21

2.   Boxplots of Acorn sizes

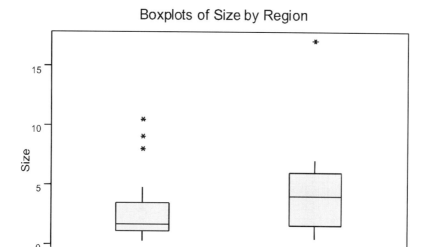

Region 1 = Atlantic
Region 2 = California

3.   Scatterplot of size of acorns versus height of trees in California Region

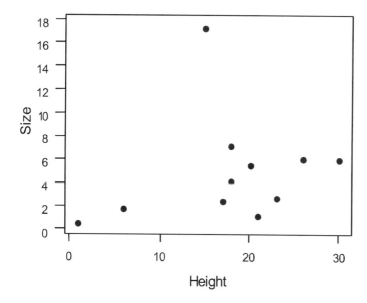

Connecting to AP Statistics:
Distributions – Measures of Center, Variability, and Shape

A distribution is the set of all values of a random variable. In AP Statistics, a distribution is often described by its center, shape, and variability (spread).

Students in Pre-AP mathematics courses should be able to use statistical terminology to describe graphical displays of data, calculate statistics that describe data, and interpret the meaning of those statistics. Students should be able to use technology as a tool for statistical analysis.

Example:

Use the graphical displays from the previous acorn data to answer the following questions:

1. Compare the distributions of acorn size for the Atlantic and California regions.

2. Does there seem to be an association between acorn size and height of tree? Explain.

Answer:

1. Using either the stem and leaf plot or the boxplots we can see that the acorn sizes for both regions are skewed to the right (toward the larger sizes).

[Teacher Note] This skewness is primarily due to the existence of three outliers at 8.1, 9.1, and 10.5 cubic centimeters in the Atlantic region and an outlier of 17.1 in the California region. These outliers are clearly identified in the boxplots but we need the stemplot to determine the actual values of these outliers.

The median acorn size for California is 4.1 cubic centimeters while the median acorn size for the Atlantic region is 1.7 cubic centimeters. It seems that, in general, acorn sizes in the Atlantic region tend to be smaller than those in the California region.

The direction of skewness is determined by the direction of the tail of the distribution. If you look at the Atlantic region, for example, the bulk of the data values are between 0 and 3 but there are a few values spread out toward the larger numbers. You could think of the bulk of the values as being the head of the distribution and the few stragglers as the tail. If we were to turn the stem scale so it looked like a number line, the larger numbers would be on the right. Thus the distribution is said to be skewed to the right. If this is confusing, it is acceptable for students to respond that the distribution is skewed toward the larger numbers (or smaller numbers depending on the distribution).

2. Based on the scatterplot of the California region there doesn't seem to be a strong association between acorn size and the height of the tree from which the acorn came. By looking at the scatterplot we can see that as the heights of the tree increase, the acorns tend to vary considerably in size. Using a calculator, we can find the correlation value is 0.21. This would indicate a weak association.

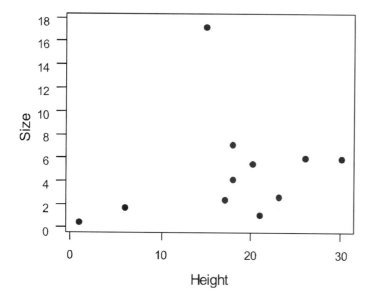

Example:

Scores on Last Week's Test for 29 Students

```
 5 |  4 6
 6 |  8
 7 |  2 3 4 4
 8 |  0 5 6 6 7 8
 9 |  1 2 2 3 6 7 9
10 |  0 0 0 0 0 0 0 0 0
```

Legend: 8 | 5 represents 85

1. Looking at the distribution of data above, would you expect the mean or median to be larger? Explain.

2. Calculate the mean, median, range, interquartile range (IQR), and then describe the distribution of the data.

Answers:

1. Since the data is skewed to the left (toward the smaller numbers), I would expect the median to be larger than the mean. The mean will be drawn in the direction of the skewness.

2. Mean = 87.8
   Median = 92
   Range = 46
   IQR = 23

(Teacher Note: It is expected that any description of a data set should include a discussion of center, spread, and shape.)

The distribution of the test scores is skewed to the left or toward the lower values. The median test score was 92. Since several test scores are quite low, the class mean will be lower than the median. From the data, we can also see that slightly more than half of the students made a grade of 90 or better and 9 students earned perfect scores. We can also calculate the lower 25% of test scores ($Q_1 = 77$) and the upper 25% of test scores ($Q_3 = 100$) giving an inter-quartile range of 23 points. This represents the middle 50% of all scores on this test.

Connecting to AP Statistics: Exploring Linear Bivariate Data

In AP Statistics, exploring bivariate data is necessary for establishing relationships and making predictions.

Students in Pre-AP mathematics courses should be able to analyze patterns in scatterplots, write equations of regression lines, and graph and analyze residual plots and outliers.

Example:

Region	Alcohol	Tobacco
North	6.47	4.03
Yorkshire	6.13	3.76
Northeast	6.19	3.77
East Midlands	4.89	3.34
West Midlands	5.63	3.47
East Anglia	4.52	2.92
Southeast	5.89	3.20
Southwest	4.79	2.71
Wales	5.27	3.53
Scotland	6.08	4.51
Northern Ireland	4.02	4.56

Family Expenditure Survey, Department of Employment, 1981 (British official statistics)

In 1981, data was collected representing the average weekly expenditures (in British pounds) for alcohol and tobacco products in the eleven different regions of Great Britain.

1. If one wanted to predict alcohol expenditures from tobacco expenditures, identify the independent (explanatory) and dependent (response) variables.

2. Draw a scatterplot of the data. Does there appear to be an association between these two variables? Explain.

3. Write the equation of the regression line (line of best fit).

4. Give the value of the slope and interpret its meaning in the context of the problem.

Answers:

1. The independent variable (explanatory) would be tobacco expenditures and the dependent (response) variable would be alcohol expenditures.

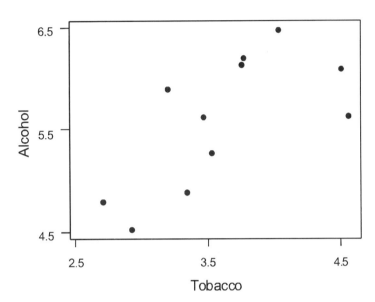

2. There appears to be a linear association between expenditures for alcohol and tobacco products. As the average weekly amount of money spent on tobacco products increases the average weekly amount spent on alcohol also increases. The relationship appears to be fairly strong.

3. It is expected that the response will not be in generic x and y form only. If the equation is written using the variables x and y, then these variables must be clearly defined. The equation may also be written in the context of the explanatory and response variables. (Note that in statistics, linear equations are usually written in the form $y = a + bx$ rather than $y = mx + b$).

    a) Alcohol = 2.9252 + 0.7365 (Tobacco)

    b) $y = 2.9252 + 0.7365x$ where x = tobacco expenditures and y = alcohol expenditures.

4. The value of the slope is 0.7365. For every one pound increase in expenditures for tobacco products there is a predicted increase of approximately 0.7365 pounds in expenditures for alcohol products.

Connecting to AP Statistics:
Exploring Non-Linear Bivariate Data

In AP Statistics, exploring bivariate data is necessary for establishing relationships and making predictions.

Students in Pre-AP mathematics courses should be able to analyze patterns in scatterplots, write equations of regression lines, graph and analyze residual plots and outliers, and transform data to achieve linearity.

Example:

Name of Note	Note above middle C	Frenquency (Hz)
Middle C	0	262
C#	1	277
D	2	294
D#	3	311
E	4	330
F	5	349
F#	6	370
G	7	392
G#	8	415
A	9	440
A#	10	466
B	11	494
C (above middle C)	12	523

Every musical note has an associated frequency measured in hertz (Hz), or vibrations per second. The table shows the approximate frequencies of the notes in the octave from middle C up to the next C on a piano. (In this case, E# is the same as F and B# is the same as C)

1. Write an appropriate regression equation to model the above data.

2. Predict the frequency for the C located two octaves above middle C (this would be note 24).

Answers:

1. The data in the left graph show a clear non-linear pattern that appears exponential so we transform the data by taking the natural log of the frequency. The result on the right looks linear.

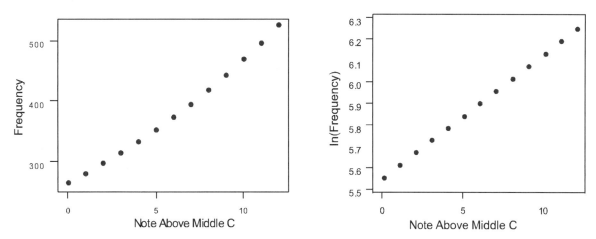

The transformed data forms an almost linear relationship, so apply a linear regression to the transformed data. The regression equation for the transformed data is given by ln(frequency) = 5.5675 + 0.0577 (note above middle C).

The residual plot is given below.

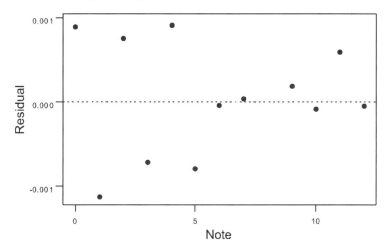

Since the plot shows no apparent pattern we will conclude that we have a good model. Transform the linearized equation back to its original form using exponential and logarithmic properties.

Frequency = $(261.779)(1.0593^{\text{note}})$

2. The frequency for the C two octaves above middle C would be F(24) = 1043.25 Hz.

Note: We might question the accuracy of the value based on this model. The data point for 24 is well beyond the range of the upper limit of the given data.

Introduction to the Lessons

In this section of the guide, you will find a set of lessons that you can use in teaching your classes. Each lesson includes a teacher page that provides you with important information to help you determine where it might fit into your normal scope and sequence. Each lesson includes a particular objective, but also serves as a review of previously learned material as well as a preview of some concept or skill that is important in AP Calculus or AP Statistics.

Good mathematics instruction should emphasize the connections between various approaches to a situation or problem. As often as possible, multiple representations should be used in a lesson to introduce, explore, and reinforce mathematical concepts. As we prepared lessons for this guide, we used a star icon to keep track of the types of representations being used in each lesson. The legend for the star is provided below.

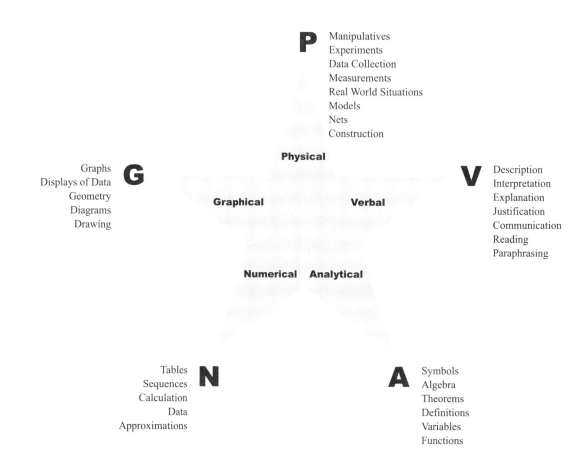

P

Manipulatives
Experiments
Data Collection
Measurements
Real World Situations
Models
Nets
Construction

Physical

Graphs
Displays of Data
Geometry
Diagrams
Drawing

G

Graphical

Verbal

V

Description
Interpretation
Explanation
Justification
Communication
Reading
Paraphrasing

Numerical   **Analytical**

Tables
Sequences
Calculation
Data
Approximations

N

A

Symbols
Algebra
Theorems
Definitions
Variables
Functions

Obviously, not all representations are appropriate to every lesson. In the upper right hand corner of each teacher page, you will notice a star icon. The points of the star that are darkened signify those representations that are used in that particular lesson. For example,   means that a lesson

includes the physical, analytic, and graphical representations of a problem situation. As students progress through their sequence of math classes, the way that a particular representation manifests itself will probably change. At the middle school level, for example, *physical* might mean the student would manipulate actual physical objects, such as algebra tiles, to model a problem. At the Algebra 2 level, *physical* would more likely mean that the student is able to model some real world situation with an algebraic function.

All of the lessons in this guide have been written by actual teachers and have been used with actual students under the normal constraints of classroom teaching. We have tried to make the lessons as user-friendly as possible, including both a student page that can be reproduced as well as an answer key for the teacher. We did not include lessons for topics that we feel are covered well in most textbooks. We intend for these lessons to serve as supplements to what you are already doing. Using them in conjunction with your textbook and lessons you have written yourself will allow you to explore what it is that makes a course "Pre-AP." Feel free to adapt the lessons to fit your own teaching style and the particular needs of your students. We hope that these will also serve as inspiration to allow you to develop lessons of your own that you can then share with other members of your team.

Algebra 1 Lessons

Use Line Plots to Determine Mean, Median, Mode, and Range

Objective:
Students will use a line plot to determine mean, median, mode and range.

Connections to Previous Learning:
Students should be able to construct a line plot and to find mean, median, mode, and range.

Connections to TEKS:
111.32 b2D

Connections to AP:
The AP Statistics objective of measures of center, shape, and variability

Time Frame:
30 minutes

Materials:
A sticky note and a copy of the student page for each student, butcher paper or chalk/white board

Teacher Notes:
Often one of the responsibilities of a Pre-AP Algebra I teacher is to search for students who have been "missed", to open the gate to a wider number of students. The first two lessons are designed to give this time before moving on to the meat of algebra and yet to provide meaningful statistical connections. While students should be able to find measures of central tendency of data, few have used a line plot to aid in finding that information. The first activity in this lesson is teacher directed and requires a sticky note for each student. Have the student write the number of letters in her/his last (or first) name. Have the chalk board or a piece of butcher paper pre-marked with numbers from 3 to 12. Leave enough space between marks for the width of the sticky plus a little. Have students come up one group (or row) at a time to place their sticky notes in the correct column. Take some time here to let them review the arithmetic necessary to find each measure. This activity can be done very quickly, but resist that temptation. Take the time to discuss questions such as which of these four measures can be most quickly found from the line plot. Show students how to work to the middle to find the median. Investigate what happens if there are two pieces of data in the middle. Be especially careful finding mean. Some students will divide by the number of points on the horizontal axis, not by the number of pieces of data. Also, if students are using a calculator, a common calculator mistake made here is to add, then divide without either using parentheses or first finding the sum. Let them make the mistake and then take the opportunity to talk about reasonableness of an answer.

The written exercise is intended to be done in groups; however, it can also be done as an individual homework assignment. In order to do this exercise, have students collect and organize a second set of data (20 to 30 points) to make a line plot. This data can be of the teacher's choosing or the students' choosing. It could be the height of each student, the number of letters in each student's first name, the number of pets in their homes, etc.

Use Line Plots to Determine Mean, Median, Mode, and Range

Using the data that you collected, make a line plot (on the back of this sheet or on another sheet of paper). Explain how you used the line plot to help find each piece of information below.

1. Mode

2. Median

3. Mean

4. Range

5. As of September 2, 2002, the top 10 home run leaders in the American League had hit 48, 42, 38, 34, 32, 31, 31, 28, 27, and 27 home runs. The top 10 home run leaders in the National League had hit 43, 40, 38, 37, 35, 33, 33, 32, 32, and 28 home runs. Make **ONE** line plot from this information. Use it to determine mean, median, mode, and range. Be sure to explain how you used the line plot as you find each measure.

Use Line Plots to Determine Mean, Median, Mode, and Range

Answers:

1. Check to see that students have made an accurate line plot from the data they collected.

2. Mode - *The student should give the mode and explain that it is the "tallest" column on the line plot.*

3. Median - *The student should give the answer and explain how to get to the middle of a line plot in order to find the median.*

4. Mean - *The student should give the answer. If you did not give rounding instructions, take any appropriately rounded answer. The majority of points here should go to checking to see if the students actually used the information from the line plot to find mean. It's important in mathematics to value the new information in a lesson when grading; therefore, don't count a problem totally wrong for an arithmetic error.*

5. What is the range of this data? How did you use the line plot to help you determine that? *Check for an accurate range, but more importantly that they can explain how to check the line plot for the smallest and largest pieces of data.*

6. As of September 2, 2002, the top 10 home run leaders in the American League had hit 48, 42, 38, 34, 32, 31, 31, 28, 27, and 27 home runs. The top 10 home run leaders in the National League had hit 43, 40, 38, 37, 35, 33, 33, 32, 32, and 28 home runs. Make **ONE** line plot from this information. Use it to determine mean, median, mode, and range. Be sure to explain how you used the line plot as you find each measure.

```
                          X
        X  X        X  X  X              X
        X  X        X  X  X  X  X     X  X     X     X  X                 X
       _____
        27 28 29 30 31 32 33 34 35 36 37 38 39 40 41 42 43 44 45 45 47 48
```

The mean is determined by (27 x 2 + 28 x 2 + 31 x 2 + 32 x 3 + 33 x 2 + 34 + 35 + 37 + 38 x 2 + 40 + 42 + 43 + 48) ÷ 20. This results in 34.45 or 34.5 rounded to the nearest tenth. The median is 33. The student can either show getting to the middle on the line plot or explain it in words. The mode is 32 as it has the highest column. The range is 48 – 27, or 11.

Analyzing Mean, Median, Mode, and Range

Objective:
Students will analyze mean, median, mode and range to determine favorable and unfavorable situations.

Connections to Previous Learning:
Students should be able to find mean, median, mode, and range.

Connections to TEKS:
111.32 b2D

Connections to AP:
The AP Statistics objective of measures of center, shape, and variability

Time Frame:
40 minutes

Materials:
Butcher paper, a transparency, or notebook paper (if you have a projector which will project print), a copy of the student page for each student for activities 1 and 2

Teacher Notes:
This lesson helps students learn how to analyze mean, median, and mode when those pieces of information are given without the accompanying data.

This lesson depends upon a whole group activity set up by the teacher. A favorite is: An employer states that "The mean salary for all employees at my software company is $300,000. I'll hire you right out of high school, no college is needed. I'll also give you a 5% cost of living pay increase each year. Would you like to come work for my company?" After the class agrees to work for the employer (and most will), explain the actual salaries. She's the CEO and design engineer with an annual salary of $1,000,000. Her mother (husband, sister, best friend, ...) is the CFO and salesperson making $750,000 annually. The company has a receptionist, secretary, maintenance engineer, and a packing specialist. Each earns $15,000 a year. Ask the class if the employer was dishonest with them. This should lead to a discussion of how statistics can be used to distort or mislead.

The first exercise is a group activity. After students have completed the exercise, take the time to thoroughly go over their answers as a whole group activity before going on to the second activity.

The second activity can be done individually, either as homework or as an assessment.

Analyzing Mean, Median, Mode, and Range

In your working group, consider the situations below. Create two sets of data for each. In the first set, create data which is favorable to the situation described. In the second set, create data which is unfavorable. Be prepared to share your work with the class.

1. At professional skating competitions, skaters are given scores ranging from 1 to 10 by 10 judges. The high and the low scores are thrown out, and the skater then receives the mean of the other 8 scores.

2. You have 6 test grades in algebra. Your average is the median of your test grades.

3. You own a small company with 11 employees. You entice new employees by telling them that most of the people in your company make $100,000 a year. Give a situation where using the mode is favorable to entry level employees. Give a situation where using the mode is unfavorable to an entry level employee.

Analyzing Mean, Median, Mode, and Range – Independent Assignment

Respond to each of the following. Use your own paper.

1. The July 2002 median resale price of a home in Dallas, Texas was $130,800. The median per capita income was $32,406. In San Antonio, the median resale price of a home was $151,100 with a per capita income of $22,500. Out on the coast, the median resale price of a home in San Francisco, California was $571,000 while the per capita income was $40,357. Use these statistics to answer the following questions.

   a) Choose one of these cities to explain exactly what the median resale price of a home is. Explain it so that I can understand it, even if I don't know the word median.

   b) What is a per capita income?

   c) Choose a city to live in. Use this data to defend your choice.

   d) What generalizations can you make from this data? Do you think that they are always true? Why or Why not.

2. Attached is a list of Major League Baseball's mean attendance by team, as of September 1, 2002.

   a) Round the mean attendance in the highlighted column to the nearest 5000. Make a line plot, and use it to find the mean, median, and mode of the data. Be sure to explain how you used the line plot to find these averages.

   b) What is the range of mean attendance?

   c) As you look at your answers in A, are there any ways in which these averages are misleading?

   d) What predictions would you make about the future of Major League Baseball, in general or by specific tcam bascd on this data?

Major League Baseball Home Attendance – September 1, 2002

Team	Games	Total Att.	Home Att.
Anaheim	71	1,938,242	27,299
Arizona	68	2,720,175	40,002
Atlanta	66	2,210,047	33,485
Baltimore	64	2,158,432	33,725
Boston	67	2,208,708	32,965
Chicago Cubs	66	2,343,994	35,515
Chicago Sox	68	1,491,362	21,931
Cincinnati	70	1,610,776	23,011
Cleveland	71	2,326,839	32,772
Colorado	68	2,382,706	35,039
Detroit	68	1,294,332	19,034
Florida	71	711,085	10,015
Houston	71	2,221,392	31,287
Kansas City	64	1,165,195	18,206
Los Angeles	68	2,633,777	38,732
Milwaukee	69	1,706,490	24,731
Minnesota	69	1,656,169	24,002
Montreal	67	687,737	10,264
New York Mets	66	2,422,934	36,711
New York Yankees	63	2,830,794	44,933
Oakland	69	1,758,431	25,484
Philadelphia	67	1,423,322	21, 243
Pittsburgh	67	1,566,771	23,384
St. Louis	65	2,449,482	37,684
San Diego	69	1,955,701	28,343
San Francisco	65	2,619,341	40,297
Seattle	69	3,035,868	43,998
Tampa Bay	65	862,678	13,271
Texas	69	2,072,956	30,042
Toronto	69	1,421,224	20,597

3. The Center for Disease Control gives statistics relating to the leading cause of death by age group. The number given is the percentage of total deaths. The following data gives the 6 leading causes of death for two age groups, 10-14 and 15-19. Use it to answer the questions below.

Leading Causes of Death ages 10-14		Leading Causes of Death ages 15-19	
Unintentional Injuries	39.6	Unintentional Injuries	48.5
Cancer	12.2	Homicide	15.2
Homicide	6	Suicide	11.7
Suicide	5.9	Cancer	5.4
Congenital Defects	5.4	Heart Disease	3.4
Heart Disease	3.9	Congenital Defects	1.6

a)   The mode for each age group is unintentional injuries. Are mean and median useful ways to look at this data? Why or why not?

b)   In what other types of real world data is mode the most useful?

c)   While the six leading causes of death are the same in both age groups, there are some marked differences in the two groups. Name three and give some possible "educated" guesses as to why these differences may exist.

Analyzing Mean, Median, Mode, and Range

Answers:
As analysis is a new activity for most students, these exercises' effectiveness increases in proportion to class time spent discussing them.

1. At professional skating competitions, skaters are given scores ranging from 1 to 10 by 10 judges. The high and the low scores are thrown out, and the skater then receives the mean of the other 8 scores. *One way to be favorable to the skater would be for 9 scores to be close to the high score. The 10th score would be considerably lower than the other 9. One way to be unfavorable would be for 9 scores to be clustered near the bottom score and the tenth score to be very high in relationship to the others.*

2. You have 6 test grades in algebra. Your average is the median of your test grades.

   One way for the median to be favorable would be for the top four scores to be close to the median and the other two much lower. One way for the median to be unfavorable would be for the bottom four scores to be close to the median and the other two scores to be much higher.

3. You own a small company with 11 employees. You entice new employees by telling them that most of the people in your company make $100,000 a year. Give a situation where using the mode is favorable to entry level employees. Give a situation where using the mode is unfavorable to an entry level employee. *A mode of $100,000 would be favorable to new employees if the $100,000 was the bottom salary. It would be unfavorable if the mode came from experienced employees, and it was the top salary.*

Sample exercises for Activity 2

1. The July 2002 median resale price of a home in Dallas, Texas was $130,800. The median per capita income was $32,406. In San Antonio, the median resale price of a home was $151,100 with a per capita income of $22,500. Out on the coast, the median resale price of a home in San Francisco, California was $571,000 while the per capita income was $40,357. Use these statistics to answer the following questions.

   a) Choose one of these cities to explain exactly what the median resale price of a home is. Explain it so that I can understand it, even if I don't know the word median. *The hope here is that students understand that median resale price means that there were as many homes that sold for less than $130,800 (Dallas) as there were that sold for more.*

   b) What is a per capita income? *Per capita income means that that is the average income for each person.*

c)   Choose a city to live in. Use this data to defend your choice. *For this question, the answers that students make should be justified by the data given. Accept any answer which fits this criteria.*

d)   What generalizations can you make from this data? Do you think that they are always true? Why or Why not. *It's important to accept any generalization that students make and justify.*

2. Attached is a list of Major League Baseball's mean home attendance by team, as of September 1, 2002.

a)   Round the mean attendance in the highlighted column to the nearest 5000. Make line plot, and use it to find the mean, median, and mode of the data. Be sure to explain how you used the line plot to find these averages.

```
                                                    X
                                       X            X
                             X         X            X
                             X         X            X        X
                             X         X      X     X        X
              X              X         X      X     X        X        X
              X        X     X         X      X     X        X        X
           ┌──────────────────────────────────────────────────────────────
            10,000   15,000  20,000  25,000  30,000  35,000  40,000  45,000
```

The mean is (10,000 x 2 + 15,000 + 20,000 x 5 + 25,000 x 6 + 30,000 x 3 + 35,000 x 7 + 40,000 x 4 + 45,000 x 2) ÷ 30. This gives 29,000. The median is 30,000, and the mode is 35,000.

b)   What is the range of mean attendance? *The range is 45,000 – 10,000 = 35,000*

c)   As you look at your answers in A, are there any ways in which these averages are misleading?

The mode is a little misleading since it's so far from the mean and median.

d)   What predictions would you make about the future of Major League Baseball, in general or by specific team based on this data? *Answers will widely vary here. They may know that there are teams in difficulty and comment on the teams with the lowest mean attendance.*

44

3. The Center for Disease Control gives statistics relating to the leading cause of death by age group. The following data gives the 6 leading causes of death for two age groups, 10-14 and 15-19. Use it to answer the questions below.

Leading Causes of Death ages 10-14		Leading Causes of Death ages 15-19	
Unintentional Injuries	39.6	Unintentional Injuries	48.5
Cancer	12.2	Homicide	15.2
Homicide	6	Suicide	11.7
Suicide	5.9	Cancer	5.4
Congenital Defects	5.4	Heart Disease	3.4
Heart Disease	3.9	Congenital Defects	1.6

a) The mode for each age group is unintentional injuries. Are mean and median useful ways to look at this data? Why or why not? *Take any meaningful analysis here. Students should realize that what occurs most often, the mode, is the useful data in this situation.*

b) In what other types of real world data is mode the most useful? *Answers will vary widely. Some examples are medical research, car sales, fashion, etc.*

c) While the six leading causes of death are the same in both age groups, there are some marked differences in the two groups. Name three and give some possible "educated" guesses as to why these differences may exist. *Sample answers: Unintentional injuries rise in 15-19 because this age group is driving. Homicide rises in 15-19 year olds because of life style choices. Suicide rises in 15-19 year olds because this age is more stressful than early teens. I will choose to let this discussion go on to the point of asking students to think about what they can do to decrease their risk of an early demise.*

Introduction to Function Notation

Objective:
Students will describe independent and dependent quantities in functional relationships and introduce function notation.

Connections to Previous Learning:

No prerequisite knowledge is required for the student.

Connections to TEKS:
111.32 b1A, b1C, b3A

Connections to AP:
The AP Calculus objective of analysis of functions

Time Frame:
40 minutes

Materials:
Butcher paper or board space, marking pens, masking tape if butcher paper is used

Teacher Notes:
This is the first of five lessons which are intended to build an informal foundation for functions. Notice that the "one range element for each domain element" definition of function is not introduced in this lesson set.

Present the following situation (or a similar scenario) to explore the terms: **variable, function, independent variable, dependent variable and function notation.**

The Math and Science Team at Smedley Middle School must decide on several fund-raisers to pay entry fees for contests and other expenses. In August, the students decide to have a Problem-A-Thon. Each student will work as many problems as possible in 20 minutes. They will get sponsors to give donations based on how many problems they work correctly.

Have students brainstorm the question: What factors might affect the success of this fund raiser? After students have brainstormed possibilities in their groups, take at least one response from each group. Lead students to the idea that factors which affect the success of the fund raiser are variables. The question: "What are the key variables in this situation?" should get students to come to an understanding of problems solved and money earned as key pieces of information, the key variables, in this situation. Begin the process of having students formally define variables by assigning each factor a letter which can be identified with the variable. Write these in a form such as p = problems solved and m = money earned.

The next step in this lesson is to get students to understand an informal definition of independent and dependent variables and the notion of function as a dependent relationship. Have groups use problems worked and money earned in sentences using the language **"depends on"** and **"is a function of"**. Give several examples of other dependent relationships focusing on using the variables in a sentence. Examples could include perimeter and side of a square, calories used and amount of exercise, number of cats and number of cat hairs, etc.

Have the class brainstorm several examples of dependent relationships. Write all examples given on the overhead, board, or butcher paper, being sure to write them in sentence form (such as "My weight depends on how much I eat or My weight is a function of how much I eat."). Conclude the whole group portion of this exercise quickly. Leave the whole group examples posted as individual groups write as many examples as possible of dependent relationships. After ten to fifteen minutes, have groups stand by their examples with pens in hand. Rotate groups clockwise through all posters, 3 minutes per poster, until all are back at their work. Have students put any questions or comments on each group's poster. (Note: Sticky notes can work well here.) Once students have returned to their station, give a few minutes for the groups to ponder responses made to their work. This activity can lead to some good discussion of dependent and independent variables. Conclude this portion of the activity by having students define dependent variable, independent variable, and function in their own words.

Use examples from the previous activity to show students the basics of function notation. If a group offered that money earned depends on hours spent babysitting, write that as response as m(h) where m is money earned and h is hours spent babysitting. Write the fact that circumference depends on diameter as c(d). After writing several class examples using the stem for function notation, give examples that start with the stem and a definition of the variables. Be sure that students can reverse the process and write a sentence for each of these before giving the student page as classwork or homework.

Examples could include:
s(e), where s = surface area and e = edge of a cube,
a(s), where s = side and a = area,
m(g), where m = miles and g = gallons,
G(s), where s = hours studied and G = grade,
and s(r), where r = rate of speed and s = stopping distance.

Introduction to Function Notation

For each pair of variables below,
a) tell which is the independent variable, and
b) write a sentence giving the relationship between the two variables using either "depends on" or "is a function of.

1. spring rainfall and wildflowers

2. number of wild rabbits and available food supply

3. number of predators and number of rabbits

4. amount of money spent and articles of clothing bought

5. amount of stagnant water and number of mosquito larva

For each of the following, write a sentence giving the relationship between the two variables using either "depends on" or "is a function of". Vary your responses using each option at least four times.

6. W(c), where c = calories and W = weight

7. T(t), where T = temperature and t = time of day

8. A(d), where A = area and d = diameter

9. W(e), where e = exercise and W = weight

10. B(k), where B = electric bill and k = kilowatt hours

11. G(t), where G = grade and t = hours of TV watched

12. R(r), where r = amount of rainfall and R = river level

13. P(s), where s = length of a side of a square and P = perimeter of a square

14. D(n), where n = number of lawns mowed and D = dollars earned

15. M(n), where M = money spent and n = number of cd's bought

Introduction to Function Notation

Answers:

For each pair of variables below,

a) tell which is the independent variable, and

b) write a sentence giving the relationship between the two variables using either "depends on" or "is a function of.

1. spring rainfall and wildflowers *Spring rainfall is the independent variable. Wildflowers depend on spring rainfall.*

2. number of wild rabbits and available food supply *Available food supply is the independent variable. Number of rabbits depends on available food supply.*

3. number of predators and number of rabbits *Number of predators is the independent variable. The number of rabbits depends on the number of predators.*
    Note: This is an example of a situation where a valid argument can be made for the opposite answer. If time permits, discuss why either answer is correct.

4. amount of money spent and articles of clothing bought *Articles of clothing bought is the independent variable. The amount of money spent depends on the articles of clothing bought. Again: If buying shirts at $20 per shirt, the number of articles of clothing bought depends on how much money was spent.*

5. amount of stagnant water and number of mosquito larva *Amount of stagnant water is the independent variable. The number of mosquito larva depends on the amount of stagnant water.*

For each of the following, write a sentence giving the relationship between the two variables using either "depends on" or "is a function of". Vary your responses using each option at least four times.

6. W(c), where c = calories and W = weight *Weight depends on calories.*

7. T(t), where T = temperature and t = time of day *Temperature depends on time of day.*

8. A(d), where A = area and d = diameter *Area depends on diameter.*

9. W(e), where e = exercise and W = weight *Weight depends on exercise.*

10. B(k), where B = electric bill and k = kilowatt hours *The electric bill is a function of kilowatt hours used.*

11. G(t), where G = grade and t = hours of TV watched *The grade is a function of hours of TV watched.*

12. R(r), where r = amount of rainfall and R = river level   *The level of the river depends on the amount of rainfall.*

13. P(s), where s = length of a side of a square and P = perimeter of a square   *The perimeter of a square depends on the length of a side of a square.*

14. D(n), where n = number of lawns mowed and D = dollars earned   *The dollars earned depends on the number of lawns mowed.*

15. M(n), where M = money spent and n = number of cd's bought   *The money spent depends on the number of cd's bought.*

Write Your Notes and Ideas Here!

Connecting a Verbal Description to Table and Graph

Objective:
Students will show the relationship between a real world scenario as a verbal description, a table, a pattern that can be derived from that table, and a verbal description of the table.

Connections to Previous Learning:
Students should be able to do simple multiplication and graphing in the first quadrant. *It is helpful, but not necessary, for students to know how to set the viewing window on a graphing calculator.

Connections to TEKS:
111.32 b1A, b1B, b1C, b1D, b1E, b3A, c1C

Connections to AP:
The AP Calculus objective of analysis of functions

Time Frame:
60 minutes

Materials:
One copy of each page for each student

Teacher Notes:
Notice the directions on question 1 of the student pages: "If your group has questions, raise your hands and I will come to you." These are written to get groups to try to settle questions within the group. This lesson is written to be done in groups followed by a whole group discussion.

*The page breaks on these pages are deliberate. Stop after question 12 and do question 13 as a whole group activity if students have no prior knowledge of setting the viewing window on a graphing calculator.

Connecting a Verbal Description to Table and Graph

The Math and Science Team at Smedley Middle School must decide on several fund-raisers to pay entry fees for contests and other expenses. In August, the students decide to have a Problem-A-Thon. Each student will work as many problems as possible in 20 minutes. They will get sponsors to give donations based on how many problems they work correctly. Ginny gets pledges from her friends and parents totaling $2 per problem. Genaro gets pledges of $3 per problem.

1. In the previous lesson, you determined the independent and dependent variables in the verbal description above. Write a sentence using "is a function of" that describes the relationship between those two variables.

2. Complete the following table to show how much money Ginny and Genaro raise for each number of problems that they work correctly. Be sure you understand the labels for each column. The first column, number of problems, refers to the number of problems worked correctly and is used for both Ginny and Genaro's columns. In the process column you will show **how** you figured Ginny's and Genaro's total money raised which you will put in the money raised column. If everyone in your group understands these 5 columns, finish this page. If your group has questions, raise your hands and I will come to you.

Number of Problems	Process Column Ginny	Money Raised by Ginny	Process Column Genaro	Money Raised by Genaro
5				
10				
15				
20				
30				
50				
70				
90				
100				

3. Describe in words a pattern that you see in Ginny's process column.

4. How much will Ginny earn for 40 correct problems? Explain your answer.

5. How much will Ginny earn for 61 correct problems? Explain your answer.

6. How many problems will Ginny have to work correctly to earn $120? Remember to explain how you got your answer.

7. Describe in words a pattern that you see in Genaro's process column.

8. Considering the patterns that you noticed, extend the table to fill in the nth row below.

Number of Problems	Process Column Ginny	Money Raised by Ginny	Process Column Genaro	Money Raised by Genaro
n				

9. How much will Genaro earn for 17 problems? Explain your answer.

10. How much will Genaro earn for 111 problems? Explain your answer.

11. How many problems will Genaro have to work to earn $120? Remember, explain!

12. Ginny is very frustrated that Genaro got more in pledges per problem than she did. What variables determine how much she makes? How could she make the same amount of money that Genaro makes? How could she make more?

13.   On a coordinate plane, the independent variable is always graphed on the x-axis (the horizontal axis) while the dependent variable is always graphed on the y-axis (the vertical axis). Carefully considering your independent variable (x), your dependent variable (y), and the data in your table, determine an appropriate viewing window to use to graph both Ginny's and Genaro's functions. In the space provided below, give the minimum and maximum values that you will use and your scale. **Justify your choices**.

   $x$min

   $x$max

   $x$scale

   $y$min

   $y$max

   $y$scale

14.   Sketch each function below. Be sure to label your both your axes and your graph.

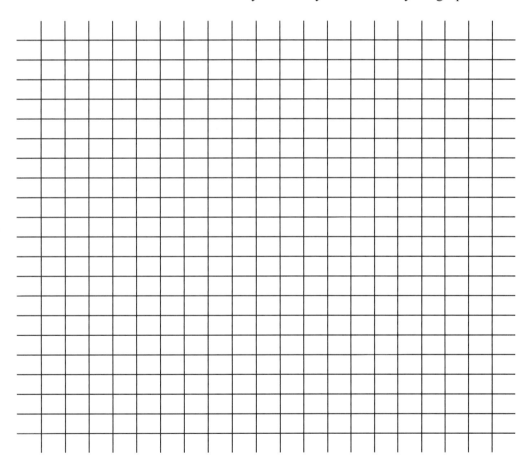

15.   What is the same about the graphs of Ginny's and Genaro's data?

16.   What differences are there between the graph of Ginny's and Genaro's data?

17.   What effect does the $2 pledge per problem have on the graph of the Ginny's function?

18.   What effect does the $3 pledge per problem have on the graph of the Genaro's function?

19.   At what point do Ginny's and Genaro's graphs intersect? If they never intersect, explain why not.

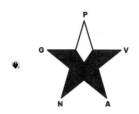

Connecting a Verbal Description to Table and Graph

Answers:

1. The independent variable is number of problems worked. The dependent variable is money raised. The money raised is a function of the number of problems worked.

2.
Number of Problems	Process Column Ginny	Money Raised by Ginny	Process Column Genaro	Money Raised by Genaro
5	2 x 5	10	3 x 5	15
10	2 x 10	20	3 x 10	30
15	2 x 15	30	3 x 15	45
20	2 x 20	40	3 x 20	60
30	2 x 30	60	3 x 30	90
50	2 x 50	100	3 x 50	150
70	2 x 70	140	3 x 70	210
90	2 x 90	180	3 x 90	270
100	2 x 100	200	3 x 100	300

As this is the first process column that students have done, it is possible that their answers will show addition. For example, they may have 2+2+2+2+2+2 for Ginny's first column. Since this exercise is written for a Pre-AP algebra class, it has been staged to hopefully "force" students to move immediately to multiplication. Since the situation is dealing with problems that are each worth $2, it is less likely that a student would put 5+5.

3. Accept any correct answer after the student has justified it. The hoped for answer is two times the number of problems.

4. $2 x 40 = $80 or Ginny gets $2 for each correct problem, so $2 times 40 correct problems gives a total of $80. (Encourage the use of units in the problem.)

5. $2 x 61 = $122 or a verbal description

6. Ginny will earn $120 if she works 60 correct problems because 2 x 60 = 120.

    $120 ÷ $2 = 60 is also correct.

7. Accept any correct answer after the student has justified it. The hoped for answer is $3 times the number of correct problems.

8.

Number of Problems	Process Column Ginny	Money Raised by Ginny	Process Column Genaro	Money Raised by Genaro
n	2 x *n*		3 x *n*	

9. $3 x 17 = $51

10. $3 x 111 = $333

11. $120 ÷ $3 = 40

12. Possible variables: how many Ginny (Genaro) works correctly, how calm Ginny (Genaro) is, how accurate Ginny (Genaro) is...

   She can make the same amount of money if she works more correctly than Genaro. For example: if Ginny works 30 and Genaro works 20 then they will make the same amount of money.

13. Students should be given credit here for any answer that they can justify.

   $x$min   0 would be the "best" minimum
   $x$max   120 would be the "best" maximum
   $x$scale   answers will vary here — perhaps 5 or 10
   $y$min   0 would be the "best" minimum
   $y$max   while 300 would be the "best" maximum, do not penalize students
                      if they can justify a different maximum
   $y$scale   answers will vary here — perhaps 20

14. Graphs will vary according to scale. At this point most students will graph a line. These graphs should be accepted.

15. This question is very open ended. Students may say that both make a line or that both are increasing. Accept any reasonable answer. The point here is the thinking process.

16. Students should notice that Ginny's "line" is lower than Genaro's data. Again, accept any reasonable answer.

17. Hopefully students will notice that the $2 pledge per problem determines how fast Ginny's graph rises. ...any reasonable answer

18. Hopefully students will notice that the $3 pledge per problem determines how fast Genaro's graph rises. ...any reasonable answer

19. If students graphed this as discrete data, they may say that Ginny's graph is always below Genaro's. It is also possible that students will think that each must get at least one problem right. (After all, they are math/science team members). Hopefully students will notice that they intersect at the origin. It is important to give students credit for correct thinking processes.

Write Your Notes and Ideas Here!

Use Tables and Graphs to Determine the Better Deal

Objective:
Students will write a function rule and analyze table and graph to decide the better deal at a given point.

Connections to Previous Learning:
Students should understand dependent and independent variable, be able to make a table and a graph, and be able to determine an appropriate viewing window for that graph.

Connections to TEKS:
111.32 b1A, b1B, b1C, b1D, b1E, b3A, c1C, c4B, c4C

Connections to AP:
The AP Calculus objective of analysis of functions

Time Frame:
50 minutes

Materials:
One copy of each page for each student

Teacher Notes:
This lesson reviews the concepts of dependent and independent variable. It also reinforces making a table and a graph, deriving a pattern for that graph, and writing a function for that graph. It is the opinion of this author that material not consistently reviewed is material easily forgotten.

Before starting with the student written pages, put the scenario (found at the top of the first student page) on a transparency or on the board and ask the following questions:

- What are the variables in this situation?

- Which is the better offer, $1 for each program or $2 for each program?

- Which is the better offer, $10 for the job or $40 for the job?

- Considering the money earned and the number of programs sold, which is the dependent variable?

- Which is the independent variable? *Students may still have trouble with this, so encourage them to make a sentence using depends for money earned and the number of programs sold. Take the time to reinforce the idea of independent and dependent variable.*

As students work through the student pages of lesson 3, have them work in groups with each student getting a copy of each page. Follow this with a whole group discussion.

Use Tables and Graphs to Determine the Better Deal

In September, the Smedley team determined that they had enough money for the first 4 contests — **NOT ENOUGH FOR THE YEAR.** The planning committee decided to have members sell programs for the high school football games. The team must choose between two offers. The first offer is a flat fee of $40 plus $1 for each program sold. The second offer gives $10 plus $2 for each program sold. Now the team must decide which contract to sign.

As you answer the questions in this lesson, be sure to justify each answer.

1. In this situation, what variables might affect the success of the project?

2. Complete the following table to show the money made for offer 1 and for offer 2 based on the number of programs sold.

Programs Sold	Process Column Offer 1	Income Offer 1	Process Column Offer 2	Income Offer 2
5				
10				
15				
20				
30				
40				
50				
70				
100				

3. Describe in words a pattern that you see for the income from offer 1.

4. Describe in words a pattern that you see for the income from offer 2.

5. Considering the patterns that you noticed extend the table to fill in the nth row below.

Programs Sold	Process Column Offer 1	Income Offer 1	Process Column Offer 2	Income Offer 2
n				

6. In this scenario, what is the independent variable? What is the dependent variable? Write a sentence using "is a function of" that shows the relationship between these two variables.

7. Choose meaningful letters to represent your independent variable and dependent variable. Using these letters, write a function rule for the income from offer 1.

8. Using the same letters that you used in number 7, write a function rule for the income from offer 2.

9. As the number of programs sold increases, what happens to the income?

10. How many programs must the team sell to make $90 with offer 1? Remember, justify your answer.

11. How many programs must the team sell to make $90 with offer 2?

12. You are on the committee to decide which offer to choose. Carefully consider which offer to use. Once you decide and sign a contract, you cannot change your mind. Be sure to justify your answer.

13. Is there a number of programs that can be sold, where the income from both offers is the same? Justify your answer.

14.   Write an equation that represents the point at which the two offers yield the same amount.

15.   Determine an appropriate viewing window for the graphs of both functions, and justify your choice of those windows.

   $x$min
   $x$max
   $x$scale
   $y$min
   $y$max
   $y$scale

16.   Sketch each function below. Be sure to label your both your axes and your graph.

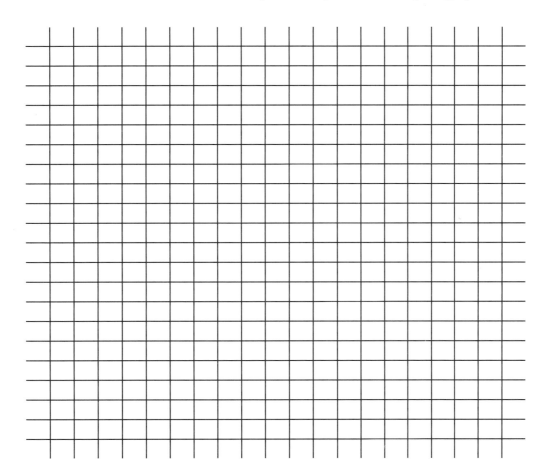

17.   What effect does the $1 income for each program have on the graph of offer 1? What effect does the $40 have on the graph?

18.   What effect does the $2 income for each program have on the graph of offer 2? What effect does the $10 have on the graph?

19.   At one point, the two graphs intersect. What are the coordinates of this point of intersection? What is the significance of this point?

20.   In question 12, you had to decide which contract you would sign. Now that you have graphed this data, would you reconsider? Why or why not? Justify your answer.

Use Tables and Graphs to Determine the Better Deal

Answers:

Young algebra students often feel that an answer is enough. It is important in the first weeks of the school year to get them accustomed to explaining an answer. Any answer that can reasonably be justified should be counted correct.

1. Sample answers: number of problems sold, attendance, cost of programs, weather, etc.

2.

Programs Sold	Process Column Offer 1	Income Offer 1	Process Column Offer 2	Income Offer 2
5	$40 + $1(5)	$45	$10 + $2(5)	$20
10	$40 + $1(10)	$50	$10 + $2(10)	$30
15	$40 + $1(15)	$55	$10 + $2(15)	$40
20	$40 + $1(20)	$60	$10 + $2(20)	$50
30	$40 + $1(30)	$70	$10 + $2(30)	$70
40	$40 + $1(40)	$80	$10 + $2(40)	$90
50	$40 + $1(50)	$90	$10 + $2(50)	$110
70	$40 + $1(70)	$110	$10 + $2(70)	$150
100	$40 + $1(100)	$140	$10 + $2(100)	$210

3. Sample: The income comes from $40 plus $1 times the number of programs sold.

4. Sample: The income comes from $10 plus $2 times the number of programs sold.

5.

Programs Sold	Process Column Offer 1	Income Offer 1	Process Column Offer 2	Income Offer 2
n	$40 + 1n$		$10 + 2n$	

6. The independent variable is number of programs sold. The dependent variable is income. The amount of income depends on the number of programs sold.

7. Let n = number of programs sold and m = money earned. A function rule for offer 1 could be $m = 40 + 1n$. (Note: This is a good time to begin the discussion that $1n = n$.)

8. Let n = number of programs sold and m = money earned. A function rule for offer 2 could be $m = 10 + 2n$.

9. As the number of programs sold increases, the income increases.

10. Fifty programs must be sold because $40 plus $1(50) gives $90. A student can also justify 50 programs by referring to the table in problem 2.

11. Forty programs must be sold because $10 plus $2(40) gives $90. Again, the answer can be justified by referring to the table.

12. The answer should include a decision based on how many programs the committee estimates that they will sell. They may note that money earned is the same when 30 programs are sold.

13. The table shows that when 30 programs are sold in both offers 1 and 2, the amount of income is $70. An alternate explanation would be to show the arithmetic yielding the $70 that occurs when 30 programs are sold in both offers.

14. The page break at this point in student pages is deliberate. You will probably have to lead your class to $40 + n = 10 + 2n$. After doing this, encourage them to do the viewing window (#15) within their groups.

15. *x*min   0 since all answers are positive. Some may give the table's minimum, 5.

    *x*max   Most will probably give 100 since it is the maximum in the table.

    *x*scale   5 is a good scale, but it will give a maximum value of 95 on the grid as given.

    *y*min   0 since all answers are positive. Some may give the table's minimum, 20.

    *y*max   210 is the maximum on the table, but some may give a max based on the scale.

    *y*scale   10 is a good scale, but it gives a maximum value of 200 on the grid as given.

16. The graph will vary based on scale.

17. The $1 income determines the steepness of the graph. The $40 gives the starting point on the *y*-axis.

18. The $2 income per program makes this graph steeper than the graph of offer 1, but the $10 starting amount gives a lower starting point on the *y*-axis.

19. The two graphs intersect at the point (30, 70). The significance of this point is that this is the point at which the earnings are that same for the two offers.

20. Even an answer of no requires a justification. It is very possible that students considered all the relevant information in problem 12. It is also possible that visually seeing information such as the much more rapid earnings for offer 2 changes their mind.

Write Your Notes and Ideas Here!

Connecting Table, Graph, and Function Notation

Objective:
Students will be introduced to **domain** and formal **function notation**.

Connections to Previous Learning:
Students should understand dependent and independent variable. Students should be able to make a table and a graph, to determine an appropriate viewing window for that graph, and to analyze information given in the table and graph.

Connections to TEKS:
111.32 b1A, b1B, b1C, b1D, b1E, b3A, c1B, c1C

Connections to AP:
The AP Calculus objective of analysis of functions

Time Frame:
75 minutes

Materials:
One copy of each page for each student

Teacher Notes:
Many algebra students have had little or no experience in connecting table, equation, and graph within the context of a real world experience. This lesson provides a review for those topics and introduces domain and function notation. A transparency master is provided to aid in the review. If students are proficient in the review topics, use the first 12 questions as an assessment. Since these 12 questions are a review, expect well worded and carefully justified answers. The new part of this lesson is an introduction to **domain** and to formal **function notation**.

Note: Although the terminology "function rule" is used in questions 7 and 8, formal function notation is not expected until question 14.

Connecting Table, Graph, and Function Notation

Lakeshia is a science team member who was not able to participate in the Problem-A-Thon or to sell programs. She is, however a whiz at computers. Ms. Alvarez, the language arts teacher, will pay her a starting wage of $10 and an additional $6 an hour to keep her computer records current. Ms. Alvarez will pay Lakeshia for whole hours only.

As you answer these questions, remember that you are expected to justify each answer.

1. In this situation, what variables might affect the amount that Lakeshia earns?

2. Complete the following table to show how much money Lakeshia can earn by working for Ms. Alvarez. (I know, I know! By now you are an expert at this!)

Number of Hours	Process Column	Money earned
1		
2		
3		
4		
5		
10		
15		
20		

3. Look for patterns in the table you just completed and describe in words a pattern you see in the amount of money earned.

4. Using your pattern, fill in the process column for *n* hours.

Number of Hours	Process Column	Money earned
n		

5. In this scenario, what is the independent variable? What is the dependent variable?

6. Lakeshia is primarily concerned with how many hours she will work and, of course, how much money she makes. Make a sentence with these variables using "depends" or "is a function of".

7. Choose and define meaningful variables to represent your independent variable and dependent variable. Using these letters, write a function rule for the amount of money Lakeshia earns.

8. Based on your pattern or function rule, how much would Lakeshia earn if she works 14 hours for Ms. Alvarez? (Remember to explain your answer in words or symbols.)

9. How long would Lakeshia have to work to earn $130?

10. Determine an appropriate viewing window for the graphs of both functions and justify your choice of viewing window.

    *x*min
    *x*max
    *x*scale
    *y*min
    *y*max
    *y*scale

11. Graph the data from your table below. Be sure to label both your axes and your graph.

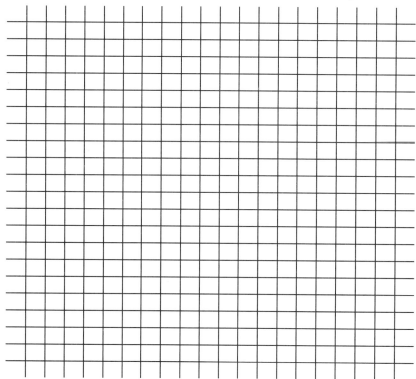

12.   What effect does the $6 pay for each hour have on the graph of the function? What effect does the $10 have on the graph?

13.   Let's revisit question 7. For the sake of consistency, let *n* be number of the hours Lakeshia worked, and let E represent the money she earned. Write an algebraic equation for the amount earned E in terms of *n*.

14.   The algebraic equation for E in terms of *n* describes E as a function of *n*. There is a specific notation that is often used for functions. The expression E(*n*) is read the function E of *n*. This means that E(*n*) would give the amount of money Lakeshia earned for *n* hours. Rewrite your algebraic equation from question 13 using this notation.

15.   In the function that you wrote in question 14, E(7) means to replace *n* with 7 and find the value of the function. What is the value of E(7)? Of E(11)?

16.   The information from the table in question 2 told us that E was 34 when *n* was 4. Write this fact using function notation.

17.   An important term that is often used in algebra is **substitution**. To find the amount of money earned for a specific number of hours, we replaced *n* with a number, that is we substituted a number for *n*. In problem 16, we substituted 4 for *n* and got $34 for the amount of money earned. Which of the following values of *n* can be meaningful substitutions? Why are they meaningful?

$n = 6$
$n = 11$
$n = 3.7$
$n = 0$
$n = 2\frac{1}{7}$

18.   If any replacement above is not meaningful, explain why it is not.

19. The set of **meaningful** replacements for *n* is called the **domain** of the function. Considering hours worked, what sort of numbers are reasonable substitutions? Using this new definition, what is the domain of the function that you wrote in question 14?

20. Think back to the Problem-A-Thon scenario. Ginny raised $2 in pledges from her friends and parents. Write Ginny's amount raised as a function of problems correctly worked. Choose meaningful variables and write your equation using function notation. Do the same thing for Genaro.

21. What is the domain for the function that you wrote in question 20? How is it the same as the domain in question 19? How is it different?

22. Look back at your graph of this situation in question 11. Now that you've thought about a meaningful domain, are there changes that you would make in this graph? If there are, explain those changes. If you would not make changes, explain why not.

Connecting Table, Graph, and Function Notation

Answers:

1. Accept all reasonable answers such as how much Ms Alvarez needs her help, number of hours she works, how fast she works, how happy Ms Alvarez is with her work, etc.

2.

Number of Hours	Process Column	Money earned
1	10 + (6 x 1)	16
2	10 + (6 x 2)	22
3	10 + (6 x 3)	28
4	10 + (6 x 4)	34
5	10 + (6 x 5)	40
10	10 + (6 x 10)	70
15	10 + (6 x 15)	100
20	10 + (6 x 20)	130

3. Sample: Lakeshia earns $10 plus $6 times n where n is the number of hours she works.

4.

Number of Hours	Process Column	Money earned
n	$10 + 6n$	

5. The independent variable is the number of hours she works. The dependent variable is the amount of money she earns.

6. The amount of money Lakeshia makes is a function of how many hours she works.

7. I'll use h for hours and m for money. My equation is $m = 10 + 6n$.

8. Lakeshia would make $10 + (6 x 14) which gives $94.

9. Sample: I'd start with $130 and subtract the $10 that Lakeshia gets to start. That gives $120. If she gets $6 an hour, I'd divide $120 by 6 and get 20 hours.

10. While I've not given a justification for these answers, students must give them.

   $x$min   0
   $x$max   about 20
   $x$scale   1's would work
   $y$min   0
   $y$max   about 130
   $y$scale   5's or 10's

11. Graphs will vary based on scale. At this point most students will probably connect the points rather than making a discrete graph.

12. Sample: The $10 represents the starting point on the *y*-axis. The $6 is the amount that the graph goes up for each hour on the *x*-axis.

13. Using *n* for hours and *E* for money earned, my equation is $E = 10 + 6n$.

14. If $E(n)$ is the amount of money that Lakeshia earns for *n* hours, then my new equation is $E(n) = 10 + 6n$.

15. $E(7) = 10 + 6(7)$, so $E(7) = \$52$ $E(11) = 10 + 6(11)$, so $E(11) = \$76$

16. $E(4) = \$34$

17. Students should be able to justify 6 and 11. They may say that 0 hours is also meaningful, but then they would have to discuss if Lakeshia gets $10 for not working.

18. Since Ms. Alvarez is only willing to pay for whole hours, 3.7 hours and $2\frac{1}{7}$ hours would not be meaningful.

19. There should be good discussion here. Is the answer whole numbers? (the most common student answer) If it is, is 0 a whole number? Is 0 meaningful? Is there an upper limit to the number of hours she could work? As this is most students' first experience with domain, this discussion should be encouraged.

20. For Ginny, I would use *p* for problems worked and *M* or money raised, so her function would be $M(p) = 2p$. For Genaro, I would use *p* for problems worked and *M* for money raised, so his function would be $M(p) = 3p$.

21. Again, the discussion is what is important here. It should be similar to the discussion in 19, but a good analysis should come more quickly this time.

22. The purpose of this question is to lead students to the difference between discrete and continuous data. The next lesson will have a very brief review and then will immediately move to this point. While students are looking at their graphs, hopefully they will realize that the points should not be connected with a solid line. (It is possible that some used points rather than a line. If they did, ask them why.) If they cannot connect the discussion in 19 and 21 with the graph, then lead them by asking what the solid line between 1 hour and 2 hours means.

Discrete and Continuous Data

Objective:
Students will determine a reasonable domain for a function and will find its range. Students will determine if the domain of a function is discrete or continuous.

Connections to Previous Learning:
Students should understand dependent and independent variable, domain, function notation, be able to make a table and a graph, to determine an appropriate viewing window for that graph, and to analyze information given in the table and graph.

Connections to TEKS:
111.32 b1A, b1B, b1C, b1D, b1E, b2B, b3A, c1B, c1C

Connections to AP:
The AP Calculus objective of analysis of functions

Time Frame:
90 minutes

Materials:
One copy of each page for each student

Teacher Notes:
This final lesson in the Laying a Foundation for Functions series reviews the concepts learned in the first four lessons. This lesson is written to be done in groups followed by a whole group discussion. The new part of this lesson is an introduction to **range** and to **discrete** and **continuous** data. Do the first student page before continuing so that students see the points where the data is separated so that no other number can be put between the two points. For the second paragraph, discuss each group's "situation that requires measurement". Try to find points of discontinuity. With situations that **do** require measurement, challenge the students to find numbers, within a reasonable range, that do not work. Thoroughly explore this topic.

Discrete and Continuous Data

In the past four lessons, you have looked at a several real world problem situations, and you have collected data for these situations, in the form of table, graph, and equation. You have found out that the specific real world situation in a problem determines the set of meaningful replacements that should be used. You also know now that this set of replacements is called the domain of a function.

It is time to consider the domain of a function more carefully. When the domain elements for a function in a real world context are separated from each other so that no other element can be put between two specific elements, we say that the function has a **discrete domain** and the information is called **discrete data**. These situations usually involve counting and are graphed using dots. Don't go on until you have wrapped your mind around this concept. Discuss first in your group and then with your teacher what it means for the domain elements of a function to be separated from each other. You may use the space below or another sheet of paper to summarize this discussion.

What happens to the domain when a situation requires measurement? In your groups, come up with a real world situation which is measured rather than counted. Does your situation have a discrete domain? If it does, explain why. If it does not, how is the domain different? Use the space below to give your group's answer to these questions. Be sure to justify your answers. You may consider situations that involve counting (such as those involving the math/science team) along with those that involve measurement to prepare your answer.

When the domain elements are not separated, the function is said to have a **continuous domain**, and the information is called **continuous data**. These situations are graphed using a line. Again, take the time to discuss first in your group and then with your teacher what it means for the domain elements of a function **not** to be separated from each other. You may use the space below or another sheet of paper to summarize this discussion.

77

In your group, consider the situations described below. Decide if they would result in discrete data or continuous data. Be sure to justify your answer.

1. Your weight from ages 12 to 14

2. Your algebra grades this six weeks

3. The number of problems you have for homework

4. The temperatures throughout the week

5. The high temperatures each day for a week.

Consider the function g(p) = 3p, a possible way to write the function for Genaro's function in the first lesson of this set. Suppose that Mrs. Snurd, the sponsor, changed the rules of the fund raiser to make it easier for sponsors to determine how much they owed a student. Mrs. Snurd decided that correct problems would be rounded to the nearest 10. She also decided that the upper limit of problems available would be 200. This considerably changes the set of meaningful replacements, the domain, for this situation.

6. List below the complete domain for p.

7. The set of values for each domain element is called the **range** of the function. Below, list the set of all ordered pairs for this function. List the set of ordered pairs with the domain element first, and the range element second, or (p, g(p)).

8. In problem 10, you will sketch the graph of the function g(p) such that g(p) = 3p. You will use the set of ordered pairs from problem 7. A short way to write the terminology for this domain is D = {p such that p is a multiple of 10 and $0 \le p \le 200$}. Before you go on to the graph, take a few minutes to discuss this notation first in your group and then with your teacher to be sure that you understand the notation.

9. Determine an appropriate viewing window for the graph of the function g(p) = 3p, and justify your choice of this window.

   *p*min

   *p*max

   *p*scale

   *g(p)*min

   *g(p)*max

   *g(p)*scale

10. Sketch the function below. Be sure to label your both your axes *p* and *g(p)* and to label your graph.

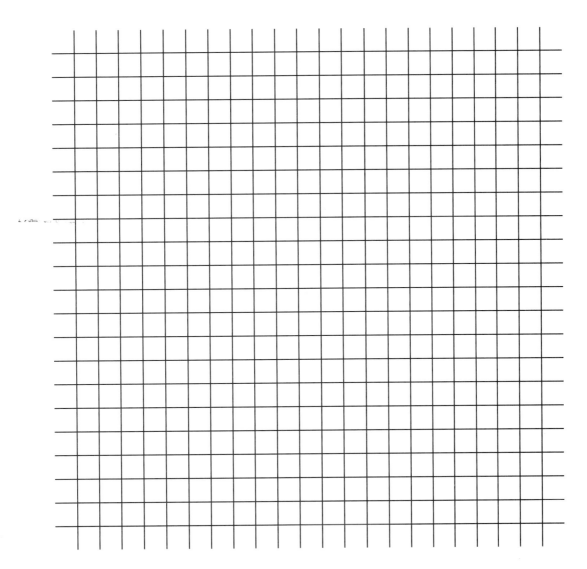

11. In questions 6-10 Genaro's fund raiser function is written as $g(p) = 3p$. In an algebraic expression, such as $3p$, the numerical factor is called the **coefficient** of the variable. In other words, the coefficient of $3p$ is _____. What does the coefficient of p tell about the rate of change in the amount of money that Genaro raises?

12. The table and the graph of a function represent the same information as the function's algebraic expression. How can the coefficient of p be observed in the table and in the graph?

Consider another scenario:

Davis, a new student, wants to be a part of the math/science team, but he has missed all the fund raisers. Davis is a cross country runner. He recruits 3 math/science team members to run with him on the local high school track. Each one got pledges for a length of time not to exceed one hour. (After all, the sponsors didn't want to be totally broke!) Davis gets pledges of $6 for each mile plus fixed pledges totaling $30.

Use this information to answer the questions below.

13. Use *a* for amount of money earned and *m* for the number of miles Davis runs. What is the dependent variable? The independent variable? Use these terms (amount of money earned and number of miles Davis runs) in a sentence to show that you understand the meaning of independent and dependent variables.

14. Using the variables from problem 13, write an equation which represents Davis' situation. Use function notation.

15. What is the coefficient of the variable in your function? What is the meaning of this coefficient?

16. Consider the following domain elements. Which are **not** meaningful in this situation?

   $m = 6$

   $m = 11$

   $m = 3.7$

   $m = 0$

   $m = 2\frac{1}{7}$

   $m = -3$

17. What is the domain of this function? Be sure to justify your answer.

18. Considering the domain you gave in question 16, what is the range of this function?

19. How many miles will Davis have to run to earn $55? $97.80? $9? $2002? Justify your answers.

20. You have finished this series of lessons which introduces functions. Come up with your own fundraising scenario for the Smedley team. First, make a table, write an equation, and draw a graph for this scenario. Second, use this scenario to show that you understand all of the special language of functions in these five lessons.

Discrete and Continuous Data

Answers:

Comments on the questions on the first page are included with the teacher notes.

1. Your weight from ages 12 to 14 - *This data is continuous. One explanation is that weight is measured and not counted. A student could explain that if their weight goes from 100 pounds to 101 pounds, there is also a point when the weight is 100.5 pounds, 100.4 pounds, 100.45 pounds, etc.*

2. Your algebra grades this six weeks - *This data is discrete. There will be a fixed number of grades. That number of grades can be counted.*

3. Problems you have for homework - *This data is can be counted and is discrete.*

4. The temperatures throughout the week - *This data is continuous. Temperature is measured. A point of discontinuity cannot be found as temperature rises or falls.*

5. The high temperatures each day for a week - *This data is discrete. Because it asks for the specific high temperature it can contain at most 7 pieces of data.*

6. Using g(p) = 3p, with problems rounded to the nearest 10 and with an upper limit of 200, the complete *domain for p is 0, 10, 20, 30, 40, ... , 180, 190, 200. (This would be a good point to discuss how to write a sequence of numbers with omitted members.)*

7. *The solution set for this function is {(0, 0), (10, 30), (20, 60), (30, 90), (40, 120), (50, 150), ... , (180, 540), (190, 570), (200, 600)}. Be sure students understand the notation (p, g(p)).*

8. *To be sure that students understand this notation, ask them to use the same notation for situations such as a domain greater than 0 but less than or equal to 30. See if students are thinking about reasonableness of a domain by checking scenarios such as the height of a person.*

9. Determine an appropriate viewing window for the graphs of both functions, and justify...

    pmin   *0 would be a good minimum because ...*

    pmax   *200 is a good maximum because ...*

    pscale   *10 would be an excellent scale because ...*

    g(p)min   *again, 0 would be a good minimum because ...*

    g(p)max   *600 would be a good maximum because ...*

    g(p)scale   *30 would be a good scale because ...*

    At this point, it is important that students be able to do a good job of justifying their choices.

10. *Graphs will vary according to the scale that students choose. It is important that this is a discrete graph.*

11. In questions 6-10 Genaro's fund raiser function is written as g(p) = 3p. In an algebraic expression, such as 3p, the numerical factor is called the **coefficient** of the variable. In other words, the coefficient of 3p is _3_. What does the coefficient of p tell about the rate of change in the amount of money that Genaro raises?

    Sample: The coefficient tells that the rate of change in the amount of money he raises is $3 for each problem, thereby giving $30 for each 10 questions.

12. The table and the graph of a function represent the same information as the function's algebraic expression. How can the coefficient of p be observed in the table and in the graph? *Sample: Looking back at the table and graph in lesson 2, the coefficient can be observed in the process column of the table, in the fact that the money increases $3 for each additional problem worked correctly. This rise of $3 per problem can also be observed in the graph.*

13. Use a for amount of money earned and m for the number of miles Davis runs. What is the dependent variable? The independent variable? Use these terms (amount of money earned and number of miles Davis runs) in a sentence to show that you understand the meaning of independent and dependent variables.

    Sample: The independent variable is number of miles that Davis runs. The dependent variable is the amount of money earned. The amount of money earned depends on the number of miles that Davis runs.

14. Using the variables from problem 13, write an equation which represents Davis' situation. Use function notation.

    a(m) = 6m + 30

15. What is the coefficient of the variable in your function? What is the meaning of this coefficient? *The coefficient is 6. This means that Davis raises $6 for each mile he runs.*

16. Consider the following domain elements. Which are not meaningful in this situation?

    Students will realize that 6 and 11 are meaningful. Have them examine the scenario if they think that 3.7 and $2\frac{1}{7}$ are not meaningful. They should not be able to find a reason to eliminate them.
    Most should decide that 0 is meaningful. After all, Davis could break his leg and not run. Students should agree that -3 is not meaningful since Davis cannot run a negative number of miles.

17. What is the domain of this function? Be sure to justify your answer.

    The domain of this function is the set of real numbers that are greater than or equal to 0. Students may be able to give a reasonable upper limit for this function by determining how many miles Davis might reasonably run in an hour. If they do not give an upper limit, have them defend this point.

18. Considering the domain you gave in question 17, what is the range of this function?

    The range is the set of real numbers that are at least 30, since Davis could conceivably not run at all. Again, make students think about an upper limit.

19. How many miles will Davis have to run to earn $55? $97.80? $9? $2002? Justify your answers.
    To earn $55, he must run $4\frac{1}{6}$ miles. To earn $97.80, he must run 11.3 miles. He cannot earn $9. A case can be made for starting at 0 (if he doesn't run and takes no money) or $30 (runs but takes the fixed $30), but he cannot earn $9. Hopefully all students realize that he cannot run fast enough, in one hour, to make $2002.

20. You have now finished this series of lessons which introduces functions. Come up with your own fundraising scenario for the Smedley team. First, make a table, write an equation, and draw a graph for this scenario. Second, use this scenario to show that you understand all of the special language of functions in these five lessons.

    Question 20 can be used for an assessment. Be sure to tell students how you will grade this assessment ahead of time, especially if you use a rubric.

Write Your Notes and Ideas Here!

Rate of Change

Objective:
Students will explore a graph showing positive, negative, and zero rates of change within the context of a real world situation.

Connections to Previous Learning:
Students should be able to graph ordered pairs on a Cartesian coordinate system. Given two data points and the unit of rate of change, students should be able to determine the rate of change.

Connections to TEKS:
111.32 c2A, c2B

Connections to AP:
The AP Calculus objective of rate of change

Time Frame:
120 minutes

Materials:
One copy of each page for each student, graph paper

Teacher Notes:
Before beginning this activity, review finding rate of change from real world data by doing a few class examples such as

Susan was 4'11" tall in 2000 and 5'4" tall in 2002. What was the rate of change of her height (in inches per year)? (2.5 inches per year)

The cost of 4 tickets to the movies is $40. The cost for 10 tickets is $70. What is the average rate of change in cost (in cost per ticket)? (–$0.50 per ticket)

In 8 minutes Andrew read 10 pages and in 20 minutes he read 25 pages. What is the average change in his reading speed? Include the unit of measure in your rate. (1.25 pages per minute)

Set up the Hurricane Lili activity for the students before giving them the data for their graphs. Be sure students understand that they will only have to graph a third of the data before they see the data set. Extend this activity by having students clip a graph from the financial page of a newspaper or magazine. The student will then use this graph to explain the rate of change for the graph as a whole and for specific intervals of the graph.

Rate of Change

During late September and early October, 2002, Tropical Storm, and later Hurricane, Lili meandered through the Gulf of Mexico and came ashore on the Louisiana coast west of New Orleans. This hurricane caused great concern as it approached the Louisiana coastline because of its power, and because of the damage caused by Hurricane Isadore in the weeks preceding it. The wind speed data on the data page provided was gathered and is provided by the National Oceanic and Atmospheric Administration (NOAA).

The website http://www.nhc.noaa.gov/archive/2002/LILI.shtml can be used if you would like to take a closer look at the data:

1. You will graph the data from the separate data page. It is divided into 3 tables so that your group may make, and combine, three separate graphs. Decide on a uniform scale for number of hours so that you <u>can</u> join your graphs. ***This is very important. Decide NOW if you will make the x scale by one hour intervals, two hour intervals, four hour intervals, etc.*** Be sure to label both your axes and your graph. **Notice that the increments from the data table are NOT uniform.** As the storm approached land NOAA reported data more frequently. If you have a four member group, decide who is going to monitor the work to be sure that the graphing is done correctly. In the space below, explain the *x* scale that your group chose and explain your reasoning.

2. What is a reasonable domain? What is a reasonable range?

3. The purpose of this exercise is to study rate of change from a graph. This data shows a positive rate of change, a negative rate of change, and zero rate of change. Graph your data points. Connect them with a red line segment if the rate of change is negative, a blue line segment if the rate of change is positive, and a black line segment if there is zero rate of change.

4. As you look at the graph, what does it tell you? When do you think the hurricane came ashore? Why?

5. What is the specific unit of measure for each rate of change?

6. What time frame shows the greatest rate of decrease? How can you tell from looking at the graph?

7. Determine the specific rate of change for the following time intervals:

    9-24-02 from 4 p.m. to 10 p.m.
    9-28-02 from 4 a.m. to 10 a.m.
    10-2-02 from 10 a.m. to 2 p.m.

    a) Explain how to determine the rate of change using arithmetic.

    b) Explain how to determine the rate of change by looking at the graph.

8. Explain how to determine rate of change in wind speed per hour for (t_1, wp_1) and (t_2, wp_2).

9. Use the internet to research the history of Hurricane Lili. Were there any conclusions that you made in question four that are historically inaccurate?

Rate of Change – Data Page

During late September and early October, 2002, Tropical Storm, and later Hurricane, Lili meandered through the Gulf of Mexico and came ashore on the Louisiana coast west of New Orleans. This hurricane caused great concern as it approached the Louisiana coast line because of its power, and because of the damage caused by Hurricane Isadore in the weeks preceding it. The wind speed data below was gathered and is provided by the National Oceanic and Atmospheric Administration (NOAA).

The website http://www.nhc.noaa.gov/archive/2002/LILI.shtml can be used if you would like to take a closer look at the data:

Date/Time EDT	Wind Speed	Date/Time EDT	Wind Speed	Date/Time EDT	Wind Speed
9-22; 4 AM	35 mph	9-27; 4 AM	35 mph	10-1; 7 PM	105 mph
10 AM	35 mph	10 AM	40 mph	10 PM	105 mph
4 PM	35 mph	4 PM	45 mph	10-2; 2 AM	110 mph
10 PM	35 mph	10 PM	50 mph	4 AM	110 mph
9-23; 4 AM	35 mph	9-28; 4 AM	50 mph	7 AM	110 mph
10 AM	35 mph	10 AM	35 mph	10 AM	120 mph
4 PM	60 mph	4 PM	50 mph	2 PM	134 mph
10 PM	60 mph	10 PM	45 mph	4 PM	140 mph
9-24; 4 AM	60 mph	9-29; 4 AM	45 mph	7 PM	145 mph
10 AM	70 mph	10 AM	50 mph	10 PM	145 mph
4 PM	70 mph	4 PM	60 mph	10-3; 4 AM	120 mph
10 PM	40 mph	10 PM	65 mph	6 AM	100 mph
9-25; 4 AM	40 mph	9-30; 4 AM	70 mph	8 AM	100 mph
10 AM	45 mph	10 AM	75 mph	10 AM	90 mph
4 PM	40 mph	4 PM	80 mph	2 PM	70 mph
10 PM	40 mph	10 PM	80 mph	4 PM	50 mph
9-26; 4 AM	40 mph	10-1; 4 AM	85 mph	10 PM	40 mph
10 AM	35 mph	10 AM	90 mph	10-4; 4 AM	35 mph
4 PM	35 mph	2 PM	100 mph		
10 PM	35 mph	4 PM	105 mph		

Rate of Change

Answers:

1. In the space below, explain the x scale that your group chose and explain your reasoning.

    Several scales are reasonable. What is important is that students justify the scale that they chose.

2. What is a reasonable domain? What is a reasonable range?

    The wording for this domain will vary. Students may describe it in terms of date or hours. It should match the scale that they chose in question 1. The range is wind speed from zero to about 150 mph.

3. Graph your data points. Connect them with a red line segment if the rate of change is negative, a blue line segment if the rate of change is positive, and a black line segment if there is no change.

    Check graphs to see that all sections used the agreed upon scale and that data points are connected according to directions given.

4. As you look at the graph, what does it tell you? When do you think the hurricane came ashore? Why?

    Answers will vary greatly here. Points that can be made are: loss of wind speed over land or cooler water, strengthening of wind speed over warmer water, etc. Students who "understand" hurricanes probably will say that the hurricane came ashore at 7 p.m. on October 2nd.

5. What is the specific unit of measure for each rate of change?

    The unit of measure is (miles per hour) per hour.

6. What time frame shows the greatest rate of decrease? How can you tell from looking at the graph?

    From 4am to 6am on October 2nd, the wind speed decreased 10 miles per hour per hour. The greatest rate of change on the graph occurs when the graph is "steepest".

7. Determine the average rate of change for the following time intervals:

    9-24-02 from 4 p.m. to 10 p.m.
    9-28-02 from 4 a.m. to 10 a.m.
    10-2-02 from 10 a.m. to 2 p.m.

    a) Explain how to determine the average rate of change using arithmetic.

    b) Explain how to determine the average rate of change by looking at the graph.

    Arithmetic explanations for each should include the difference quotients and the unit of the rate. The graphical explanation may be very similar to the arithmetic explanation if the student gets the points from the graph and finds the difference quotients. Some students may explain how to count the rate of change from the graph.

8. Explain how to determine rate of change in wind speed per hour for (t_1, wp_1) and (t_2, wp_2).

   The wind speed between these two points can be found by $(wp_2 - wp_1)/(t_2 - t_1)$

9. Use the Internet to research the history of Hurricane Lili. Were there any conclusions that you made in question four that are historically inaccurate?

   Because of Hurricane Isadore's lingering effects, Hurricane Lili weakened BEFORE it came ashore on October 3rd. The most likely incorrect conclusion would be that it came ashore at the highest wind speed on October 2nd.

Slope – Investigation

Objective:
Students will define slope as constant rate of change and find the slope of a line given two points, a table, or a graph.

Connections to Previous Learning:
Students should be able to find the rate of change between two points.

Connections to TEKS:
111.32 b3A, c1C, c2A, c2B

Connections to AP:
The AP Calculus objective of rate of change.

Time Frame:
45 minutes

Materials:
One copy of each page for each student

Teacher Notes:
This lesson reinforces making a table and a graph, deriving a pattern for that graph, writing a function for the graph, and determining rate of change from a real world situation. The new portion of this lesson is defining a constant rate of change as slope. The investigation is written to be done as a group activity. The assignment can be done as a continuation of the group activity or as individual work.

Slope – Investigation

Consider the following situation: At her annual physical, Mrs. Smith, the health teacher at Smedley Middle School, found that she was 153 centimeters tall and that she weighed 120 kilograms. After being diagnosed with hypertension (high blood pressure) and high cholesterol, she decided that she would follow a diet planned and supervised by her doctor. On this diet, Mrs. Smith planned to lose 0.5 kg per week.

1. Fill in the table at right to show Mrs. Smith's weight during the first 10 weeks of her diet, if she continues this pattern. Also give her weight for the nth week in the process column.

Week	Process Column	Weight
0		120kg
1		
2		
3		
4		
5		
6		
7		
8		
9		
10		
n		

2. Using the variables n for week number and w for weight, write a function rule to describe Mrs. Smith's weight after n weeks. Be sure to use function notation.

3. In a previous lesson, you learned how to find rate of change. Using the ordered pairs $(n, w(n))$, write the ordered pairs that represent her weight for weeks 3 and 4. What is Mrs. Smith's rate of change in kilograms per week between weeks 3 and 4?

In each of the following problems, be sure to justify your answer.

4. What is her rate of change in kilograms per week between weeks 3 and 5?

5. What is her rate of change in kilograms per week between weeks 2 and 8?

6. Stop now and compare your answers with those of your group. What conclusion can you draw about the rate of change in this function?

7. Determine an appropriate viewing window for the graph of this function, and **justify your choice of windows**.

    *x*min

    *x*max

    *x*scale

    *y*min

    *y*max

    *y*scale

8. Graph the function on the grid provided below. Be sure to draw and label your axes, label the tick marks, and label the graph.

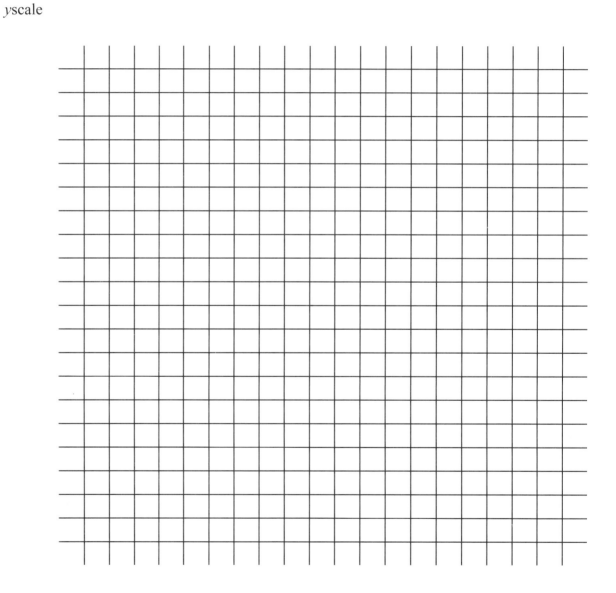

9. Discuss with your group the appearance of the points that you graphed above. Write any conclusions that you consider important about that appearance in the space below.

In every situation in which there is a **constant rate of change** between points, the points will always lie on a line. **This constant rate of change is called the slope of the line.**

In mathematics the Greek symbol Δ means "**change**". In problems 3, 4, and 5, you found that the rate of **change** was -0.5 kg per week. You found this by finding the **change** in kilograms and dividing it by the **change** in weeks. This is exactly what slope is. If you have two ordered pairs (x_1, y_1) and (x_2, y_2), then the slope is:

$$\frac{\Delta y}{\Delta x} = \frac{y_2 - y_1}{x_2 - x_1}$$

10. Pick any two points on the graph that you made in problem 8. List those two points as ordered pairs and show how to determine the slope between them.

11. Pick two points, different from the ones you chose for problem 10. List those two points as ordered pairs and determine the slope between them.

12. Consider the function that you wrote in problem 2, the rate of change that you found in problems 3 - 5, and the graph that you made in problem 8. Explain how to find the slope from the function, from the rate of change, and visually from the graph.

Slope – Independent Activity

Do this assignment on your own paper. Show each step for each problem. Carefully give each explanation.

1.   In the class work, you learned the formula for slope. That formula is $\dfrac{\Delta y}{\Delta x} = \dfrac{y_2 - y_1}{x_2 - x_1}$. The practical way to find slope is (difference in y) divided by (difference in x). Use that formula to find the slope between the points (0, 2) and (1, 7).

2.   Find the slope between the points (5, 0) and (6, 0). This is a special slope. Graph these two points so that you notice the appearance of the line between them.

3.   Find the slope between the points (0, 5) and (0, 6). Again, this is a special case. Graph these two points so that you notice the appearance of the line between them.

4.   One way to show that 3 or more points lie on the same line is to **determine that the slope between pairs of points is the same.**   Prove that the points (0, 2), (2, 5), and (6, 11) do or do not lie on the same line.

5.   Prove that the points (3, 2), (1, 0), and (-2, -5) do or do not lie on the same line.

6.   Given the function f(x) = 2x + 3, find two points on the graph, and find the slope between these two points. Remember, you CAN find two points on this line. If x is 0, what is f(x)? That gives you one ordered pair (0, 3). Find another point. Calculate the slope.

7.   Given the function g(x) = 3x – 2, find two points on its graph, and find the slope between these two points.

8.   Given the function m(n) = $\dfrac{2}{3}$n + 2, find two points on its graph, and find the slope between these two points.

9.   Look carefully at the slopes of the lines in 6, 7, and 8. Do you notice the slope that you determined somewhere in the equation? Explain what you notice.

10.   Find the slope of the equation 2x + 3y = 6. **Remember, find two points, then find the slope.** Is this slope as obvious in the equation? Can you find it in the equation? Where?

Slope – Investigation

Answers:

1. Fill in the table at right to show Mrs. Smith's weight during the first 10 weeks of her diet, if she continues this pattern. Also give her weight for the *n*th week in the process column.

Week	Process Column	Weight
0	$120 - 0(.5)$	120 kg
1	*120 – 1(.5)*	*119.5 kg*
2	*120 – 2(.5)*	*119 kg*
3	*120 – 3(.5)*	*118.5 kg*
4	*120 – 4(.5)*	*118 kg*
5	*120 – 5(.5)*	*117.5 kg*
6	*120 – 6(.5)*	*117 kg*
7	*120 – 7(.5)*	*116.5 kg*
8	*120 – 8(.5)*	*116 kg*
9	*120 – 9(.5)*	*115.5 kg*
10	*120 – 10(.5)*	*115 kg*
n	*120 – n(.5)*	

2. Using the variables *n* for week number and *w* for weight, write a function rule to describe Mrs. Smith's weight after n weeks. Be sure to use function notation.

3. In a previous lesson, you learned how to find rate of change. Using the ordered pairs $(n, w(n))$, write the ordered pairs that represent her weight for weeks 3 and 4. What is Mrs. Smith's rate of change in kilograms per week between weeks 3 and 4?

   (3, 118.5) and (4, 118). The rate of change is (118.5 – 118)/ (3 – 4), so the rate of change is -0.5 kg/week.

4. What is her rate of change in kilograms per week between weeks 3 and 5?

   (3, 118.5) and (5, 117.5). The rate of change is (118.5 – 117.5)/ (3 – 5), so the rate of change is -0.5 kg/week.

5. What is her rate of change in kilograms per week between weeks 2 and 8?

   (2, 119) and (8, 116). The rate of change is (119 – 116)/ (2 – 8), so the rate of change is -0.5 kg/week.

6. Stop now and compare your answers with those of your group. What conclusion can you draw about the rate of change in this function?

   The rate of change in these problems was always -0.5 kg/week.

7. Determine an appropriate viewing window for the graph of this function, and **justify your choice of windows**.

    Answers will vary widely. Any window which can be reasonably justified should be accepted.

    xmin – 0, There are no negative weeks.
    xmax – 10, The largest number of weeks on the table is 10
    xscale – 1 to match the table
    ymin – Answers may widely vary here, from near 150 kg to 0.
    ymax – 120, One hundred twenty kg was the largest, the starting, amount.
    yscale – Answers will vary here depending on the minimum given.

8. Graph the function.

    As graphs will vary according to scale, no sample is given. Be sure to check labeling of axes, tick marks, and graph.

9. Discuss with your group the appearance of the points that you graphed above. Write any conclusions that you consider important about that appearance in the space below.

    Any reasonable conclusion should be accepted; however, it is hoped that groups will notice that these points lie on a line.

10. Pick any two points on the graph that you made in problem 8. List those two points as ordered pairs, and show how to determine the slope between them.

    Check students' work to be sure that they listed the points as ordered pairs, showed determining the slope, and arrived at an answer of -0.5 kg/week.

11. Pick two points, different from the ones you chose for problem 10. List those two points and determine the slope between them.

    Check students' work to be sure that they listed the points as ordered pairs, showed determining the slope, and arrived at an answer of -0.5 kg/week.

12. Consider the function that you wrote in problem 2, the rate of change that you found in problems 3 - 5, and the graph that you made in problem 8. Explain how to find the slope from the function, from the rate of change, and visually from the graph.

    Students should be able to explain that the slope in each situation was -0.5. They may simply state that the slope is the coefficient of x in the function, that it is the same as the rate of change, and that it can be found in the graph by looking at the change between any two points. They may also explain how to find the slope in each of these situations.

Slope – Independent Activity

Answers:

1. Find the slope between the points (0, 2) and (1, 7).

$$\frac{7-2}{1-0} = \frac{5}{1} = 5$$

2. Find the slope between the points (5, 0) and (6, 0). $\frac{0-0}{6-5} = \frac{0}{1} = 0$ *Note: this solution should also show a graph of these two points.*

3. Find the slope between the points (0, 5) and (0, 6). $\frac{6-5}{0-0} = \frac{1}{0} =$ undefined. It is very probable that a discussion and/or proof of why division by zero is impossible will be required here. This solution should also show a graph of these two points.

4. Prove that the points (0, 2), (2, 5), and (6, 11) do or do not lie on the same line.

$$\frac{11-5}{6-2} = \frac{6}{4} = \frac{3}{2} \qquad \frac{11-2}{6-0} = \frac{9}{6} = \frac{3}{2}$$ *Since the slopes are the same, they lie on the same line.*

5. Prove that the points (3, 2), (1, 0), and (-2, -5) are or are not on the same line.

Students will get different slopes here and will prove that the points do not lie on the same line.

6. Given the function f(x) = 2x + 3, find two points on the graph, and find the slope of the line.

Once students find another point and do the difference quotient, they will find that the slope is 2.

7. Given the function g(x) = 3x – 2, find two points on its graph, and find the slope between these two points.

Students should use the difference quotient to show that the slope is 3.

8. Given the function m(n) = $\frac{2}{3}$n + 2, find two points on that line, and find the slope between these two points.

Students should use the difference quotient to show that the slope is $\frac{2}{3}$.

9. Look carefully at the slopes of the lines in 6, 7, and 8. Do you notice the slope that you determined somewhere in the equation? Explain what you notice.

The slope is the coefficient of x.

10. Find the slope of the equation $2x + 3y = 6$. **Remember, find two points, then find the slope.** Is this slope as obvious in the equation? Can you find it in the equation? Where?

    After choosing two points, the students will find that the slope is $-\frac{2}{3}$. Answers may vary here.

    Hopefully students noticed the 2 and 3 as coefficients of x and y and perhaps even noted that the fraction is the coefficient of x if the equation is in $y = mx + b$ form.

Write Your Notes and Ideas Here!

Calculating Average Rates of Change

Objective:
Students will connect the concept of slope to finding the average rate of change.

Connections to Previous Learning:
Students should know how to calculate a slope given the coordinates of two points.

Connections to TEKS:
111.32 c2A and c2B

Connections to AP:
The AP Calculus objective of rate of change

Time Frame:
45 minutes

Materials:
Student worksheet

Teacher Notes:
1. Emphasize to students that they have calculated average rates of change. That means that the rate of change might have been different at various points during the interval, sometimes higher than the average and sometimes lower than the average.

2. Problems # 14 and 15 are based on tabular data provided to AP Calculus students on free response questions 1999 AB 3 and 2001 AB 2.

Calculating Average Rates of Change

Instructions: Read each problem carefully and determine the coordinates of the two points mentioned. Use the coordinates to calculate the slope of a line passing through those two points. Show the difference quotient that leads to your answer. Write a sentence interpreting the slope as an average rate of change. Be sure to include units in your answer.

Example: While working on her English essay, Tammy noticed that her clock read 12:32 and the word count for her paper was 568. When she finished the paper, her clock read 12:48 and the final word count was 1128.

Answer: (32, 568) and (48, 1128)

$$\frac{1128 - 568 \text{ words}}{48 - 32 \text{ minutes}} = \frac{560 \text{ words}}{16 \text{ minutes}} = 35 \text{ words per minute}$$

Tammy can type at an average rate of 35 words per minute.

1. The population of Austin, Texas in 1990 was 472,000 people. The population in 1980 was 346,000 people.

2. At 3 o'clock, Sharon passes mile marker 295 on Highway 35. At 6 o'clock she passes mile marker 475.

3. The value of my new car after 2 years was $11,200. When the car is 6 years old, the value has dropped to $6100.

4. A lab technician is growing a bacteria sample. After one hour, she notes that there are 250 bacteria in the sample. After 3 hours, she notes that there are 1000 bacteria in the sample.

5. Mr. Suarez joined a gym to lose weight. After three weeks of membership, he weighed 189 pounds. When he had been a member for twelve weeks, he weighed only 162 pounds.

6. On his fifth birthday, Paul was 42 inches tall. On his seventh birthday, he was 48 inches tall.

7. In 1984, the price of a VCR was $375. In 1996, the price was $125.

8. Dixie left Austin with a full tank of gas (16 gallons) and an odometer reading of 12,584 miles. Upon arriving in Houston, her gas tank was only half full and her odometer reading was 12,792.

9. Dara works in the clothing department of a large store. When she began her shift at 4 p.m., the register showed sales of $10,550. When she clocked out at 9 p.m., the register showed sales of $40,620.

10.   At one o'clock the temperature outside registered 85 degrees. At seven o'clock, the temperature was 61 degrees.

11.   When an amusement park opened, the counter on the turnstile at the entrance read 1278. Seven hours later, the counter read 3672.

12.   The concession stand at the amusement park begins the day with 500 popcorn containers. When the park closes, twelve hours later, an inventory shows there are only 44 containers left.

13.   Scott began printing his history paper at 3:15. At 3:20, he found that it had printed 12 of his 15 pages.

14.   The rate at which water flows out of a pipe, in gallons per hour, is given by a function R of time t. The table shows the rate as measured every 3 hours for a 24-hour period. Determine how fast the rate of flow is increasing between 3 and 12 hours.

t (hours)	$R(t)$ (gallons per hour)
0	9.6
3	10.4
6	10.8
9	11.2
12	11.4
15	11.3
18	10.7
21	10.2
24	9.6

15.   The temperature, in degrees Celsius $(°C)$, of the water in a pond is a function W of time t. The table shows the water temperature as recorded every 3 days over a 15-day period. Over what time interval is the water temperature increasing most rapidly and how fast is it rising? Over what time interval is the water temperature falling most rapidly and how fast is it dropping?

t (days)	$W(t)$ $(°C)$
0	20
3	31
6	28
9	24
12	22
15	21

Calculating Average Rates of Change

Answers:

1. (1990, 427,000) and (1980, 346,000)

$$\frac{472,000 - 346,000}{1990 - 1980} = \frac{126,000}{10} = 12,600 \frac{\text{people}}{\text{year}}$$

The population of Austin was increasing at an average rate of 12,600 people per year.

2. (3, 295) and (6, 475) $\quad \frac{475 - 295}{6 - 3} = \frac{180}{3} = 60 \frac{\text{miles}}{\text{hour}}$

Sharon is traveling at an average rate of 60 miles per hour.

3. (2, 11,200) and (6, 6100) $\quad \frac{6,100 - 11,200}{6 - 2} = \frac{-5100}{4} = -1275 \frac{\text{dollars}}{\text{year}}$

The new car is decreasing in value at an average rate of $1275 per year.

4. (1, 250) and (3, 1,000) $\quad \frac{1000 - 250}{3 - 1} = \frac{750}{2} = 375 \frac{\text{bacteria}}{\text{hour}}$

The bacteria is growing at an average rate of 375 bacteria per hour.

5. (3, 189) and (12, 162) $\quad \frac{162 - 189}{12 - 3} = \frac{-27}{9} = -3 \frac{\text{pounds}}{\text{week}}$

Mr. Suarez is losing weight at an average rate of 3 pounds per week.

6. (5, 42) and (7, 48) $\quad \frac{48 - 42}{7 - 5} = \frac{6}{2} = 3 \frac{inches}{year}$

Paul is growing at an average rate of 3 inches per year.

7. (1984, 375) and (1996, 125) $\quad \frac{125 - 375}{1996 - 1984} = \frac{-250}{12} = \frac{-125}{6} = -20.83\overline{3} \frac{\text{dollars}}{\text{year}}$

The price of a VCR was dropping at an average rate of $20.83 per year.

8. (16, 12584) and (8, 12792) $\quad \frac{12584 - 12792}{16 - 8} = \frac{-208}{8} = -26 \frac{\text{miles}}{\text{gallon}}$

Dixie drives an average of 26 miles for every gallon of gasoline.

9. (4, 10550) and (9, 40620) $\dfrac{40620 - 10550}{9 - 4} = \dfrac{30070}{5} = 6014 \dfrac{\text{dollars}}{\text{hour}}$

Merchandise is being sold at an average rate of $6014 per hour.

10. (1, 85) and (7, 61) $\dfrac{61 - 85}{7 - 1} = \dfrac{-24}{6} = -4 \dfrac{\text{deg}}{\text{hour}}$

The temperature is decreasing at an average rate of 4 degrees per hour.

11. (0, 1278) and (7, 3672) $\dfrac{3672 - 1278}{7 - 0} = \dfrac{2394}{7} = 342 \dfrac{\text{people}}{\text{hour}}$

People are entering the park at an average rate of 342 people per hour.

12. (0, 500) and (12, 44) $\dfrac{44 - 500}{12 - 0} = \dfrac{-456}{12} = -38 \dfrac{\text{containers}}{\text{hour}}$

Popcorn sells at an average rate of 38 containers per hour.

13. (15, 0) and (20, 12) $\dfrac{12 - 0}{20 - 15} = \dfrac{12}{5} = 2.4 \dfrac{\text{pages}}{\text{min}}$

The printer prints pages at an average rate of 2.4 pages per minute.

14. (3, 10.4) and (12, 11.4) $\dfrac{11.4 - 10.4}{12 - 3} \dfrac{\text{gallons per hour}}{\text{hours}} = \dfrac{1 \text{ gallons per hour}}{9 \text{ hours}}$

The rate of flow is increasing at an average rate of $\dfrac{1}{9}$ (gallons per hour) per hour.

15. **Water temperature is increasing most rapidly between 0 and 3 days. It is increasing at an average rate of $3\dfrac{2}{3}$ °C per day. Water temperature is falling most rapidly between 6 and 9 days. It is dropping at an average rate of $1\dfrac{1}{3}$ °C per day.**

Write Your Notes and Ideas Here!

The Amusement Park Problem

Objective:
Students will examine a function that relates to the rate at which people enter and leave an amusement park. They will interpret function notation and determine particular values. They will solve a variety of problems pertaining to the situation presented.

Connections to Previous Learning:
Students should have worked with function notation and accumulation previously. They should be able to plot points and solve word problems.

Connections to TEKS:
111.32 b1A, b1C, b1D, b1E, b2D

Connections to AP:
The AP Calculus objectives of rate of change and accumulation

Time Frame:
45 minutes

Materials:
Worksheet for each student, graphing paper

Teacher Notes:
Depending on students' previous experiences, this lesson could be done as a whole class activity, in small groups with the teacher providing suggestions and guidance, or individually.

If unfamiliar with the methods of approximation mentioned in #7, then examine the Connecting to AP Calculus: Accumulation section of this guide. This problem is based on a question from the 2002 AP Calculus examination.

As an extension, students could graph $L(t)$ on the same set of axes as $E(t)$, perhaps in a different color. By examining the graph, students should be able to approximate the time at which the same number of people are entering the park as are leaving. Is the graphical answer supported by the table of values?

The Amusement Park Problem

The rate at which people enter an amusement park on a given day is modeled by the function E. The rate at which people leave the same amusement park on the same day is modeled by the function L.

Both $E(t)$ and $L(t)$ are measured in people per hour and time t is measured in hours after midnight. These functions are valid for $9 < t < 23$, the hours during which the park is open. At time $t = 9$, there are no people in the park.

Use the data in the chart below to answer the questions.

t	$E(t)$	$L(t)$	$E(t) - L(t)$
9	624	91	
11	918	135	
13	918	220	
15	624	396	
17	380	761	
19	240	1099	
21	161	761	
23	114	396	

1. Explain the meaning of the function notation $E(t)$.

2. What does $t = 13$ mean in the context of the problem?

3. What does $L(13)$ mean in the context of the problem and what is its value?

4. What t value corresponds to 5 p.m.?

5. Fill in the fourth column of the chart above. Why is $E(t) - L(t)$ positive at $t = 15$, but negative at $t = 17$? Explain the meaning of $E(t) - L(t)$ in the context of the problem.

6. Make a graph showing E as a function of t.

7. Use your graph and the data in the table above to approximate the number of people who have entered the park by 5 p.m. using a) a left hand approximation, b) a right hand approximation, and c) a trapezoidal approximation.

8. Approximate the number of people who are in the park at 5 p.m. Explain your method clearly.

9. Why are answers to questions # 7 and # 8 different?

109

10. The price of admission to the park is $15 until 5 p.m. After 5 p.m., the price of admission to the park is $11. Approximately how many dollars are collected from admissions to the park on the given day? Show your calculations clearly.

11. Cashiers can serve an average of one person every 30 seconds. In order to keep the lines moving quickly, how many cashiers should be on duty at the park's entrance when it is busiest? Show the calculations that support your answer.

12. Parking lot attendants can process one car every 40 seconds as they leave the parking lot. If each car has an average of 3 people in it, how many parking lot attendants should be on duty when the exit is the busiest? Show the calculations that support your answer.

The Amusement Park Problem

Answers:

1. $E(t)$ means that the rate at which people enter the park is dependent on the time of day.

2. $t = 13$ corresponds to a clock time of 1:00 p.m.

3. $L(13)$ represents the rate at which people are leaving the park at 1:00 p.m. $L(13)=220 \frac{\text{people}}{\text{hour}}$

4. $t = 17$ corresponds to 5 p.m.

5. It is positive at $t = 15$ because the number of people in the park is increasing, but negative at $t = 17$ because the number of people in the park is decreasing. $E(t) - L(t)$ means the rate at which the number of people in the park is changing.

t	$E(t)$	$L(t)$	$E(t) - L(t)$
9	624	91	533
11	918	135	783
13	918	220	698
15	624	396	228
17	380	761	-381
19	240	1099	-859
21	161	761	-600
23	114	396	-282

6.

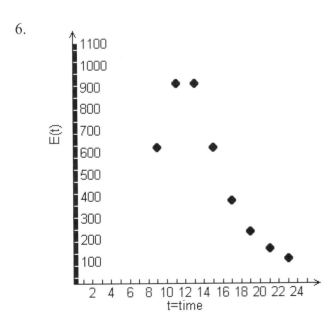

7. a) $2\,hours\,[624+918+918+624]\dfrac{people}{hour}=6168$ people

    b) $2\,hours\,[918+918+624+380]\dfrac{people}{hour}=5680$ people

    c) $\dfrac{2\,hours\,[624+918+918+624+918+918+624+380]}{2}\dfrac{people}{hour}=5924$ people

8. 3570 people One possible solution is 5924 – [91 + 2 x 135 + 2 x 220 + 2 x 396 + 761].

9. Answer to #7 is the number of people who have entered the park but some of those people have since left the park. Answer to #8 is the number of people in the park at 5 p.m.

10. (5924)($15)+(1296)($11) = $103,116

11. 2 people per minute = 120 people per hour

    $918 \div 120 = 7.65$ 8 cashiers should be on duty

12. $\dfrac{1\,car}{40\,sec}\cdot\dfrac{60\,sec}{1\,min}\cdot\dfrac{60\,min}{1\,hr}=90\dfrac{cars}{hr}$

    $\dfrac{90\,cars}{hr}\cdot\dfrac{3\,people}{car}=\dfrac{270\,people}{hr}$

    $1099 \div 270 = 4.070$

    4 or 5 parking attendants

Shoveling Dirt

Objective:
Students will examine the concepts of rates of change and continuity.

Connections to Previous Learning:
Students should be able to perform unit conversions, graph ordered pairs and lines, determine slopes of line, write equations of lines, and determine domain and range.

Connections to TEKS:
111.32 b1C, b1D, b1E, b2B, b2C, c1B c2A, c2A, c2B, c2C, c2F

Connections to AP:
The AP Calculus objective of rate of change

Time Frame:
90 minutes

Materials:
Calculator

Teacher Notes:
The purpose of this lesson is for students to physically understand rates of change – how fast is something happening as time passes. The connection to slope will be obvious. The three men filling the hole is a discontinuous function because the hole is not being continuously filled with dirt. When the truck fills the hole, the continuous activity helps the student understand why the graph is a solid line. Other topics used in this lesson are dimensional analysis, domain and range.

Shoveling Dirt

Brandon has been given the task of filling a large hole with dirt, so he is trying the come up with an efficient plan for getting the work done. He can do the job by himself, he can ask friends to help, he can work alone using a wheelbarrow, or he can pay for a dump truck to come out and fill the hole for him. The dimensions of the hole are 6 ft. x 6 ft. x 6 ft.

Brandon knows that one shovel will hold $\frac{1}{2}$ cu. ft. He also knows that he can toss one shovel full of dirt into the hole every twelve seconds.

1. What is the volume of the hole?

2. Complete the table below with cubic feet of dirt as a function of time in seconds.

time	12 seconds	24 seconds	36 seconds	48 seconds	60 seconds
cubic feet					

3. At this rate, how long will it take Brandon to fill the hole? Give the answer in seconds, in minutes, and in hours and minutes.

4. Draw the first 60 seconds of the graph of the amount of dirt in cubic feet that Brandon shovels into the hole.

5. This is not a continuous graph. Why?

6. Brandon asks his friend Jim to help. Jim works at the same rate as Brandon, and they throw the dirt into the hole at the same time.

    a) Draw a graph of the amount of dirt in the hole for the first minute that they work.

    b) How does this graph compare to the graph in problem #3?

    c) What is the domain of their work as a function of seconds?

    d) What is the domain of the entire job as a function of minutes?

    e) What is the range of their work?

    f) When is the hole half filled?

7. If they want to fill the hole in 5 minutes, how many people, working as fast as Brandon, are needed for the job? Explain why this probably not a good plan.

8. Cooper, another friend of Brandon's, has a shovel that will hold 1 ft³, twice as much dirt as the ones used by Brandon and Jim. Cooper still needs 12 seconds to fill his shovel, so he throws dirt into the hole at a rate of $\dfrac{1}{12}\dfrac{ft^3}{sec}$.

   a) If all three men are working together, how long will it take them to completely fill the hole?

   b) Draw the graph of their work for the first minute. Discuss how this graph differs from the first two graphs.

9. Brandon decides to purchase a wheelbarrow and to work alone. The wheelbarrow holds 4 cubic feet of dirt. Brandon requires two minutes to fill the wheelbarrow and then one minute to unload it.

   a) Draw a graph of Brandon's work for the first 10 minutes?

   b) How much time will Brandon need to complete the job using the wheelbarrow? Give the answer in minutes and in hour and minutes.

10. Instead of using a shovel, Brandon contracts with a large dump truck to bring in a load of dirt. The driver tells Brandon that he will need exactly 5 minutes to fill the hole.

    a) At what rate will the dump truck pour dirt into the hole?

    b) Draw a graph to describe the work of the dump truck.

    c) How is this graph different from all the other graphs?

11. The dump truck cannot be brought in until after Brandon shovels dirt for one hour.

    a) How much dirt does the truck need to bring?

    b) If the truck can unload the dirt at the same rate as before, write an equation to describe the amount of dirt in cubic feet that the dump truck unloads into the hole as a function of the time in minutes.

12. If you have the task of filling the hole with dirt, how would you get the job done? Explain your choice.

Shoveling Dirt

Answers:

1. 216 cubic feet

2. Complete the table below with cubic feet of dirt as a function of time.

time	12 seconds	24 seconds	36 seconds	48 seconds	60 seconds
cubic feet	0.5 cu ft.	1 cu ft.	1.5 cu ft.	2 cu ft.	2.5 cu ft.

3. At this rate, how long will it take Brandon to fill the hole? Give the answer in seconds, in minutes, and in hours and minutes.

$$216\,\text{ft}^3 = \frac{1\,\text{ft}^3}{24\,\text{seconds}} \times t \text{ seconds}$$

$$t = 5184 \text{ seconds}$$

Brandon can fill the hole in 5184 seconds, 86.4 minutes, or 1 hour and 26.4 minutes

4. Draw the first 60 seconds of the graph of the amount of dirt in cubic feet that Brandon shovels into the hole.

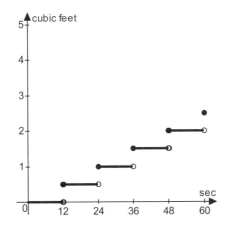

5. This is not a continuous graph. Why?

The amount of dirt in the hole changes only every 12 seconds.

117

6. Brandon asks his friend Jim to help. Jim works at the same rate as Brandon, and they throw the dirt into the hole at the same time.

    a) Draw a graph of the amount of dirt in the hole for the first minute that they work.

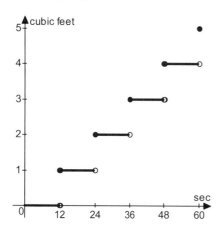

    b) How does this graph compare to the graph in problem #3?

    The graph is steeper and in 1 minute the hole has been filled with 5 cu ft of dirt.

    c) What is the domain of their work as a function of seconds?

    Domain: $\{0, 12, 24, 36, \ldots , 2592\}$

    d) What is the domain of their work as a function of minutes?

    Domain: $\left\{0, \dfrac{12}{60}, \dfrac{24}{60}, \dfrac{36}{60}, \cdots, \dfrac{2592}{60}\right\}$

    e) What is the range of their work?

    Range: $\{0,1,2,3,\cdots,216\}$

    f) When will their work be half completed?

    $$\frac{216\,\text{ft}^3}{2} = \frac{1\,\text{ft}^3}{12\,\text{seconds}}t$$

    $$t = 1296\,\text{seconds}$$

    The work was half completed in 1296 seconds or 21.6 minutes.

7. If they want to fill the hole in 5 minutes, how many people, working as fast as Brandon, are needed for the job? Explain why this probably not a good plan.

Each person is working at a rate of $\dfrac{1}{24}\dfrac{\text{ft}^3}{\text{sec}}$. Let n be the number of people required to complete

the job. The rate for all of the workers together will be $\dfrac{n}{24}\dfrac{\text{ft}^3}{\text{sec}}$. Thus,

$$216\,\text{ft}^3 = \frac{n}{24}\frac{\text{ft}^3}{\text{sec}} \times 5\,\text{min} \times \frac{60\ \text{seconds}}{\text{min}}$$
$$n = 17.28$$

This means that 18 people will be needed to complete the job within 5 minutes. (This probably is not a good plan because this is too large of a crowd for one hole!)

8. Cooper, another friend of Brandon's, has a shovel that will hold 1 ft³, twice as much dirt as the ones used by Brandon and Jim. Cooper still needs 12 seconds to fill his shovel, so he throws dirt into the hole at a rate of $\dfrac{1}{12}\dfrac{\text{ft}^3}{\text{sec}}$.

a) If all three men are working together, how long will it take them to completely fill the hole?

Since Cooper works at a rate of $\dfrac{1}{12}\dfrac{\text{ft}^3}{\text{sec}} = \dfrac{2}{24}\dfrac{\text{ft}^3}{\text{sec}}$ the group of three boys working together

will work at a rate of $\dfrac{1}{24}\dfrac{\text{ft}^3}{\text{sec}} + \dfrac{1}{24}\dfrac{\text{ft}^3}{\text{sec}} + \dfrac{2}{24}\dfrac{\text{ft}^3}{\text{sec}} = \dfrac{4}{24}\dfrac{\text{ft}^3}{\text{sec}}$ or $\dfrac{1}{6}\dfrac{\text{ft}^3}{\text{sec}}$

$$216\,\text{ft}^3 = \frac{1\,\text{ft}^3}{6\,\text{seconds}}\,t$$
$$t = 1296\,\text{seconds}$$

The three boys will complete the job in 1296 seconds or 21.6 minutes.

Note: It would be good to point out here that the 3 people completed the whole job in the same amount of time it took 2 people to do ½ the job.

b)   Draw a graph of their work for the first minute. Discuss how this graph differs from the first two graphs.

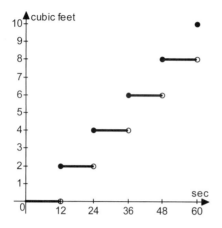

The graph is steeper and reaches 10 cubic feet in 60 seconds. The domain is still the same since each boy still requires 12 seconds to fill his shovel.

9.   Brandon, working alone, decides to use a wheelbarrow that holds 4 cubic feet of dirt. He requires two minutes to fill the wheelbarrow and then one minute to unload it.

a)   Draw a graph of Brandon's work for the first 10 minutes?

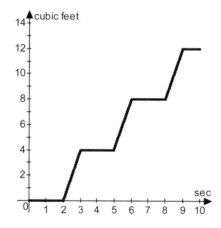

b)   How much time will Brandon need to complete the job using the wheelbarrow? Give the answer in minutes and in hour and minutes.

$$\frac{4}{3}\frac{\text{ft}^3}{\text{min}}\,t = 216 \text{ ft}^3$$

$t = 162$ minutes or 2 hours and 42 minutes.

10.   A large dump truck of dirt is brought in and fills the hole in 5 minutes.

   a)   At what rate does the dump truck pour dirt into the hole?

$$\frac{216 \ \text{ft}^3}{5 \ \text{min}}$$

   b)   Draw a graph to describe the work of the dump truck.

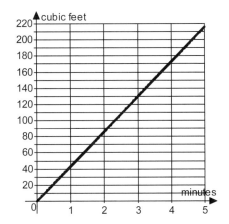

   c)   How is this graph different from all the other graphs?

   It is steeper and has a continuous domain.

11.   The dump truck cannot be brought in until after Brandon shovels dirt for one hour.

   a)   How much dirt does the truck need to bring?

   $216 - 150 = 66$. The truck needs to bring 66 cubic feet of dirt.

   b)   If the truck can unload the dirt at the same rate as before, write an equation to describe the amount of dirt in cubic feet that the dump truck unloads into the hole in cubic feet as a function of time in minutes.

   The dump truck pours dirt into the hole at a rate of $\dfrac{216 \ \text{ft}^3}{5 \ \text{min}}$. The truck does not begin until 60 minutes after Brandon goes to work so there is already 150 ft^3 of dirt in the hole. The equation $y - 150 = \dfrac{216}{5}(x - 60)$ will model the work of the dump truck beginning at 60 minutes after Brandon goes to work.

12.   Answers will vary. Give credit for any answer that is supported with reasons.

Reading the Graph

Objectives:
Students will interpret, analyze and formulate conclusions based on a graph of a two different functions, formulate an equation of a line using function notation, find the average rate of change over a specific time interval, find values from the graph and interpret the meanings of the problem situation, and interpret a graph with a verbal description.

Connections to Previous Learning:
Students should be able to determine average rate of change and write verbal descriptions of graphs.

Connections to TEKS:
111.32 b1A, b1C-E, b2C, b2D, b3A, b4A, c1C, c2A-D

Connections to AP:
The AP Calculus objectives of rate of change, position and velocity

Time Frame:
45 minutes

Materials:
One copy of the student page for each student

Teacher Notes:
This lesson can be used as an introduction to average rate of change and as such should be worked through as a class activity. It can also be used as a review or as an assessment.

Reading the Graph

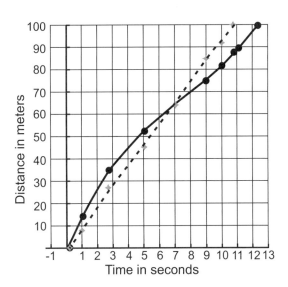

The graph above is a sketch of the time, in seconds, it took two ladies from the USA, Betty Robinson (the solid line with dots) and Marion Jones (the dotted line), to run the woman's 100-meter dash in the Olympics.

1. a)   State the independent variable.

    b)   State the dependent variable.

2. a)   Both ladies won the gold medal. Who do you think won the gold medal (1st place) in 1928 and who won the gold medal in 2000?

    b)   Explain the reasoning behind your choice of winners in part "a".

    c)   What was approximate winning time in 2000?

    d)   Approximately how many seconds were shaved off of the winning time in these 72 years?

3. a)   What was Robinson's average speed for the entire race?

    b)   What was Jones' average speed for the entire race?

4. a)   If the runners had run the race together, at what time would one runner pass the other?

    b)   How far along the course were Jones and Robinson when this happened?

    c)   Who would have overtaken whom to win the race?

123

5. a)   If d(t) = 70, find t for each runner.

    b)   Explain what this value represents.

    c)   Find d(10) for each runner.

    d)   Explain what this value represents.

6. a)   From looking at the graph, how does Robinson's speed over the interval from 0 to 2 seconds compare with Jones' speed over the same interval?

    b)   Find Jones' average speed over the interval from 5 to 9 seconds.

    c)   Find Robinson's average speed over the interval from 5 to 9 seconds.

    d)   What do the values in part "b" and "c" represent, using the units of measurement?

7. Suppose the ladies are running on the same track at the same time and you are the commentator for the race. Write a paragraph describing the race that both ladies ran. Indicate in your narrative when or if they increased or decreased their speed, and where they were in comparison to each other. In addition, be sure to speculate what Robinson was planning at about 5 seconds.

Reading the Graph

Answers:

1. a) Time in seconds

   b) Distance in meters

2. a) In 1928 Robinson won and in 2000 Jones won.

   b) Over the years, the women have gotten faster and stronger with weight training so Jones finished in a shorter amount of time.

   c) Approximately 10.8 seconds

   d) About 1.7 seconds

3. a) $\dfrac{100}{12.5}$ or 8 meters per second

   b) $\dfrac{100}{10.8}$ or 9.259 meters per second

4. a) 7 seconds

   b) About 65 meters

   c) Jones overtook Robinson.

5. a) Robinson is 8 seconds and Jones is about 7.4 seconds.

   b) How long it took the runner to get to the 70 meter mark

   c) Robinson has run approximately 82 meters and Jones approximately 92 meters.

   d) Exactly 10 seconds after the race started, Robinson had run approximately 82 meters and Jones had run approximately 92 meters.

6. a)   Jones ran at a constant rate of about 9 meters per second while Robinson ran at an average rate of about 13 meters per second. If they had been running on the same track, Robinson would be ahead after 2 seconds.

    b)   About 9 meters per second

    c)   6 meters per second

    d)   How their position is changing with respect to time which is velocity or the speed (in this case) of the runners.

7. Both the runners begin the race at the same time with Robinson pulling ahead and running at a faster speed because her "line" is steeper for about the first 3 seconds. Then their lines are close to parallel so they are running at the same speed for 1 second, but Robinson is still ahead. At about 4 seconds, Robinson is slowing down, maybe to rest a couple of seconds so she can run faster at the end of the race, and Jones catches up with her after 7 seconds. Now Jones is ahead of Robinson and running at a faster rate. It seems as if Robinson has run out of steam too early and Jones finishes the 100 meter race at about 10.8 seconds and Robinson comes in at a time of 12.5 seconds.

A Transformation Story

Objective:
Students will explore transformational changes in a graph using verbal descriptions.

Connections to Previous Learning:
Students should be able to graph ordered pairs and determine vertical and horizontal transformations.

Connections to TEKS:
111.32 b1A, b1B, b1C, b1D, b1E, b2B, b3B

Connections to AP:
The AP Calculus objectives of rate of change, position and velocity

Time Frame:
90 minutes

Materials:
Worksheet

Teacher Notes:
At the beginning of this assignment, a simulation of the story would be helpful for the students to understand and see what the graph is describing. Assign three students to be Amy, Julia and Jordan. Select appropriate locations in the room to match the details of the story. Have Amy walk the path that the story describes. As shifts are made in the problem, shift the locations in the classroom. As Amy's speed is increased, have Amy walk faster.

A Transformation Story

I. Amy was at Julia's house from 12 noon to 2 p.m. She stopped by to visit Jordan. Jordan lives two miles from Julia's house. Jordan was not at home. Amy arrived home at 6 p.m. The following graph describes Amy's distance from home.

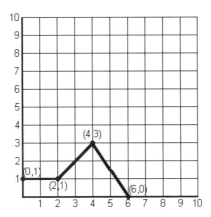

Each of the following graphs describes a change in the problem situation. Rewrite the story that each graph describes.

a)

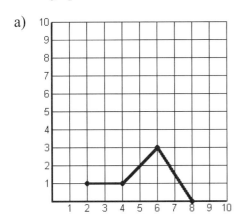

c)

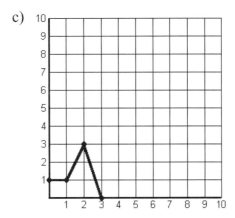

b)

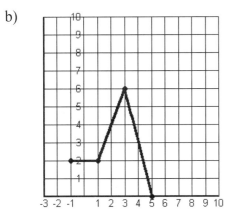

d)

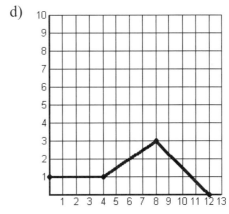

129

e)

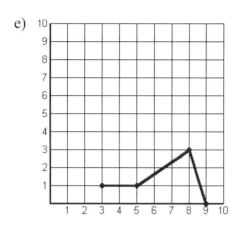

Which graph describes the following changes?

1. Amy left Julia's house at 4 p.m.
2. Amy's trip took half the time.
3. Amy stayed at Julia's house from 11 a.m. to 1 p.m.
4. Julia's house is twice as far from Amy's was in the original problem.
5. Amy traveled slower on her way home.
6. Amy was at Jordan's house at 2 p.m.
7. It took Amy 4 hours to go home from Jordan's house.
8. Amy was traveling the slowest.
9. Amy's speed is 2 mph.
10. The total distance traveled is 10 miles.

II.   Write a story to describe the graph below.

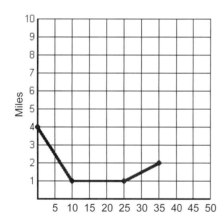

If each graph describes a change in the story, explain the change.

1.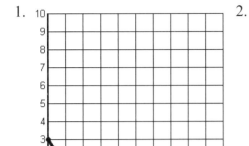

2.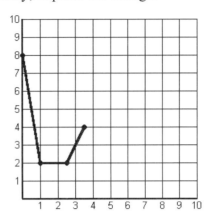

A Transformation Story

Answers:

I. a) Amy was at Julia's house from 2 p.m. to 4 p.m. She stopped by to visit Jordan. Jordan lives two miles from Julia's house. Jordan was not at home. Amy arrived home at 8 p.m.

b) Amy was at Julia's house from 11 a.m. to 1 p.m. She stopped by to visit Jordan. Jordan lives four miles from Julia's house. Jordan was not at home. Amy arrived home at 5 p.m.

c) Amy was at Julia's house from 12 noon to 1 p.m. She stopped by to visit Jordan. Jordan lives two miles from Julia's house. Jordan was not at home. Amy arrived home at 3 p.m.

d) Amy was at Julia's house from 12 noon to 4 p.m. She stopped by to visit Jordan. Jordan lives two miles from Julia's house. Jordan was not at home. Amy arrived home at 12 midnight.

e) Amy was at Julia's house from 3 p.m. to 5 pm. She stopped by to visit Jordan. Jordan lives two miles from Julia's house. Jordan was not at home. Amy arrived home at 9 p.m.

1. a
2. c
3. b
4. b
5. d
6. c
7. d
8. d
9. c
10. b

II. As these are students' stories, they will vary. The following are samples. Alex lives 4 miles from school. Jackson lives one mile from school and Allen lives 2 miles from school. Alex can get to Jackson house in 10 minutes and Jackson's house is 10 minutes from Allen's house. The graph shows that Alex went to Jackson's house for 15 minutes, then went to Allen's.

1. Alex lives 3 miles from school. Jackson lives one mile from school and Allen lives 3 miles from school. Alex can get to Jackson house in 10 minutes and Jackson's house or to school is 10 minutes from Allen's house. The graph shows that Alex went to Jackson's house for 15 minutes, then went to Allen's.

2. Alex lives 8 miles from school. Jackson lives 2 miles from school and Allen lives 4 miles from school. Alex can get to Jackson house in 5 minutes and Jackson's house is 5 minutes from Allen's house. The graph shows that Alex went to Jackson's house for 7 ½ minutes, them went to Allen's.

Write Your Notes and Ideas Here!

Translations of Linear Functions

Objective:
Students will examine the effects of horizontal and vertical shifts on linear functions.

Connections to Previous Learning:
Students should know how to graph equations of lines, write equations of lines from their graphs, and transform equations from one form to another.

Connections to TEKS:
111.32   b3A, b3B, b4A, b4B, c1C, c2A, c2C, c2D, c2E

Connections to AP:
The AP Calculus objective of analysis of functions

Time Frame:
50 minutes

Materials:
Worksheet for each student, graph paper

Teacher Notes:
This is a discovery activity. Students will work several specific problems and then are asked to draw a general conclusion. By looking at horizontal and vertical translations of linear functions and connecting them to the $y = m(x - h) + k$ notation, students will more easily understand the translations of quadratic functions in the form $y = a(x - h)^2 + k$, as well as similar translations of other parent functions.

As an extension, the students can determine at least one additional translation which results in the graphs given in the answer key.

Translations of Linear Functions

1. a) Graph $y = 2x$

   b) Translate the graph 4 units to the right.

   c) Write the equation for the translated graph in slope-intercept form.

   d) Write the equation in 'c' in factored form, $y = m(x - h)$.

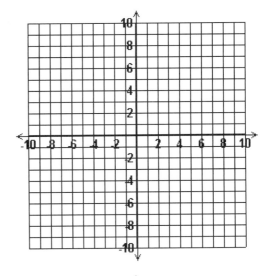

2. a) Graph $y = 3x$

   b) Translate the graph 2 units to the right.

   c) Write the equation for the translated graph in slope-intercept form.

   d) Write the equation in 'c' in factored form.

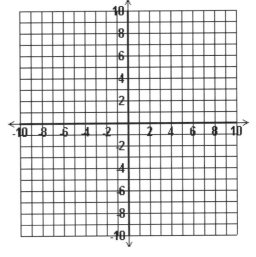

3. a) Graph $y = \dfrac{1}{2}x$

   b) Translate the graph 6 units to the right.

   c) Write the equation for the translated graph in slope-intercept form.

   d) Write the equation in 'c' in factored form.

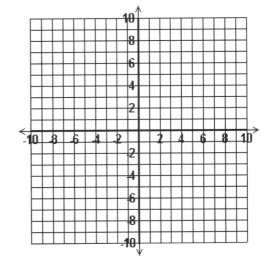

135

Based on your work in questions 1-3, what conclusions can be drawn about the relationship between the graphs of $y = mx$ and $y = m(x - h)$, $h > 0$?

4.　a)　Graph $y = 4x$

　　b)　Translate the graph 2 units to the left.

　　c)　Write the equation for the translated graph in slope-intercept form.

　　d)　Write the equation in 'c' in factored form.

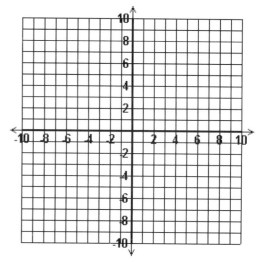

5.　a)　Graph $y = -2x$

　　b)　Translate the graph 3 units to the left.

　　c)　Write the equation for the translated graph in slope-intercept form.

　　d)　Write the equation in 'c' in factored form.

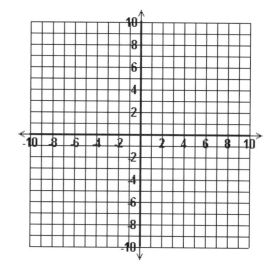

6.　a)　Graph $y = \dfrac{1}{3}x$

　　b)　Translate the graph 9 units to the left.

　　c)　Write the equation for the translated graph in slope-intercept form.

　　d)　Write the equation in 'c' in factored form.

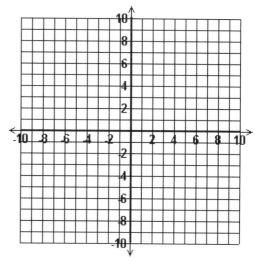

Based on your work in 4-6, what conclusions can be drawn about the relationship between the graphs of $y = mx$ and $y = m(x + h)$, $h < 0$?

7. a)   Graph $y = -3x$

    b)   Translate the graph 2 units up.

    c)   Write the equation for the translated graph in slope intercept form.

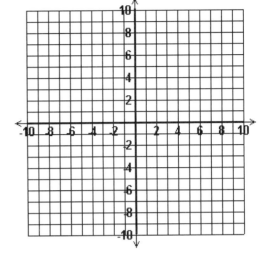

8. a)   Graph $y = \frac{1}{4}x$

    b)   Translate the graph 5 units up.

    c)   Write the equation for the translated graph in slope intercept form

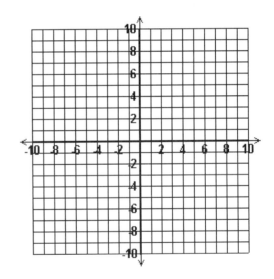

Based on 7 and 8, what conclusion can be drawn about the relationship between the graphs of $y = mx$ and $y = mx + k$, $k > 0$?

9.   a)   Graph $y = 5x$

     b)   Translate the graph 2 units down.

     c)   Write the equation for the translated graph in slope intercept form.

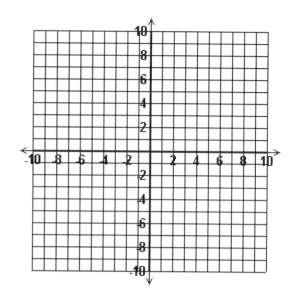

10. a)   Graph $y = -\dfrac{1}{2}x$

     b)   Translate the graph 6 units down.

     c)   Write the equation for the translated graph in slope intercept form.

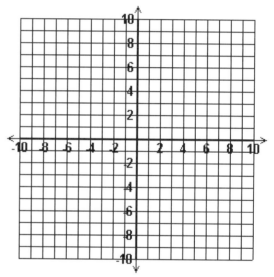

What conclusion can be drawn about the relationship between the graphs of $y = mx$ and $y = mx + k$, $k < 0$?

11. a)   Based upon your previous conclusion, speculate how the graphs of $y = 2x$ and $y = 2(x - 3) + 4$ are related.

     b)   Graph $y = 2x$

     c)   Simplify $y = 2(x - 3) + 4$ by distributing and combining like terms. Graph the resulting equation to check your answer to 'a'.

12. a)   Based upon your previous conclusions, speculate how the graphs of $y = -3(x + 1) - 5$ and $y = -3x$ are related.

    b)   Graph $y = -3x$

    c)   Simplify $y = -3(x + 1) - 5$ by distributing and combining like terms. Graph the resulting equation to check you answer to 'a'.

13.   How would you translate the equation, $y = 5x$, 4 units to the right and 2 units down?

14.   How would you translate the equation $y = \dfrac{-1}{3}x$ 6 units to the left and 4 units up?

Translations of Linear Functions

Answers:

1.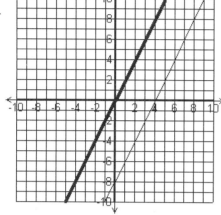

    c) $y = 2x - 8$

    d) $y = 2(x - 4)$

2.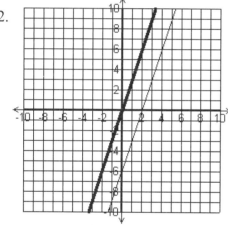

    c) $y = 3x - 6$

    d) $y = 3(x - 2)$

3.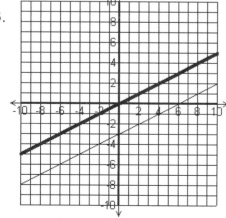

    c) $y = \dfrac{1}{2}x - 3$

    d) $y = \dfrac{1}{2}(x - 6)$

Conclusion: The second equation will translate the graph of the first equation h units to the right.

4.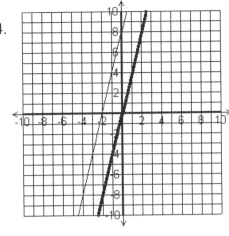

c) $y = 4x + 8$

d) $y = 4(x + 2)$

5.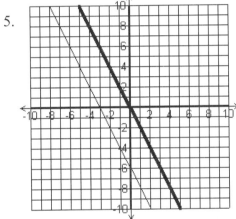

c) $y = -2x - 6$

d) $y = -2(x + 3)$

6.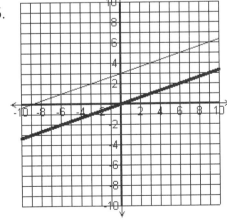

c) $y = \frac{1}{3}x + 3$

d) $y = \frac{1}{3}(x + 9)$

Conclusion: The second equation will translate the graph of the first equation h units to the left.

7.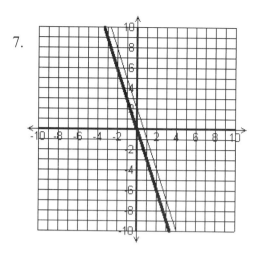

c) $y = -3x + 2$

8.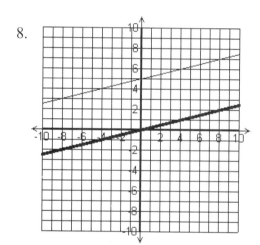

c) $y = \dfrac{1}{4}x + 5$

Conclusion: The second equation will translate the graph of the first equation k units upward.

9.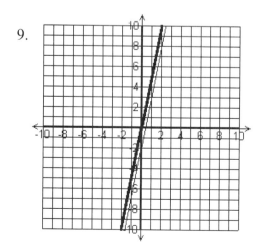

c) $y = 5x - 2$

10.

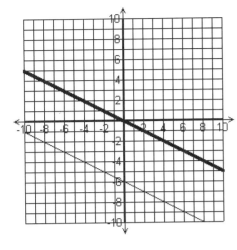

c) $y = -\dfrac{1}{2}x - 6$

Conclusion: The second equation will translate the graph of the first equation *k* units downward.

11.

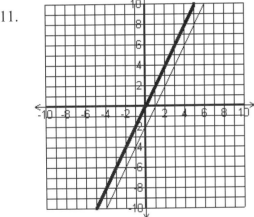

a) Second graph will be a translation of the first graph, 3 units to the right, 4 units upward.

12.

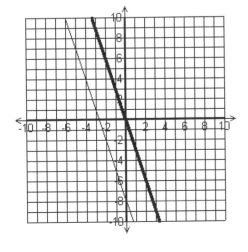

a) Second graph will be a translation of the first graph, 1 unit to the left, 5 units downward.

13. $y = 5(x-4) - 2$

14. $y = \dfrac{-1}{3}(x+6) + 4$

Write Your Notes and Ideas Here!

Analysis of Functions

Objective:
Students will be able to describe behavior of functions in terms of whether they are positive/negative and increasing/decreasing/constant on various intervals of x. Students will practice writing inequalities for various domains and see how the behavior of a function relates to its slope.

Connections to Previous Learning:
Students should be familiar with graphing in the coordinate plane and be able to write inequalities of a single variable. Students should know that f(x) is referring to the y values of a function and should also be familiar with positive, negative and zero slopes of linear functions.

Connections to TEKS:
111.32 b1D, b2B, c1C, d1A

Connections to AP:
The AP Calculus objective of analysis of functions

Time Frame:
50 minutes

Materials:
A worksheet for each student, an overhead transparency with the graphs on it

Teacher Notes:
The teacher might want to do one or two problems with the students and then let them work the rest on their own or in pairs. Teachers should point out to students that the graph of a function is "read" from left to right. If the y values are going up as the graph is "read", then the function is said to be increasing. If the y values are going down as the graph is read, then the function is said to be decreasing. If the y values remain the same, then the function is said to be constant. Teachers might also want to discuss positive, negative and zero slopes of linear functions. Finally remind students that the function is positive if it is above the x-axis, zero if it is on the x-axis (emphasize that zero is neither positive nor negative) and negative if it is below the x-axis.

Analysis of Functions

1.

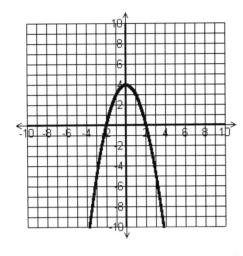

   a) On what intervals of x is $f(x)$ increasing?

   b) On what intervals of x is $f(x)$ positive?

2.

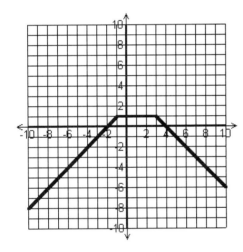

   a) On what intervals of x is $f(x)$ constant?

   b) On what intervals of x does $f(x)$ have zero slope?

   c) On what intervals of x is $f(x)$ negative?

3.

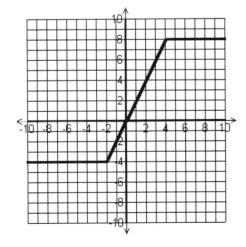

   a) On what intervals of x is $f(x)$ positive?

   b) On what intervals of x does $f(x)$ have positive slope?

   c) On what intervals of x is $f(x)$ increasing?

4.

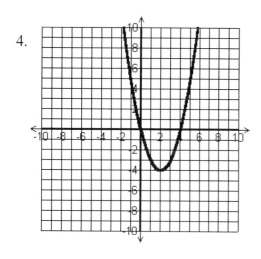

a) On what intervals of *x* is *f*(*x*) decreasing?
b) On what intervals of *x* is *f*(*x*) negative?

5.

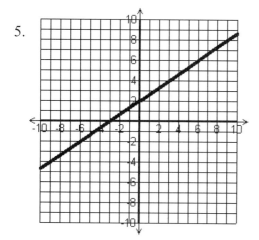

a) On what intervals of *x* is *f*(*x*) positive?
b) On what intervals of *x* does *f*(*x*) have positive slope?
c) On what intervals of *x* is *f*(*x*) increasing?

6.

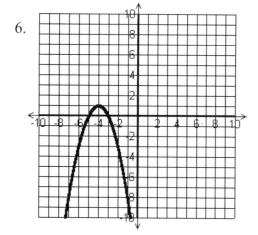

a) On what intervals of *x* is *f*(*x*) decreasing?
b) On what intervals of *x* is *f*(*x*) negative?

7.

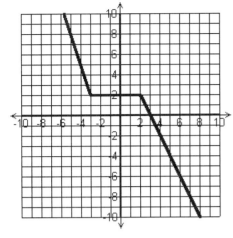

a) On what intervals of *x* is *f*(*x*) decreasing?

b) On what intervals of *x* does *f*(*x*) have positive slope?

c) On what intervals of *x* is *f*(*x*) positive?

d) On what intervals of *x* does *f*(*x*) have zero slope?

8.

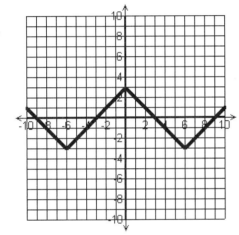

a) On what intervals of *x* is *f*(*x*) negative?

b) On what intervals of *x* is *f*(*x*) decreasing?

c) On what intervals of *x* does *f*(*x*) have negative slope?

9.

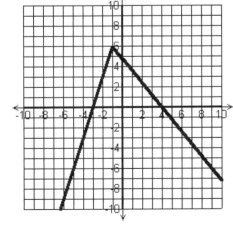

a) On what intervals of *x* is *f*(*x*) increasing?

b) On what intervals of *x* does *f*(*x*) have a negative slope?

c) On what intervals of *x* is *f*(*x*) negative?

10.

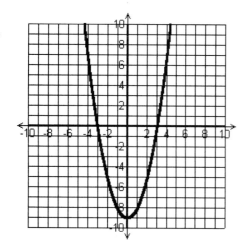

a) On what intervals of x is $f(x)$ positive?

b) On what intervals of x is $f(x)$ increasing?

11.

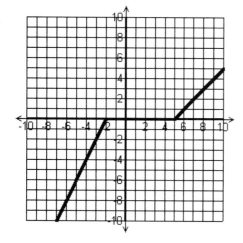

a) On what intervals of x is $f(x)$ constant?

b) On what intervals of x is $f(x)$ positive?

c) On what intervals of x is $f(x)$ increasing?

d) On what intervals of x does $f(x)$ have positive slope?

12. Petunia says, "If a function is positive, then it is increasing." Do you agree or disagree with this statement? Support your answer.

Analysis of Functions

Answers:

1. a) $f(x)$ is increasing for $x \leq 0$

   b) $f(x)$ is positive for $-2 < x < 2$

2. a) $f(x)$ is constant for $-1 \leq x \leq 3$

   b) $f(x)$ has zero slope for $-1 < x < 3$

   c) $f(x)$ is negative for $x < -2$ or $x > 4$

3. a) $f(x)$ is positive for $x > 0$

   b) $f(x)$ has positive slope for $-2 < x < 4$

   c) $f(x)$ is increasing for $-2 \leq x \leq 4$

4. a) $f(x)$ is decreasing for $x \leq 2$

   b) $f(x)$ is negative for $0 < x < 4$

5. a) $f(x)$ is positive for $x > -3$

   b) $f(x)$ has positive slope for all values of x.

   c) $f(x)$ is increasing for all values of x.

6. a) $f(x)$ is decreasing for $x \geq -4$

   b) $f(x)$ is negative for $x < -5$ or $x > -3$

7. a) $f(x)$ is decreasing for $x \leq -3$ or $x \geq 2$

   b) $f(x)$ has positive slope for no values of x.

   c) $f(x)$ is positive for $x < 3$

   d) $f(x)$ has zero slope for $-3 < x < 2$

8. a) $f(x)$ is negative for $-9 < x < -3$ and $3 < x < 9$

   b) $f(x)$ is decreasing for $x \leq -6$ and $0 \leq x \leq 6$

   c) $f(x)$ has negative slope for $x < -6$ and $0 < x < 6$

9. a) $f(x)$ is increasing for $x \leq -1$

   b) $f(x)$ has negative slope for $x > -1$

   c) $f(x)$ is negative for $x < -3$ or $x > 4$

10. a) $f(x)$ is positive for $x < -3$ or $x > 3$

    b) $f(x)$ is increasing for $x \geq 0$

11. a) $f(x)$ is constant for $-2 \leq x \leq 5$

    b) $f(x)$ is positive for $x > 5$

    c) $f(x)$ is increasing for $x \leq -2$ or $x \geq 5$

    d) $f(x)$ has positive slope for $x < -2$ or $x > 5$

12. The statement is not correct. Look at number 10. $f(x)$ is positive for $x < -3$, but the function is decreasing there. Students might give other examples. Ask them how they could correct the statement. Some possibilities: "If a function is positive then its graph is ABOVE the x-axis," or "If a function has a positive slope, then it is increasing."

Write Your Notes and Ideas Here!

Finding Area and Writing Equations for Bounded Regions

Objective:
Students will practice writing equations for lines in both slope-intercept and standard form. They will also practice finding areas of geometric figures such as rectangles, triangles, trapezoids and combination figures.

Connections to Previous Learning:
Students should know how to write equations for horizontal and vertical lines, given the slope and y-intercept of a linear function or given a point and a slope. They should also know how to calculate areas of geometric figures.

Connections to TEKS:
111.32 b4A, c1C, c2A, c2D, c2E

Connections to AP:
The AP Calculus objective of area

Time Frame:
45 minutes

Materials:
Worksheet for each student

Teacher Notes:
Teachers should specify the form in which the equations should be written. Both slope-intercept form and standard form are provided in the answer key. Having students do both forms can provide them with practice in algebraic manipulation. If students finish early, the teacher can challenge them to graph their own region that looks like some common object. Students would also provide the equations for the lines that bound their region.

As an independent assignment, students can use the equations for their boundaries in problems 1-9 to write sentences to describe each of the shaded regions. If the teacher chooses to use this activity, the following instructions can be used:

Use the equations of the boundaries you found in problems 1-9 to write a sentence that could be used to describe to someone how to draw each of the shaded regions.

Finding Area and Writing Equations for Bounded Regions

Instructions: Determine the area of each of the regions shown below. Then determine the equations of the lines that bound each region. Ask your teacher if answers should be given in slope-intercept form, standard form or both of those forms.

1.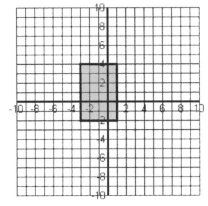

2.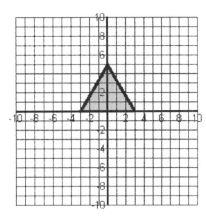

3.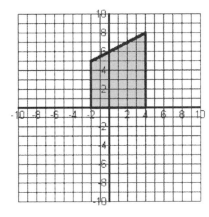

4.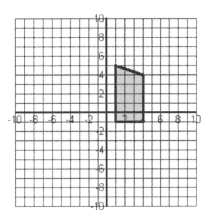

5.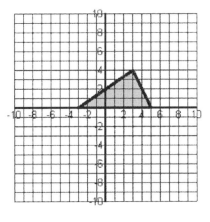

6.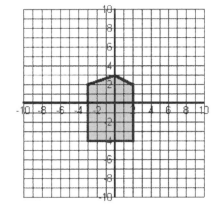

7.

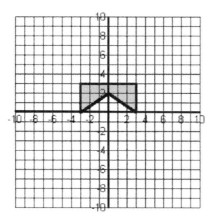

8.

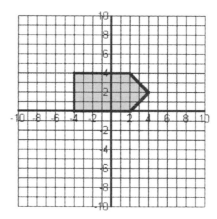

9.

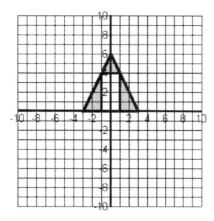

Finding Area and Writing Equations for Bounded Regions

Answers: In the following, u stands for "units".

1. $A = 24u^2$ bounded by $x = -3$, $y = -2$, $x = 1$, and $y = 4$

2. $A = 15u^2$ bounded by $y = 0$, $y = \dfrac{5}{3}x + 5$ and $y = \dfrac{-5}{3}x + 5$

$$(5x - 3y = -15) \quad (5x + 3y = 15)$$

3. $A = 39u^2$ bounded by $x = -2$, $y = 0$, $x = 4$ and $y = \dfrac{1}{2}x + 6$

$$(x - 2y = -12)$$

4. $A = 16.5$ or $\dfrac{33}{2}u^2$ bounded by $x = 1$, $y = -1$, $x = 4$ and $y = -\dfrac{1}{3}x + \dfrac{16}{3}$

$$(x + 3y = 16)$$

5. $A = 16u^2$ bounded by $y = 0$, $y = \dfrac{2}{3}x + 2$ and $y = -2x + 10$

$$(2x - 3y = -6) \quad (2x + y = 10)$$

6. $A = 32.5$ or $\dfrac{65}{2}u^2$ bounded by $x = -3$, $y = -4$, $x = 2$, $y = -\dfrac{1}{2}x + 3$ and $y = \dfrac{1}{3}x + 3$

$$(x + 2y = 6) \quad (x - 3y = -9)$$

7. $A = 12u^2$ bounded by $y = \dfrac{2}{3}x + 2$, $y = -\dfrac{2}{3}x + 2$, $x = 3$, $y = 3$ and $x = -3$

$$(2x - 3y = -6) \quad (2x + 3y = 6)$$

8. $A = 28u^2$ bounded by $x = -4$, $y = x - 2$, $y = -x + 6$, $y = 4$, and $y = 0$

$$(x - y = 2) \quad (x + y = 6)$$

9. $A = 10u^2$ bounded by $y = 2x + 6$, $y = -2x + 6$, $y = 0$, $y = 4$, $x = 1$, $x = -1$

$$(2x - y = -6) \quad (2x + y = 6)$$

Alternate Activity

Instructions: Determine the area of each of the shaded regions.

1. Draw and shade the rectangular region bounded by the lines $x = -3$, $y = -2$, $x = 1$, and $y = 4$.

2. Draw and shade the triangular region bounded by $y = 0$, $y = (5/3)x + 5$, and $y = -(5/3)x + 5$.

3. Draw and shade the trapezoidal region bounded by the lines $x = -2$, $y = 0$, $x = 4$, and $y = (1/2)x + 6$.

4. Draw and shade the trapezoidal region bounded by the lines $x = 1$, $y = -1$, $x = 4$, and $y = -(1/3)x + (16/3)$.

5. Draw and shade the triangular region bounded by the lines $y = 0$, $y = (2/3)x + 2$, and $y = -2x + 10$.

6. Draw and shade the region bounded by the lines $x = -3$, $y = -4$, $x = 2$, $y = -(1/2)x + 3$, and $y = (1/3)x + 3$.

7. Draw and shade the region inside the rectangle bounded by the lines $x = 3$, $x = -3$, $y = 0$, and $y = 3$ but outside the triangle bounded by $y = 0$, $y = (2/3)x + 2$, and $y = -(2/3)x + 2$.

8. Draw and shade the region bounded by $x = -4$, $y = x - 2$, $y = 0$, $y = -x + 6$, and $y = 4$.

9. Draw and shade the region inside the triangle bounded by $y = 2x + 6$, $y = -2x + 6$, and $y = 0$ but outside the rectangle bounded by $y = 0$, $y = 4$, $x = 1$, and $x = -1$.

Write Your Notes and Ideas Here!

Literal Equations – Reviewing and Foreshadowing

Objective:
Students will review solving literal equations while at the same time working with formulas from algebra, geometry, and science.

Connections to Previous Learning:
Students should be able to solve first-degree equations.

Connections to TEKS:
111.32 b4A, b4B

Connections to AP:
The AP Calculus objectives of area and volume

Time Frame:
30 minutes

Materials:
One copy of the worksheet for each student

Teacher Notes:
This lesson can be used as a review or as an assessment. In order to reach its full potential, students need to not only perform the algebraic manipulations, but consider what each revised formula means. The idea of using what they already have mastered to foreshadow what they are going to learn is very powerful. Students should realize that they have the ability to solve number 12. Even though it is exponential, that skill is not needed to solve for P.

Literal Equations – Reviewing and Foreshadowing

I. For each equation below, solve for the given variable. Show each step needed to justify your answer.

1. Solve $2x + 3y = 9$ for y.

2. Solve $4x - 7y = 7$ for x.

3. Solve $5x - 2y = 8$ for y.

4. Solve $ax + by = c$ for y.

II. For each equation below, solve for the given variable. Explain the meaning of the "new" equation. Example: Solve $D = \dfrac{m}{V}$, for V, where D = density, m = mass, and V = Volume. To receive full credit for this section, first, show the steps needed to solve for the given variable, in this case $V = \dfrac{m}{D}$. Second, explain the meaning of the answer. In this case, it means that Volume is mass divided by density.

5. Solve $I = prt$ for r, where I = interest, p = principal, r = rate of interest, and t = time in years

6. Solve $T = p + prt$ for p, where T = total money, and p, r, and t are as defined in number 5.

7. Solve $F = ma$ for a, where F = force, m = mass, and a = acceleration.

8. Solve $W = mg$ for g, where W = weight, m = mass, and g = gravity.

9. Solve $A = \dfrac{1}{2}h(b_1 + b_2)$ for b_1, where A = area of a trapezoid, h = height of the trapezoid, and b_1 and b_2 are the lengths of the two bases of the trapezoid.

10. Solve $p = 2l + 2w$ for w, where p is a rectangle's perimeter, l is the length, and w is the width.

11. Solve $L = a + (n - 1)d$ for d, where L = the last term of an arithmetic sequence, a = the first term of the sequence, n = the number of terms, and d = the common difference.

12. Solve $T = P(1 + r)^t$ for P, where T = total investment, P = initial investment, r = rate of interest, and t = number of "growth periods". In this case let t = number of years.

13. Solve $y = mx + b$ for m, where x and y are independent and dependent variables, m = slope, and b = y-intercept.

14. Solve $m = \dfrac{y - y_1}{x - x_1}$ for y, where m = slope and (x, y) and (x_1, y_1) are ordered pairs.

15. Solve $y + mx_1 = mx + y_1$ for m, where variables are defined as in number 14.

16. Solve $a = \dfrac{v_f - v_0}{t_f - t_0}$ for t_f, where a = acceleration, v_f = final velocity, v_0 = initial velocity, t_f = final time, t_0 = initial time.

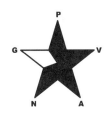

Literal Equations – Reviewing and Foreshadowing

Answers:

I. For this section, only final answers are given in the solution key. Be sure that your students show work in the manner that you expect.

1. $y = -\dfrac{2}{3}x + 3$

2. $x = \dfrac{7}{4}y + \dfrac{7}{4}$

3. $y = \dfrac{5}{2}x - 4$

4. $y = -\dfrac{a}{b}x + \dfrac{c}{b}$

II. The final answer and a sample explanation is given for each of the following.

5. $r = \dfrac{I}{pt}$ Rate of interest equals Interest divided by the product of principal and time in years.

6. $p = \dfrac{T}{1 + rt}$ Principal equals total money divided by the sum of 1 and the product of rate and time.

7. $a = \dfrac{F}{m}$ Acceleration equals Force divided by mass.

8. $g = \dfrac{W}{m}$ Gravity equals weight divided by mass.

9. $b_1 = \dfrac{2A}{h} - b_2$ or $b_1 = \dfrac{2A - b_2 h}{h}$ One base of a trapezoid equals the difference of two times the Area divided by the height and the second base.

10. $w = \dfrac{p - 2l}{2}$ Width of a rectangle equals one-half the difference of the perimeter and twice the length.

11. $d = \dfrac{L - a}{n - 1}$ The common difference in an arithmetic sequence equals the quotient of the difference of the last term and the first term divided by the difference of the number of terms and 1.

12. $P = \dfrac{T}{(1 + r)^t}$ The initial investment equals the total amount of the investment divided by the sum, raised to the power of the number of years, of 1 and the rate of interest.

13. $m = \dfrac{y - b}{x}$ The slope equals the quotient of the difference of y and the y-intercept divided by x.

14. $y = m(x - x_1) + y_1$ y equals the sum of the product of the slope and the difference of x and x_1 and y_1.

15. $m = \dfrac{y - y_1}{x - x_1}$ Slope equals the quotient of the difference of y and y_1 divided by the difference in x and x_1.

16. $t_f = \dfrac{v_f - v_0}{a} + t_0$ The final time equals the difference between the final velocity and initial velocity divided by acceleration added to the initial time.

Write Your Notes and Ideas Here!

Adaptation of AP Calculus 1999 AB-6

Objective:
Students will review rate of change and will analyze the behavior of a function as "x" gets large.

Connections to Previous Learning:
Students should know how to determine rate of change, area under the curve, equation of a line, and function values.

Connections to TEKS:
111.32 b1C, b1D, b1E, b2C, b2D, b3A, b4A, c1A, C; c2A, c2D, c2E

Connections to AP:
The AP Calculus objectives of rate of change and position

Time Frame:
45 minutes

Materials:
Calculator

Teacher Notes:
The first concern for the students is probably that the graph is so "busy". Have the students focus on one specific goal at a time and not the global picture.

The purpose of this lesson is to utilize an AP Calculus exam question, in free response style, to continually recycle previously learned material into the yearly curriculum while introducing new material, such as the tangent line to a curve at one point.

Some graphical examples of tangent lines:

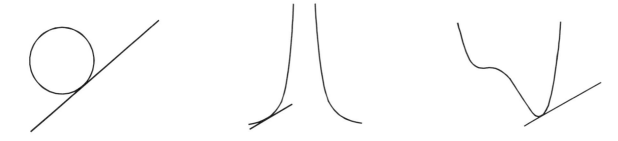

Some graphical examples that we would **not** call tangent lines:

On question 8, the lesson is leading the student to a general concept of end behavior as x approaches positive infinity. In other words, what is happening to $g(x)$ as x gets larger and larger? This is also a precursor to a limit in calculus.

Adaptation of AP Calculus 1999 AB-6

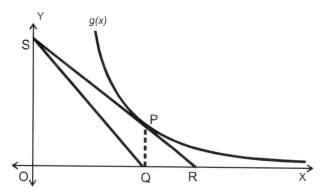

In the figure above, $\overline{SR}$ is tangent to the graph of $g(x) = \dfrac{1}{x^2}$ at point P, where $x = 3$. Point Q has coordinates $(3,0)$ and $\overline{SR}$ crosses the x-axis at point R, with coordinates $(k,0)$. Use this information to answer the following questions.

1. The slope of $\overline{SR}$ is $\dfrac{-2}{27}$. Determine the y value of point S.

2. Find the coordinates for point R.

3. Formulate the equation for $\overline{SR}$, in standard form. This line is the tangent line at point P.

4. Evaluate the area of $\triangle SOR$.

5. Determine the length of $\overline{SQ}$ rounded to the nearest thousandths place.

6. a) Sketch in a vertical line segment from the x-axis to $g(x)$ at $x = 4$.

   b) Find the height of that line segment.

7. a)   Evaluate *g*(7).

    b)   Evaluate *g*(300).

    c)   Evaluate *g*(90,000).

    d)   As *x* gets really large, what value does *g*(*x*) approach?

    e)   Explain how can you defend your conclusion in part "d" analytically.

    f)   Does the function ever actually reach the *y*-axis? Explain your reasoning.

8. Suppose that Pedro and Alex are friends who are riding their bicycles. In this figure, the *x*-axis represents time (in minutes) and the y-axis represents the distance (in miles) Pedro and Alex are away from home. Pedro's distance from home at a given time is represented by $\overline{SR}$ and Alex's path is represented by $\overline{SQ}$. Create a story about each of their bike trips, using the correct units. Be sure to address speed, starting position, stops along the way, etc. for both boys.

Adaptation of AP Calculus 1999 AB-6

Answers:

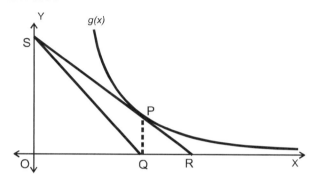

In the figure above, $\overline{SR}$ is tangent to the graph of $g(x) = \dfrac{1}{x^2}$ at point P, where $x = 3$. Point Q has

coordinates $(3,0)$ and $\overline{SR}$ crosses the x-axis at point R, with coordinates $(k,0)$. Use this information to answer the following questions.

1. The slope of $\overline{SR}$ is $\dfrac{-2}{27}$. Determine the y value of point S.

    $$y = \frac{1}{3}$$

2. Find the coordinates for point R.

    $$(\frac{9}{2}, 0)$$

3. Formulate the equation for $\overline{SR}$, in standard form. This line is the tangent line at point P.

    $$2x + 27y = 9$$

4. Evaluate the area of $\triangle SOR$.

    $$\frac{3}{4}$$

5. Determine the length of $\overline{SQ}$ rounded to the nearest thousandths place.

    3.018

6. a) Sketch in a vertical line segment from the x-axis to $g(x)$ at $x = 4$.

    b) Find the height of that line segment.

        $\dfrac{1}{16}$

7. a) Evaluate $g(7)$.

        $\dfrac{1}{49}$

    b) Evaluate $g(300)$.

        $\dfrac{1}{90,000}$

    c) Evaluate $g(90,000)$.

        $\dfrac{1}{8,100,000,000}$

    d) As x gets really large, what does $g(x)$ approach?

        0

    e) How can you defend your conclusion in part "d" analytically?

        As x gets really large in the function $g(x) = \dfrac{1}{x^2}$, you would have 1 divided by some really large number. One divided by a really large number is close to zero so the outcome of $g(x)$ is very close to 0.

    f) Does the function ever actually reach the y-axis? Explain your reasoning.

        For the function to reach the y-axis, the equation $g(x) = \dfrac{1}{x^2}$ would have to be solved for $g(x) = 0$. This is mathematically impossible.

8. Suppose that Pedro and Alex are friends who are riding their bicycles. In this figure, the x-axis represents time (in minutes) and the y-axis represents the distance (in miles) Pedro and Alex are away from home. Pedro's distance from home at a given time is represented by $\overline{SR}$ and Alex's path is represented by $\overline{SQ}$. Create a story about each of their bike trips, using the correct units. Be sure to address speed, starting position, stops along the way, etc. for both boys.

    Pedro and Alex are start riding their bikes from the same place, $\dfrac{1}{3}$ of a mile away from home.

    They both travel at a constant speed, and have to travel the same distance, but Alex is going faster because his line is steeper and he gets back home in a shorter amount of time, that is before Pedro. Neither one of the boys stopped along the way, because the lines are never horizontal.

Accumulating Area

Objective:
Students will investigate the concept of accumulating area bounded by a vertical line, the y-axis and a given function.

Connections to Previous Learning:
Students should be able to graph linear functions, determine area for a triangle and rectangle, and describe the nth term of a series.

Connections to TEKS:
111.32 b1A, B, E, b2C, b2F

Connections to AP:
The AP Calculus objectives of area and accumulation

Time Frame:
90 minutes

Materials:
Calculator

Teacher Notes:
Accumulating Area can be used as a discovery lesson or a teacher directed lesson to briefly introduce the students to the concept of area under the graph of a function, using sequences and tables to generalize answers. The emphasis should not be on area itself, but on the whole concept of accumulation of area. Help the students to visualize what is happening by drawing various frames of the accumulation. This lesson lays the foundation for area under the curve and integration. When accumulation is introduced early in mathematics, integration becomes a much easier topic to understand. The lesson begins with accumulating rectangles under a horizontal line then advancing to adding triangles under an oblique line passing through the origin to accumulating trapezoids under an oblique line if the y-intercept is non-zero. Drawing a picture of the problems in this lesson is very important. All oblique lines will have a positive slope so that the process of accumulating will be easier for the students to visualize.

Accumulating Area

Add the following series of numbers:

$1 + 2$

$1 + 2 + 4$

$1 + 2 + 4 + 8$

$1 + 2 + 4 + 8 + 16$

The process above is called accumulating powers of two. Predicting the next term is possible and predicting the answer is possible. Can you predict what the 100th term will be? Can you predict the sum of the first 100 terms? The answer is yes, however it requires advanced formulas to get the answer. In advanced mathematics, the idea of accumulation is very important, because it allows one to find a value for the sum of a large number of terms without a great deal of arithmetic through the use of algebraic expressions. The process above is called the sequence of partial sums. The purpose of the process is to discover a pattern to the sequence of partial sums that will allow one to generalize about a sum of an infinite number of terms.

1. The figures below show a series of rectangles bounded on top by a horizontal line y = 2, on the bottom by the x-axis, on the left the y-axis and on the right by a vertical line x = k where k is an increasing value. Find the area of each rectangle. Make a table of values of answers to find the area of the last entry on the table.

a) 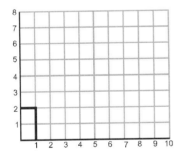 Area = _____

b) 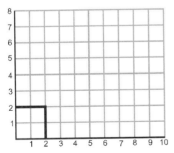 Area = _____

c)

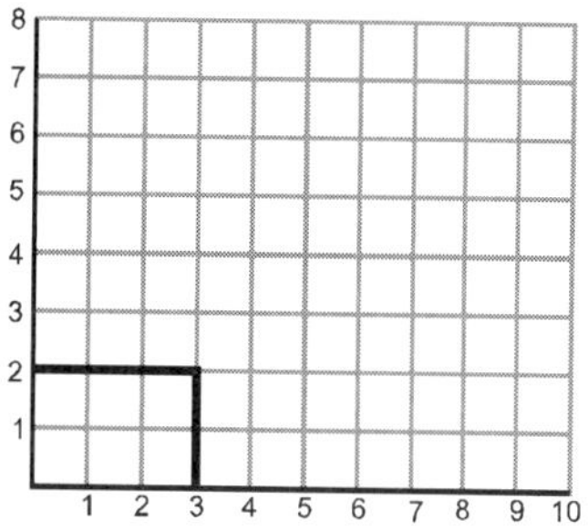

Area = _____

d)

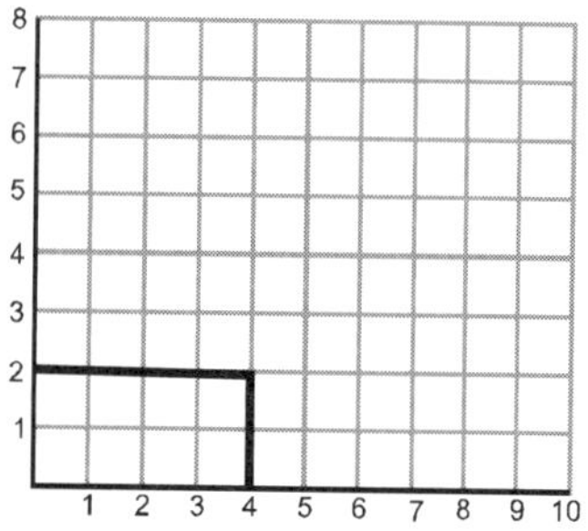

Area = _____

e)   Complete the table using answers from above.

BASE	HEIGHT	AREA
1	2	2
2		
3		
4		
x		

f)   What is the area of a rectangle in the sequence above whose base is 100?

2. The figures below show a series of triangles bounded by the line y = 2x on the top, the x-axis and a vertical line. Find the area of each triangle. Make a table of values of answers to find the area of the last triangle.

a)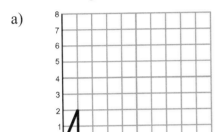

Area = _____

b)

Area = _____

c)

Area = _____

d)

Area = _____

e)   Complete the table below using the answers above:

BASE x	HEIGHT y = 2x	AREA ½ bh
1		
2		
3		
4		
x		

f)   What would be the area of a triangle in this sequence whose base is 100?

3.   The figures below show a series of trapezoids bounded by the line y = 2x + 2 on the top, the x-axis, the y-axis and a vertical line. Find the area of each trapezoid. Make a table of values of answers to find the area of the last trapezoid. Hint: area of a trapezoid = ½ h(b$_1$ + b$_2$)

a)   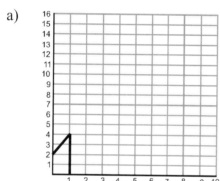   Area = _____

b)   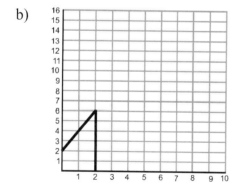   Area = _____

c)

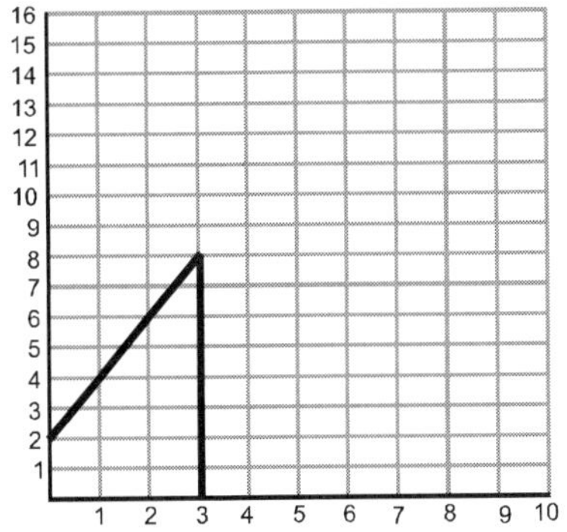

Area = _____

d)

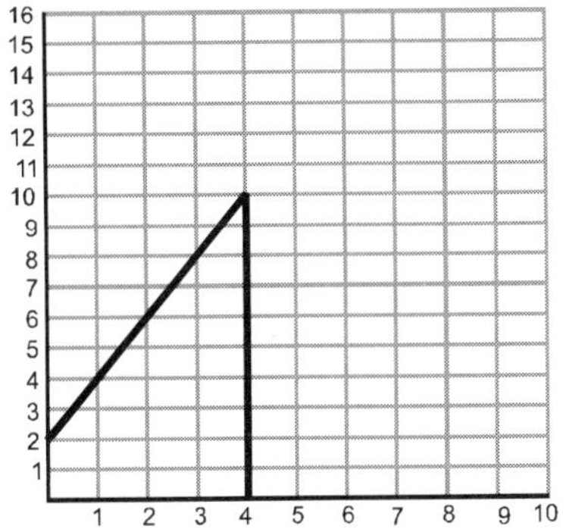

Area = _____

e)   Complete the table of values using the answers above:

Height (x)	Base 1 (2)	Base 2 (y = 2x + 2)	Area A = ½ h(b₁ + b₂)
1			
2			
3			
4			
x			

f)   If this table continued, what would be the area of a trapezoid with height 100?

g)   How could you use the general answers in problem 1 and 2 to help find the general answer to problem 3?

4.   Draw a picture of a region bounded by y = 3x + 8, y = 0, x = 0 and x = 16. Show how to divide this region into four trapezoids that could be used to find the area bounded by this region.

Accumulating Area

Answers:

1.

a)   2

b)   4

c)   6

d)   8

e)

BASE	HEIGHT	AREA
1	2	2
2	2	4
3	2	6
4	2	8
x	2	2x

f)   200

2.

a)   1

b)   4

c)   9

d)   16

e)

BASE	HEIGHT	AREA
x	Y = 2x	½ bh
1	2	1
2	4	4
3	6	9
4	8	16
x	2x	x^2

f)   10,000

3.

a) 3

b) 8

c) 15

d) 24

e)

Height (x)	Base 1 (2)	Base 2 (y = 2x + 2)	Area A = ½ h(b₁ + b₂)
1	2	4	3
2	2	6	8
3	2	8	15
4	2	10	24
x	2	2x + 2	$x^2 + 2x$

f) 10,200

g) The trapezoids are can be divided into a rectangle and a triangle which match the geometric figures in 1 and 2. The sum of the rectangles in problem 1 and the triangles in problem 2 add to be the area of the trapezoids.

4.

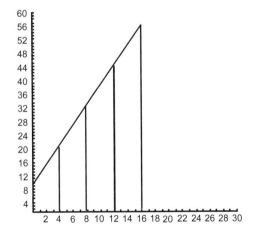

Piecewise Functions

Objectives:
Students will review linear functions and their properties and be introduced to piecewise functions.

Connections to Previous Learning:
Students should be able to write the equation of a line and to use rate of change to create a story to model a linear function.

Connections to TEKS:
111.32   b1C-E, b2B-D, b3A, b4A-B, c1A-C, c2A-F, c3A-C

Connections to AP:
The AP Calculus objectives of rate of change, analysis of functions, and position

Time Frame:
40 minutes

Materials:
Calculator

Teacher Notes:
This is an excellent introductory lesson for piecewise functions. If it is used in this manner, it should be done as a whole class activity.

Piecewise Functions

The Free Wheelers Bicycle Club went on a Saturday bicycle trip. The graph shows the relationship between time in hours and distance in miles traveled from the starting point by one female club member. Use the graph, which is $g(t)$, to answer the following questions.

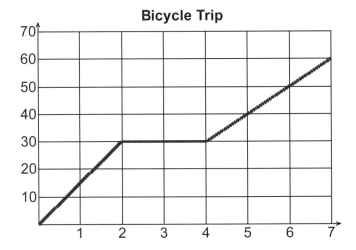

1. In this problem, _____ is a function of _____ .

2. Write these labels on the appropriate axis with the units, where distance is measured in miles and time is measured in hours.

3. During which interval is she moving the fastest? Explain your answer.

4. Describe what is happening on the bicycle trip for the first 2 hours.

5. Looking at the graph above you can see that it consists of three distinct pieces of lines. Write an equation for each part: one for the interval t = 0 to t = 2, one for the interval t = 2 to t = 4, and one for the interval t = 4 to t = 7. This is called a **piecewise function,** and would be written as

$$g(t) = \begin{cases} \underline{\quad 15t \quad} & \text{for } t = 0 \text{ to } t = 2 \\ \underline{\qquad\qquad} & \text{for } \underline{\qquad\quad} \\ \underline{\qquad\qquad} & \text{for } \underline{\qquad\quad} \end{cases}$$

6. When is $g(t) = 22$ miles? Show the work that leads to your conclusion and interpret the meaning of what you found.

7. What is the average rate of speed for the interval t = 1 to t = 3?

8. Suppose that at the beginning of the fourth hour, the bicyclist decides to go back to her starting position. Illustrate what the graph might look like for the return trip.

9. Invent a story for the graph of the function $g(t)$ for the interval t = 0 to t = 7.

Piecewise Functions

Answers:

1. **distance** is a function of **time**

2.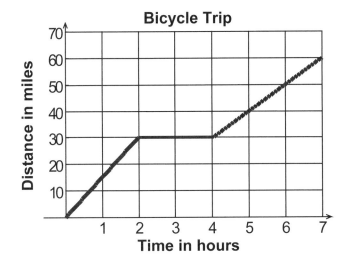

3. Between 0 and 2 hours because that is where the line is the steepest which says that is where her speed is the greatest

4. For the first two hours she is traveling at a constant rate of change going away from her starting position. By 2 hours, she has biked a distance of 30 miles and at a rate of 15 miles per hour.

5.
$$g(t) = \begin{cases} 15t \text{ for } 0 \le t \le 2 \\ 30 \text{ for } 2 < t < 4 \\ 10t - 10 \text{ for } 4 \le t \le 7 \end{cases}$$

6. Finding the equation of the line, the slope has a rise of 30 and a run of 2 so the rate of change or slope is 15. Since the line goes through (0,0) and has a slope of 15, then the equation for this portion of the graph is $g(t) = 15t$. Then to find $g(t) = 22$, we have $22 = 15t$. Solving for t gives us $\frac{22}{15}$ or 1.467 hours. This says that at 1.467 hours, the person had ridden 22 miles.

7. 7.5 miles per hour

8. Graphs may vary. They are correct as long as they decrease beginning at the 4th hour and go back to the time axis. One example of a correct graph is below.

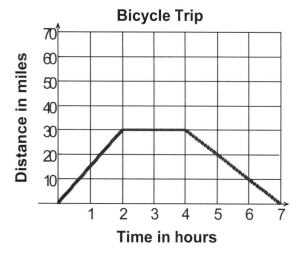

9. At the second hour she stops for 2 hours to eat lunch and take a nap under a tree in a park that is 30 miles away from where she started. At the 4th hour, she decides to continue on her bike journey still traveling away from her starting position. She is going at a constant rate of 10 miles per hour for 3 more hours. At the end of 7 hours she is 70 miles away from her starting position.

Write Your Notes and Ideas Here!

Parallel and Perpendicular Lines – An Investigation

Objective:
Students will "discover" properties of slopes for parallel and perpendicular lines.

Connections to Previous Learning:
Students should have a basic understanding of parallel and perpendicular lines and be able to determine slope of a line.

Connections to TEKS:
111.32 c2A, c2B

Connections to AP:
The AP Calculus objective of analysis of functions

Time Frame:
30 minutes

Materials:
Graph paper

Teacher Notes:
This lesson should be done after students have mastered finding the slope of a line, and it can be used as a review of this skill. It is meant to be done in groups of 3 or 4 with no two students having the same set of parallel or perpendicular lines. The fact that they all have different pairs of lines will add power to the conclusions that the group makes. There is an independent assignment included in addition to the 30 minutes of estimated class time. The teacher can also modify this lesson to have the students write the equations of the lines given in the independent assignment.

Parallel and Perpendicular Lines – An Investigation

Investigation I

Use the numbered steps below to draw a pair of parallel lines on your graph paper. For the purposes of these two investigations, do not draw any lines that have slopes of 1, -1, 0, or undefined. Also, for both, be sure that your pair of parallel lines is different from those of anyone else in your group.

1. Place your ruler on your graph paper so that the bottom edge of the ruler is on at least two integer ordered pairs on the graph paper. Label these points A and B.

2. Draw a line through the two points. Be sure to hold your ruler steady and to make a very thin, straight line.

3. Find two integer points on the graph paper on the other side of your ruler. Label these points C and D. Draw this line.

4. Be sure you drew your lines so that they are parallel. Close won't work here. One way to be sure is to fold your graph paper so that the lines are on top of each other. If your lines are parallel, the fold line in the middle will be equally distant from each line and will also be parallel to the two lines.

If you are sure that your two lines are parallel, find the slope of lines AB and CD. What do you notice about the slopes? Compare your results with those of your group members. Is there a common result?

On your graph paper, state your conclusion about the slopes of lines which are parallel. Support this conclusion by showing the calculations that you made to determine the slopes of your lines.

Investigation II

Use the numbered steps below to draw a pair of lines which are perpendicular.

1. Take a sheet of paper which has a right-angled corner. Place the corner at an integer point on your graph paper. Label this point Y.

2. Rotate this sheet of paper about your chosen point until **each** edge passes over a point that is also an integer point. Label these points X and Z.

3. Take your ruler and carefully draw angle XYZ.

Find the slope of rays YX and YZ. What do you notice about the slopes? Compare your results with those of your group members. Is there a common result?

On your graph paper, state your conclusion about the slopes of lines which are perpendicular. Support this conclusion by showing the calculations that you made to determine the slopes of your lines. Verify your conclusions with your teacher before going on to the assignment.

Parallel and Perpendicular Lines – Independent Assignment

Part I

A quadrilateral that has both sets of opposite sides parallel and one right angle is a rectangle. Verify that quadrilateral ABCD below is a rectangle. In order to do this, follow the steps below.

1.   Show that both pairs of opposite sides are parallel.

2.   Show that at least one pair of adjacent sides is perpendicular.

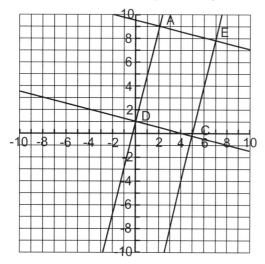

Part II

1.   Determine the coordinates for four ordered pairs so that the quadrilateral they make is a parallelogram, but not a rectangle. Be sure to justify your choice of coordinates.

2.   Determine the coordinates for four ordered pairs so that the quadrilateral they make is neither a parallelogram, a rectangle, nor a square. Be sure to justify your choice of coordinates.

Parallel and Perpendicular Lines – Independent Assignment

Answers:
Part I

Verify that quadrilateral ABCD below is, or is not, a rectangle. In order to do this, follow the steps below.

1. Show that both pairs of opposite sides are (or are not) parallel.

   The slopes of AD and BC are 4. The slopes of AB and CD are -.25. These opposite pairs of sides are parallel.

2. Show that at least one pair of adjacent sides is (or is not) perpendicular.

   From the slopes determined in #1 above, the lines are perpendicular since they are negative reciprocals.

Part II

1. Determine the coordinates for four ordered pairs so that the quadrilateral they make is a parallelogram, but not a rectangle. Be sure to justify your choice of coordinates.

   Check students' work to be sure that the slopes of opposite pairs of lines are parallel. Also check to be sure that the slopes are not negative reciprocals.

2. Determine the coordinates for four ordered pairs so that the quadrilateral they make is neither a parallelogram, a rectangle, nor a square. Be sure to justify your choice of coordinates.

   Check students' work. Slopes of both opposite pairs of sides must not be equal.

Write the Equation of the Line – Review

Objective:
Students will be assessed on their ability to write the equation of a line in multiple methods.

Connections to Previous Learning:
Students should be able to write the equation of a line using a graph, slope – intercept, two points, point – slope.

Connections to TEKS:
111.32 c2C, c2D, c2E, c2F

Connections to AP:
The AP Calculus objective of analysis of functions

Time Frame:
45 minutes

Materials:
One copy of the worksheet for each student

Teacher Notes:
This lesson can be used as a review or as an assessment.

Write the Equation of the Line – Review

1. Use the graph showing line b below to answer the following. Be sure to show the steps which justify EACH part of each answer. Your work will be graded based on the explanations that you give, not just based on your answer.

    a) What is the slope of this line? Explain how you got this answer two different ways.

    b) What is the y-intercept of this line?

    c) Explain how to use the graph to write an equation for this line in slope-intercept form. Give the equation of the line.

    d) Choose any two points on the graph and explain how to find the equation in slope-intercept form from those two points.

    e) Choose any point on the graph and the slope that you determined in part a. Write an equation in point-slope form for this line.

    f) Re-write your equation from part e in standard form.

    g) Re-write your equation from part e in slope-intercept form.

    h) If line b is shifted down 3 units, what is the equation of the new line?

    i) If line b is shifted to the right 4 units, what is the equation of the new line?

line b

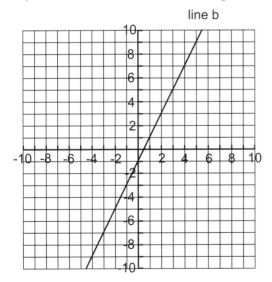
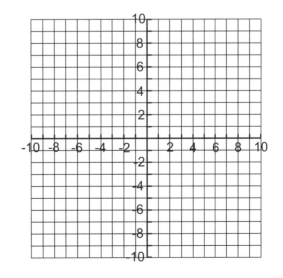

2. Use the points (3, 0) and (0, -2) to answer the following. (You may use the grid above to graph the points if you wish.)

    a) What is the slope of the line which passes through these two points?

    b) Write the equation of the line passing through these points. Use slope-intercept form.

    c) Write the equation of the line passing through these points. Use point-slope form.

    d) Write the equation of the line passing through these points in standard form.

    e) Write the equation of any line which is perpendicular to this line.

    f) Write the equation of a line which is parallel to this line which passes through the point (1, 3). Give your answer in standard form.

Write the Equation of the Line – Review

Answers:

1. Use the graph showing line b below to answer the following. Be sure to show the steps which justify EACH part of each answer. Your work will be graded based on the explanations that you give, not just based on your answer.

    a) What is the slope of this line? Explain how you got this answer two different ways. *One way is to just count on the coordinate plane. The rise is 2 and the run is 1, so the slope is 2. Another way is to pick any two points on the line. I'll use (0, -1) and (1, 1). The slope is*
    $$\frac{1-(-1)}{1-0} = \frac{2}{1} = 2.$$

    b) What is the y-intercept of this line? *The y-intercept, from looking at where the graph crosses the y-axis, is -1.*

    c) Explain how to use the graph to write an equation for this line in slope-intercept form. Give the equation of the line. *From the graph I counted the slope and found that it is 2, see part a. Then I found that the y-intercept is -1, see part b. Since the equation of the line in slope-intercept form is y = mx + b, the equation of this line is y = 2x – 1*

    d) Choose any two points on the graph and explain how to find the equation in slope-intercept form from those two points. *I'll use the points (1, 1) and (2, 3). From these points, find the slope which is* $\dfrac{3-1}{2-1} = 2$. *Next use this slope and one ordered pair. I'll use (1, 1). 1 = 2(2) + b. Solving this equation for b, I get b = -1. Substituting for the slope and y-intercept, the equation is y = 2x – 1.*

    e) Choose any point on the graph and the slope that you determined in part a. Write an equation in point-slope form for this line. *I'll use (1, 1) and the slope is 2, so y – 1 = 2(x – 1).*

    f) Re-write your equation from part e in standard form. *y – 1 = 2(x – 1)*
    y – 1 = 2x – 2
       after adding -2x and 1 to both sides *-1(y – 2x = -1)*
    2x – y = 1

    g) Re-write your equation from part e in slope-intercept form. *y – 1 = 2(x – 1)*
    y – 1 = 2x – 2
       after adding 1 to each side *y = 2x – 1*

h) If line b is shifted down 3 units, what will the equation of the new line be? *Since the original equation is y = 2x – 1, a shift down 3 units will take the y-intercept down 3 from -1. Since -1 + -3 is -4, the new y-intercept is -4, and the new equation is y = 2x – 4.*

i) If line b is shifted to the right 4 units, what will the equation of the new line be? *From looking at the graph, I see that the point (-4, -9) would move to the y-axis. This would make the new y-intercept (0, -9). The new equation would be y = 2x – 9, or y = 2(x – 4) – 1 = 2x – 9.*

2. Use the points (3, 0) and (0, -2) to answer the following. (You may use the grid above the graph the points if you wish.)

a) What is the slope of the line which passes through these points? *The slope is*
$$\frac{-2-0}{0-3} = \frac{-2}{-3} = \frac{2}{3}.$$

b) Write the equation of the line passing through these points. Use slope-intercept form. *The equation of the line passing through these points is $y = \dfrac{2}{3}x – 2$. I know the y-intercept because it is the y-coordinate when x is zero, and we were given that point.*

c) Write the equation of the line passing through these points. Use point-slope form. *Since we found the slope in part a, and using (3, 0), the equation is $y – 0 = \dfrac{2}{3}(x – 3)$.*

d) Write the equation of the line passing through these points. Give your final answer in standard form. *Since the two points given were the intercepts, the equation can be found by just working backwards. The equation is 2x – 3y = 6 since 2 times 3 is 6 and -3 times -2 is 6 or 3y = 2x – 6.*

e) Write the equation of any line which is perpendicular to this line. *The equation of a line perpendicular to this line has to have a slope of $-\dfrac{3}{2}$, so in general, a possible equation would be of the form $y = -\dfrac{3}{2}x + b$.*

f) Write the equation of a line which is parallel to this line which passes through the point (1, 3). Give your answer in standard form. *A line parallel to this line will have the same slope, $\dfrac{2}{3}$.*

Using point-slope form,	$y – 3 = \dfrac{2}{3}(x – 1)$
clearing fractions and parentheses	$3y – 9 = 2x – 2$
subtracting 3y and -2 from each side	$-7 = 2x – 3y.$
The equation in standard form is	$2x – 3y = -7.$

Write Your Notes and Ideas Here!

A Study of Olympic Winning Times

Objective:
Students will graph data, determine a line of best fit, and solve a system of equations by graphing.

Connections to Previous Learning:
Students should be able to graph on a coordinate plane and write the equation of a line.

Connections to TEKS:
111.32 b1B, b1C, b1D, b1E, b2C, b2D, c1C, c2D, c3A, c4A, c4B, c4C

Connections to AP:
The AP Statistics objectives of graphical displays and linear bivariate data
The AP Calculus objective of analysis of functions

Time Frame:
90 minutes

Materials:
Straight edge, graph paper, one copy of the student pages for each student, and access to a data source or the data provided with this lesson

Teacher Notes:
This lesson is designed to be done after students have mastered writing the equation of a line, but before a formal study of systems of equations. If used at this point, explain the instructions on number 11 of the student worksheet. Students can collect their own data from a sports event of their choice or use the data from the 100m dash which is given on a separate page. If students collect their own data, it must be an event that is performed competitively by both men and women, and one that will yield data for 1928 to 2000. They can gather data from a source such as the internet or *The World Almanac*.

To improve discussion, students should have a reasonably uniform graph. Label 1900 as the year zero on their graph, and work from that starting point for all graphs and questions.

It is important to spend some time on the final question. Encourage students to push their lines to the extreme and realize that eventually not only would women be running faster than men, but that both would also run in zero or negative time. This would be a good time to revisit, or visit, piecewise functions as this data often breaks down into distinct sections.

Note: Students are usually curious about the gap in the table – no Olympics during World War II

A Study of Olympic Winning Times

Obtain data for a specific Olympic event in which both men and women competed from 1928 to 2000. Display in a table the winning times for both men and women.

Graph both data sets on a coordinate graph. Use the horizontal axis for the year and the vertical axis for winning times. Let the year 1900 be 0 on your horizontal axis.

Determine a line of best fit for each set of points. Show your work in determining both lines.

Answer the following questions:

1. Explain why the year was place on the horizontal axis and the winning times on the vertical axis. Be sure to include appropriate mathematical terminology in the explanation.

2. What problems might be encountered if the winning times were placed on the horizontal axis?

3. What is the slope of the line of best fit for the men? What is the slope of the line of best fit for the women? Interpret the slope in terms of the problem.

4. What winning time does your line calculate for men for the year 1850? Is it a reasonable projection? Explain. What about for the year 1600? The year 0?

5. What winning time does your line calculate for women for the year 1850? Is it a reasonable projection? Explain. What about for the year 1600? The year 0?

6. Is a line a good representation of the possible data for the years before 1900? Explain.

7. What winning time does your line calculate for men for the year 2008? Is it a reasonable prediction? Explain. What about for the year 2050? The year 3000?

8. What winning time does your line calculate for women for the year 2008? Is it a reasonable prediction? Explain. What about for the year 2050? The year 3000?

9. Is a line a good representation of the possible data for the years after 2000? Explain.

10. What model might better represent how the winning times are changing over time?

11. Solve the system of equations using a method that you consider best. Justify your solution. What is the significance of this point?

A Study of Olympic Winning Times – Data Page

The following table gives the men and women's winning times for the 100m dash in the Olympics from 1928-2000.

Year	Men's 100m Dash in seconds	Women's 100m Dash in seconds
1928	10.8	12.2
1932	10.3	11.9
1936	10.3	11.5
1948	10.3	11.9
1952	10.4	11.5
1956	10.5	11.5
1960	10.2	11.0
1964	10.0	11.4
1968	9.95	11.00
1972	10.14	11.07
1976	10.06	11.08
1980	10.25	11.06
1984	9.99	10.97
1988	9.92	10.54
1992	9.96	10.82
1996	9.84	10.94
2000	9.87	10.75

A Study of Olympic Winning Times

Answers:

Check that students have provided a table and a graph for their data. These will depend on the event chosen. If you had your class use the 100m dash table, then you can simply instruct students to turn that in. Graphs for this set of data are provided below.

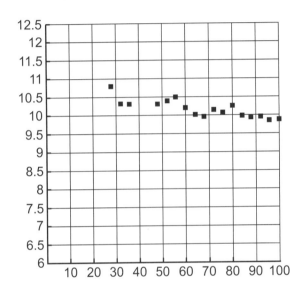
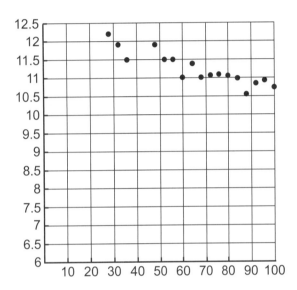

Again, the lines of best fit, and all specific answers below, are for the 100m dash data.

The level of experience your students have will determine the line that they give. The man's line should be about y = -.0085x + 10.69. The woman's line should be about y = -.018x + 12.3. My students do this as an evaluation after learning how to do line of best fit by hand. Their equations will be cruder than these.

1. Explain why the year was place on the horizontal axis and the winning times on the vertical method. Be sure to include appropriate mathematical terminology in the explanation. *The year is the variable that we are using to explain the winning times. We will consider this the independent variable. Scatter plots are always graphed with the independent variable on the horizontal axis and the dependent variable on the vertical axis.*

2. What problems might be encountered if the winning times were placed on the horizontal axis? *If we see a graph with the winning times on the horizontal axis, this tells us we are attempting to use the winning times to predict the year. In this situation, trying to predict the year based on a sporting event would not be sensible.*

3. What is the slope of the line of best fit for the men? What is the slope of the line of best fit for the women? Interpret the slope in terms of the problem. *The sample slope for the men is -.0085 and for the women is -.018. For every increase of one year, there is a decrease of .0085 seconds.*

4. What winning time does your line calculate for men for the year 1850? Is it a reasonable projection? Explain. What about for the year 1600? The year 0?

    The answers in 4-6 will vary according to the lines that students derive. Samples are given. 1850, ≈ 11.115sec; 1600, ≈ 13.24sec; 0, ≈ 25.99sec. Accept any well thought out, well explained answer for the "reasonable projection".

5. What winning time does your line calculate for women for the year 1850? Is it a reasonable projection? Explain. What about for the year 1600? The year 0?

    The answers in 4-6 will vary according to the lines that students derive. 1850, ≈ 13.2sec; 1600, ≈ 17.7sec; 0, ≈ 44.7sec. Accept any well thought out, well explained answer for the "reasonable projection".

6. Is a line a good representation of the possible data for the years before 1900? Explain. A good argument can be made that a line is/is not a good representation. *Accept any well thought out answer.*

7. What winning time does your line calculate for men for the year 2008? Is it a reasonable prediction? Explain. What about for the year 2050? The year 3000?

    2008, ≈ 9.972sec; 2050, ≈ 9.415sec; 3000, 1.34sec

8. What winning time does your line calculate for women for the year 2008? Is it a reasonable prediction? Explain. What about for the year 2050? The year 3000?

    2008, ≈ 10.356sec; 2050, ≈ 9.6sec; 3000, -7.5sec

9. Is a line a good representation of the possible data for the years after 2000? Explain. Students should recognize that the data for the years after 2000 is not linear. One reasonable explanation is that it is not possible to ever run in negative time.

10. What model might better represent how the winning times are changing over time? This question is a stretch at this point in algebra. Students might consider a piecewise function as a possibility. You will probably have to lead them to a model such as exponential.

11. Solve the system of equations using a method that you consider best. Justify your solution. What is the significance of this point. *If you do this when students have no experience solving systems of equations, they will probably get this solution by using a table (from calculator or by hand), or trial and error. An approximate answer is (170, 9.24). This means that in the year 1900 + 170 or 2070, women and men will run the 100m dash in the same time, using this mathematical model. The time will be about 9.24 seconds.*

Coding Data for Scatterplots and Trend Lines

Objective:
Students will learn how to code data to make calculations simpler.

Connections to Previous Learning:
Students should be able to draw scatterplots and write the equation of a trend line.

Connections to TEKS:
111.32 b1A, b1B, b1C, b1D, c2B, c3A

Connections to AP:
The AP Statistics objective of linear bivariate data

Time Frame:
30 minutes

Materials:
Handouts and a graphing calculator with statistical capabilities

Teacher Notes:
This lesson is designed to introduce the practice of coding data. In many cases the numbers in a data set can be quite large and cumbersome when students are trying to do calculations. Additionally, some calculators have overflow problems if the numbers get too large. Coding is one way to help reduce this problem. The first example leads students through the process of coding years such as 1940. While the example decides to use t = years since 1940, it is worth discussing that defining t in this manner is only one possibility. We could have let t = years since 1900. This leads to the familiar truncated form of 1940 as '40, and 1945 as '45. Ask students how they would define the year 2002 using this definition of t. This is a good way to relate the definition chosen for t to the graphical problem for the x-axis. If 1999 is represented as '99 then what happens to 2000? Is it '00? Where would this data point be located on the x-axis? Does that seem appropriate?

The lesson draws students to realize that using the coded data will not change to relationship of the points on the scatterplot nor the slope of the trend line (even though the coded equation will have a different y-intercept). Any predicted value would be the same whether one used the original equation or the coded equation.

Note: Examples #2 - #4 are designed for students to practice how to code data. A teacher using these examples could also extend the lesson by modifying questions #1(a) – (i), for examples #3 and #4. Both of these are linear data sets and would be appropriate for Algebra I students. Example #2 is exponential and does not have a linear trend line.

Coding Data for Scatterplots and Trend Lines

1. Below are the data on the farm population (in millions of people who live on farms) from 1940 to 1985.

Year	1940	1945	1950	1955	1960	1965	1970	1975	1980	1985
Pop	30.5	24.5	23.1	19.2	15.6	12.4	9.7	8.9	7.2	4.2

a) Based on the table describe the relationship between year and the number of people who living on American farms.

b) Construct a scatterplot of the data. Remember to include scales and labels for your axes.

c) Does the scatterplot confirm your description in part (a)? Explain your answer.

d) On your scatterplot, draw a straight line through the points (1945, 24.5) and (1975, 8.9). Give the equation of the line you just drew. Note that this line goes through the approximate middle of the data and is called a trend line. What does the variable y represent in your equation? What does the variable x represent in your equation? What is the slope of this line? Interpret the slope in the context of this problem.

e) Use your equation from part (d) to estimate the number of people who lived on farms is 1973. Do you think that your estimate will be close to the actual number of people who lived on farms in 1973? Explain your answer.

One way we can make the equation somewhat easier to calculate is to reduce the size of the numbers involved in the equation. This is called **CODING** the data. For example, if we look at the original data we notice that the years are given as 1940, 1945, etc. We could let t represent the years since 1940. Then 1940 would be represented as t = 0, 1945 as t = 5, and so forth through 1985 as t = 45.

f) Recode the years for the problem above if t = years since 1940. We will use the variable t and N = number of people who lived on farms.

t										
N	30.5	24.5	23.1	19.2	15.6	12.4	9.7	8.9	7.2	4.2

g) Construct a scatterplot of the data. Remember to include scales and labels for your axes with the new variables. How does this scatterplot compare to the scatterplot you drew in part (b)? Explain your answer.

h) On your scatterplot, draw a straight line through the points (5, 24.5) and (35, 8.9). Give the equation of this line. Use the new variables when writing your equation. What is the slope of this line? How does this slope compare to the slope of the original line in part (d)?

i) Use your equation from part (h) to estimate the number of people who lived on farms is 1973. How does your answer compare to the estimate you gave in part (e) which was based on the un-coded equation?

Summary: After you code the data which of the following remain the same as if you had used the original data?

  (i) the scatterplot of the coded data.

  (ii) the equation of the trend line based on the coded data.

  (iii) the slope of the trend line based on the coded data.

  (iv) a predicted value based on the trend line for the coded data.

We must be careful to define what the coded variable will represent. If we had let t = years since 1944, then we would have 1945 represented by $t = 1$, 1950 would be coded as $t = 6$, and so forth. We try to choose something that is convenient to use.

2. The number of cell phones and personal communications systems subscribers in the United States has increased dramatically since 1990, as shown by the following table.

Year	Number of Subscribers
1990	5,300,000
1991	8,650,000
1992	11,100,000
1993	18,400,000
1994	21,100,000
1995	32,800,000
1996	41,700,000
1997	52,800,000

a) Code the years by letting t = years since 1989 and N = number of subscribers given in millions.

b) Let t = years since 1900. List the coded years and number of subscribers (in millions) for the above data. Use the space to the right of the original table.

c) How would you code the year 2003?

3. A real estate agent would like to predict the selling price of single-family homes. After careful consideration, she concludes that the variable likely to be most related to selling price is the size of the house. As an experiment, she takes a random sample of 9 recently sold homes and records the selling price and the size of the house. See the table below.

SIZE (sq. ft)	Price (in $)
2600	146,900
3390	409,700
2050	83,100
3210	318,400
1800	66,600
3240	371,800
2750	151,400
3080	201,200
2430	133,800
3190	252,100
2860	165,800

Code the data by using size in $100 \ ft^2$ and price in $1000.

4. Car dealers across North America use the "Blue Book" to help them determine the value of used cars that customers trade in when purchasing new vehicles. The book lists on a monthly basis the amount paid at recent used-car auctions and indicates the trade-in values according to condition and optional features. A study was completed to determine whether the odometer reading would serve as a useful predictor of trade-in value. Fifteen five-year-old cars of the same make, model, condition, and options have been randomly selected. The trade-in value and mileage are shown below.

Odometer Reading	Trade-in Value ($)
58,200	3840
92,800	2400
37,500	7220
72,000	3090
52,000	4000
67,200	3110
88,340	2750
62,490	3920
95,100	2540
83,120	2600
43,000	4300
35,900	6110
31,200	8800
39,000	5520
27,800	9990

Decide what would be a convenient method for coding the data and then redo the table using the coded values.

Coding Data for Scatterplots and Trend Lines

Answers:

1. a)   As the years have increased form 1940 to 1985 the number of people living on farms has steadily decreased.

   b)

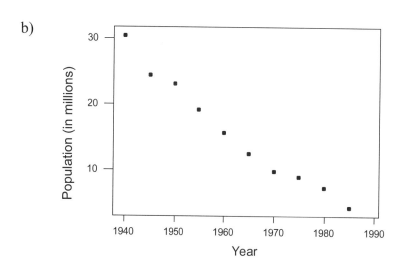

   c)   Yes. It is clear from the scatterplot that the points decrease as the years increase.

   d)   The slope of the line is m $= \dfrac{24.5 - 8.9}{1945 - 1975} = \dfrac{15.6}{-30} = -0.52$

   y – 24.5 = -0.52(x -1945)

   y = -0.52x + 1035.9 where y = population living on farms and x = time in years

   The slope is –0.52. For every one-year increase in time the population living on farms decreases by about 520,000 people.

   e)   If x = 1973, then population = -0.52 (1973) + 1035.9 = 9.94 million people.

   Based on the data in the table this seems a little high, since there were only 9.7 million people living on farms in 1970.

   f)

t	0	5	10	15	20	25	30	35	40	45
N	30.5	24.5	23.1	19.2	15.6	12.4	9.7	8.9	7.2	4.2

g)

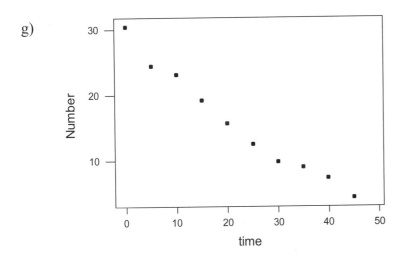

The scatterplot based on the coded data is the same as the scatterplot for the original data. The only difference is the scale on the x-axis. The relationship between the data points have remained unchanged.

h)   The slope of the line is m = $\dfrac{24.5 - 8.9}{5 - 35} = \dfrac{15.6}{-30} = -0.52$.

N – 24.5 = -0.52(t - 5)

N = -0.52t + 27.1 where N = number of people living on farms and t = time in years since 1940.

i)   If time is 1973 then t = 33 and N = -0.52 (33) + 27.1 = 9.94 million people.

This predicted value is the same as if the original data had been used.

Summary: parts (i), (iii), and (iv) remain the same.

2.   a)

Year	1	2	3	4	5	6	7	8
Number of Subscribers (in millions)	5.3	8.65	11.1	18.4	21.1	32.8	41.7	52.8

b)

Year	90	91	92	93	94	95	96	97
Number of Subscribers (in millions)	5.3	8.65	11.1	18.4	21.1	32.8	41.7	52.8

c)   Code 2003 as t = 14 if t is defined as years since 1989 and as t = 103 if t is defined as years since 1900.

3.

SIZE (in 100 sq ft)	Price (in 1000s)
26	146.9
33.9	409.7
20.5	83.1
32.1	318.4
18	66.6
32.4	371.8
27.5	151.4
30.8	201.2
24.3	133.8
31.9	252.1
28.6	165.8

4.

Odometer (in 1000s)	Trade-in Value (in $100)
58.2	38.4
92.8	24
37.5	72.2
72	30.9
52	40
67.2	31.1
88.34	27.5
62.49	39.2
95.1	25.4
83.12	26
43	43
35.9	61.1
31.2	88
39	55.2
27.8	99.9

Write Your Notes and Ideas Here!

Fitting a Line to Data

Objective:
Students will learn to draw a line of good fit and to write its equation.

Connections to Previous Learning:
Students should be able to draw scatterplots and write the equation of a line.

Connections to TEKS:
111.32 b1A, b1B, b1C, b1D, c2B, c3A

Connections to AP:
The AP Statistics topic of linear bivariate data

Time Frame:
50 minutes

Materials:
Handouts, rulers, and graph paper.

Teacher Notes:
This lesson is designed to introduce constructing a trend line from data in order to make a prediction. This lesson can be introduced when students are learning how to write the equations of lines either in slope-intercept or point-slope form. While most linear regression equations are written in the form $y = a + bx$, it would not complicate matters to let students write their equation in $y = mx + b$ form.

This is a non-calculator lesson so students should use graph paper to construct their scatterplots and a ruler to draw their trend lines. The objective is to draw a line that fits the data so many teachers start to use the terminology "best fit line" or "fitted line" instead of "trend line" as this is more in keeping with statistical terminology. This line will be a line of "good" fit while it may not be the line of best fit. In order to determine a line of "best fit" students would have to use techniques beyond the realm of Algebra I.

Note: When drawing the scatterplot, the variable that is being <u>predicted</u> goes on the vertical axis and the other variable (explanatory or independent) goes on the horizontal axis. Emphasize with students that the line they are going to draw needs to go through the middle of the data so they should think about this and experiment a little with their ruler before drawing their line.

Another concept that is introduced is that of a <u>residual</u>. One objective in regression is to make a prediction for the y-value when you are given some x-value. The difference between the actual y-values and the predicted y-values determined from the fitted line are called residuals (residual = actual value – predicted value). If the line is a good fit we would anticipate that most of the residuals will be small.

The first example is a group instruction problem. The second can be a partner problem or an individual problem

Fitting a Line to Data

1. A large company is expanding its workforce and needs to hire some new administrative assistants. The company wants to know what the relationship is between the amount of experience that its current administrative assistants possessed when they were hired and their starting salary with the company. The data for ten randomly selected administrative assistants is given below.

Experience (in months)	Starting Salary (in $1000)
4	25
13	34
3	22
0	21
10	33
7	27
22	38
15	35
5	26
20	36

a) What kind of the relationship would you expect between length of experience and starting salary for the randomly selected administrative assistants.

b) Construct a scatterplot of the data. Which variable should be the independent variable and which is the dependent variable? Remember to include scales and labels for your axes.

c) Does the scatterplot confirm your description in part (a)? Explain your answer.

d) Suppose you wanted to hire an administrative assistant who had 17 months experience. Predict what the starting salary would be. Describe how you used the scatterplot to help you. How does your prediction compare with other student's predictions?

Since there seems to be an almost linear relationship between starting salary and amount of job experience in months, a line can be drawn on the scatterplot to summarize this relationship. Such a line helps us to predict the value of the variable on the vertical axis (the dependent variable) from the value of the variable on the horizontal axis (the independent variable).

On your scatterplot in part (b), draw a line that you think summarizes or *fits* the data. This line should go through the middle of the set of data points.

e) Use the line you drew to predict the approximate starting salary for an assistant with 12 months experience.

f) According to the data, the actual salary of an assistant with 12 months experience was $33,000. How close was your prediction? Calculate this by subtracting the predicted value from the actual value. This difference in called a <u>residual</u>. Did you over-predict or under-predict your estimate? Justify your answer.

g) Compare your prediction to those made by others in your class. Who was the closest to the actual value? What can we say about the residual of the person with the closest prediction?

h) Look at the line drawn by the person who had the smallest residual value. Do you think that this person had the line that best fits the data? Explain your answer.

i) Instead of using the graph of the fitted line to predict a starting salary based on experience, you can use an equation for the line to do it. Pick two ordered pairs on the line you drew on the scatterplot of length of experience and starting salary. Use your ordered pairs to write an equation of the line. Write your answer in the form of $y = mx + b$.

j) What does the variable y represent in your equation? What does the variable x represent in your equation?

k) What is the slope of this line? Interpret the slope in the context of this problem.

l) Use your equation from part (i) to predict the starting salary for an assistant who has 17 months experience.

m) Compare your prediction from part (l) to your estimate from the scatterplot in part (d). Are they reasonably close? Do you think having the equation for the fitted line makes it easier to predict a value? Explain your answer.

2. Car dealers across North America use the "Blue Book" to help them determine the value of used cars that customers trade in when purchasing new vehicles. The book lists on a monthly basis the amount paid at recent used-car auctions and indicates the trade-in values according to condition and optional features. A study was completed to determine whether the odometer reading would serve as a useful predictor of trade-in value. Five-year-old cars of the same make, model, condition, and options have been randomly selected. The trade-in value and mileage are shown below.

Odometer Reading	Trade-in Value ($)
58,000	3800
93,100	2400
72,200	3100
52,000	4000
67,700	3200
88,100	2700
62,500	3900
95,100	2500
83,100	2600
43,400	4300
39,000	5500

a) What kind of relationship would you expect between trade-in value and odometer reading for the randomly selected cars. Explain your answer.

b) Code the data to make it easier to use.

c) Construct a scatterplot of the coded data. Which variable should be the independent variable and which is the dependent variable? Do you think that odometer reading depends on trade-in value or trade-in value depends on the odometer reading? Remember to include scales and labels for your axes.

d) Does the scatterplot confirm your description in part (a)? Explain your answer.

e) On your scatterplot in part (b), draw a line that you think summarizes or *fits* the data. Pick two ordered pairs on the line you drew on the scatterplot of trade-in value and odometer reading. Use your ordered pairs to write an equation of the line. Write your answer in the form of $y = mx + b$.

f) What does the variable y represent in your equation? What does the variable x represent in your equation?

g) What is the slope of this line? Interpret the slope in the context of this problem.

h) Use your equation from part (e) to predict the trade-in value of a vehicle with 52,000 miles.

i) According to the data, the actual trade-in value of a car with 52,000 miles was $4,000. How close was your prediction? Calculate the <u>residual</u>. Did you over-predict or under-predict your estimate? Justify your answer.

Fitting a Line to Data

Answers:

1. a) I would expect that as the level of experience increases the starting salary for an administrative assistant will also increase.

   b) The independent variable should be experience and the dependent variable should be starting salary.

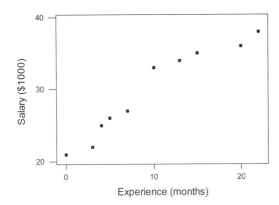

   c) The scatterplot confirms the description in part (a) since the data forms a positive relationship between experience and starting salary.

   d) There is no data point corresponding to an assistant with 17 months experience. If you were to lay a ruler on the scatterplot going through the data points around 17 months we can see that the salary range is in the neighborhood of $35,000 to $37,000, so let's estimate it as $36,000

   Answers may vary depending on what students describe as their method.

   e) Answers will vary depending on the line that the student drew and how accurate the student can estimate.

   f) Suppose that the student estimates the salary to be $32,500. The residual would be $33,000 – $32,5000 or $500. If the residual is positive, then the actual value is more than the predicted value so the line is under-predicting; if the residual is negative, then the predicted value is more than the actual value so the line would be over-predicting at that point.

   g) Answer will vary.

   h) It is possible that this is the line that fits the data best but it could just be that the line is off substantially for other points and just happens to be close for this particular value. Ideally the best line should consistently give residuals that are small for each of the data points in the problem.

i) Answers will vary depending on the chosen points but should be close to the equation
y = 0.80x + 21.8.

j) The variable y represents the starting salary in $1000 and the variable x represents the
experience in months for an administrative assistant. It is helpful to write the equation
representing the line in the context of the situation. This helps emphasize the relationship
between the variables in the problem. Thus the equation would be written as
Salary = 0.80 (months) + 21.8.

k) The slope of the line is 0.80. This means that for every 1 month increase in experience the
starting salary increases by approximately 0.80(1000) = $800.

l) Answers will vary depending on the student's equation but should be approximately
y = 0.80(17) + 21.8 = 35.4. The predicted starting salary for an administrative assistant
who possesses 17 months experience would be approximately $35,400.

m) Part (d) the predicted value from the scatterplot was $36,000 and from the fitted line the
prediction was $35,400. They are reasonably close to each other but it is easier to use the
fitted equation rather than eyeball an estimate form the scatterplot.

2. a) As odometer readings increases a car has been driven more so the trade-in value will
decrease.

b) Code the data by using odometer readings in thousands of miles and the trade-in value in
hundreds of dollars.

Odometer Reading (1000s)	Trade-in Value ($100)
58	38
93.1	24
72.2	31
52	40
67.7	32
88.1	27
62.5	39
95.1	25
83.1	26
43.4	43
39	55

c)

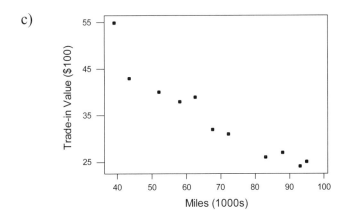

d) Yes. There is a negative linear relationship between odometer reading and trade-in value.

e) Student responses may vary considerably depending where they draw their line to account for the high point of (39,55). Ideally it should be close to y = -0.46x + 66.05.

f) The variable y represents the trade-in value in hundreds of dollars and the variable x represents the odometer reading in thousands of miles. The equation could therefore be written in the context of the situation as Value = (-0.46 $\frac{mileage}{1000}$ + 66.05)(100 dollars)

g) Answers will vary depending on student's work. If the slope of the line is given by -0.46, then for every 1000 mile increase in odometer reading the trade-in value of the car will decrease by approximately (.46)(100) = $46.00. Note: the units of the slope are given by $\frac{units\ of\ y}{units\ of\ x}$; that is, hundreds of dollars per thousand miles.

h) Value = -0.46(52) + 66.05 = 42.13. The predicted trade-in value for a car with 52,000 miles is approximately $4213.

i) Residual = actual-predicted = 4000 – 4213 = -$213. Since the residual has a negative value the fitted line is over-predicting the trade-in value.

Linear Regression with Coded Data

Objective:
Students will make predictions using regression lines.

Connections to Previous Learning:
Students should be able to create scatterplots and find lines of good-fit (this could be changed to lines of best fit if done with a graphing calculator).

Connections to TEKS:
111.32 c1C, c2D

Connections to AP:
The AP Statistics objective of linear bivariate data

Time Frame:
30 minutes

Materials:
Worksheet (graphing calculator optional)

Teacher Notes:
The purpose of this lesson is to provide students practice with data that has been coded in some way. The lesson is written to find lines of good-fit without using a graphing calculator, but it can easily be adapted to find lines of best fit if a calculator is employed. The interpretation of slope is emphasized as well as the uncoding of the data.

Linear Regression with Coded Data

1. The following table shows the birth rates (per 1000 people) in the United States since 1920. (The variable year is the number of years since 1920.)

Year	10	20	30	40	50	60	70
Birth rate	21.3	19.4	24.1	23.7	18.4	15.9	16.7

    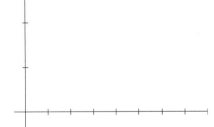

    a) Construct a scatterplot for the data.

    b) What year is represented by year 40?

    c) Calculate a good-fitting line for the data.

    d) In the context of the problem, what does the intercept mean?

    e) In the context of the problem, what does the slope mean?

    f) Predict the birth rate for the year 2000.

2. Suppose you work at the stadium of a major league baseball team. Your job is to order food for the concession stands. In order to determine the number of hotdogs that you need to order for the next game, you examine data from previous games. You have found that the expected attendance at a game can be determined from advanced ticket sales. The data below show the number of advanced tickets sold (in thousands) and the number of hotdogs purchased (in thousands) at each game.

Ticket Sales	45	64	37	58	41	29
Hotdogs sold	32	46	25	44	32	18

    a) Construct a scatterplot for the data.

    b) Calculate a good-fitting line for the data.

    c) In the context of the problem, what does the slope mean?

    d) If advanced ticket sales are 52,000, approximately how many hotdogs would you expect to sell at the game?

219

3. A real estate agent must often determine the price of a house that is to be sold. One of the factors that help determine the cost of the house is its size, or the number of square feet of living space in the house. The data below gives the number of square feet (in hundreds) and the cost (in thousands of dollars) of houses that sold recently in a town.

Size of house	15	31	22	18	26	14	35	25	23
Cost of house	130	280	195	160	225	140	315	210	205

a) Construct a scatterplot for the data.

b) Calculate a good-fitting line for the data.

c) In context of the problem, what is the meaning of the slope?

d) What is the approximate cost of a house that has 2000 square feet of living space? 3000 square feet?

e) If a house cost $260,000, approximately how many square feet would you expect it to have?

4. The Leaning Tower of Pisa leans more and more each year. The data that follows gives the lean of the tower for the years 1975 to 1987. The lean is the distance (in meters) between where a point on the tower would be if the tower were straight and where it really is. In 1975, the lean of the tower was 2.9642 meters and appears as 642 in the table. In 1976, the lean of the tower was 2.9644 meters.

Year	75	76	77	78	79	80	81	82	83	84	85	86	87
Lean	642	644	656	667	673	688	696	698	713	717	725	742	757

a) Construct a scatterplot for the data.

b) Calculate a good-fitting line for the data.

c) Predict the lean of the tower for 1990.

d) Would it be reasonable to use this data to predict the lean of the tower for the year 2005? Explain. If so, what would the lean be in 2005?

Linear Regression with Coded Data

Answers:

1. a)

b) $1920 + 40 = 1960$

c) $y = -.09x + 23.71$ (best-fit line); students' answers should be close to this line.

d)   The birth rate in the year 1920 was approximately 23.71 babies per 1000 people.

e)   For an increase in one year, there is approximately a .09 decrease in births per thousand people.

f) $x = 2000 - 1920 = 80$, so $y = -.09(80) + 23.71 = 16.51$ births/1000 people

2. a)

b) $y = .81x - 4.12$ (best-fit line)

c)   For an increase of 1000 advanced ticket sales, there is an approximate increase of 810 (.81 x 1000) hotdogs purchased at the game.

d) $y = .81(52) - 4.12 = 38$ thous. hotdogs or 38,000 hotdogs

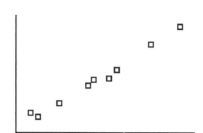

3. a)

b) $y = 8.7x + 4.6$ (best-fit line)

c) For an increase in 100 square feet of living space, there is an approximate increase of $8700 in cost of the house.

d) $y = 8.7(20) + 4.6 = \$178.6$ thousand,

$y = 8.7(30) + 4.6 = \$265.6$ thousand

e) $260 = 8.7x + 4.6 = 29.4$ hundred sq ft

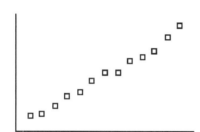

4. a)

b) $y = 9.32x - 61.12$ (best-fit line)

c) $y = 9.32(90) - 61.12 = 778;$ lean $= 2.9778$

d) Assuming that the rate that the tower leans remains relatively constant, then it would be acceptable to predict for 2005, but typically extrapolation (using values outside the given data) is not advised in a regression setting if the values are far outside the given data.

$y = 9.32(105) - 61.12 = 917;$ lean $= 2.9917$

Write Your Notes and Ideas Here!

Using a Calculator to Determine a Fitted Line and to Extrapolate Beyond the Range of Data

Objective:
Students will use a calculator to write the equation for a fitted line to data and examine the problem of attempting to extrapolate a prediction from data.

Connections to Previous Learning:
Students should be able to write a linear equation for data.

Connections to TEKS:
111.32 b1A, b1B, b1C, b1D, c2B, c3A

Connections to AP:
The AP Calculus objective of analysis of functions
The AP Statistics objective of linear bivariate data

Time Frame:
40 minutes

Materials:
Handouts, graph paper, and a graphing calculator with statistical capabilities

Teacher Notes:
This lesson is designed to introduce using a calculator to construct a fitted line from data in order to make a prediction. This lesson can be introduced after students have learned to write the equations of lines either in slope-intercept or point-slope form. While most linear regression equations are written in the form $y = a + bx$, it would not complicate matters to let students write their equation in $y = mx + b$ form.

This is a calculator lesson so students should use graph paper to construct their scatterplots and then their calculators to do the equation work. The objective is to determine the equation of the line that best fits the data so teachers start to use the terminology "best fit line" or "fitted line" instead of "trend line" as this is more in keeping with statistical terminology.

Note: When drawing the scatterplot, the variable that is being <u>predicted</u> goes on the vertical axis and the other variable (explanatory or independent) goes on the horizontal axis.

We want to write the equation of the best-fit line for the data above. How do we use our calculator to accomplish this? It is important to go slowly with the students at first since there is a fair amount of button pushing. It might be useful to post the steps on the board for a while until the students are clear on the mechanics. A graphing overhead unit in the classroom is also immensely useful.

Below are the steps for computing a best-fit line on the calculator. This and other techniques for fitting curves to data is often called regression analysis.

1. Decide which variable should be the independent variable, and which is the dependent variable.

2. Enter X (independent)-values in L_1.

3. Enter corresponding Y (dependent)-values in L_2.

4. To calculate the linear model there are two options: Choose either $\boxed{\text{STAT}}$, $\boxed{\text{CALC}}$, $\boxed{4}$:**LinReg(ax + b) or** $\boxed{\text{STAT}}$, $\boxed{\text{CALC}}$, **8: LinReg(a+bx).**

    The only difference is that #4 writes the equation in the more familiar $y = mx + b$ format and #8 writes it in the format used by most statistical software programs.

5. Add L_1, L_2 at the end. The screen should look like **LinReg(ax + b)** L_1, L_2

    Note: L_1 is gotten by using the 2nd key on your calculator: $\boxed{2^{nd}}\boxed{1}$ **and** L_2 by $\boxed{2^{nd}}\boxed{2}$.

6. Press $\boxed{\text{ENTER}}$. This will give the best-fit line in the form $y = mx + b$.

    We can use the best-fit line to make a reasonable prediction for the dependent variable from a value of the explanatory (independent variable) that was used to determine the line.

Extrapolation is the use of a best-fit line for prediction outside the range of values of the independent variable. These predictions may not be very accurate far outside the known range of values since we do not know whether the linear pattern exhibited in the scatterplot continues outside of the given range.

Using a Calculator to Determine a Fitted Line and to Extrapolate Beyond the Range of Data

1. Below are the data on the farm population (in millions of people who live on farms) from 1940 to 1985.

Year	1940	1945	1950	1955	1960	1965	1970	1975	1980	1985
Pop	30.5	24.5	23.1	19.2	15.6	12.4	9.7	8.9	7.2	4.2

   a) Construct a scatterplot of the data. Remember to include scales and labels for your axes. Think about which variable should be the independent and which the dependent variable.

   b) Based on the scatterplot, describe the relationship between year and the number of people who living on American farms.

We want to write the equation of the best-fit line for the data above. Year is the independent variable, so input the years in L_1. (Reminder: you could decide to code the years first). The farm population is the dependent variable so input the numbers into L_2.

Run the regression. If you did not code the years you should get the equation y = -.558x + 1110.96 where y = population living on farms and x = years. Remember that it can also be written in context such as Population = -.558 (Year) + 1110.96.

If you coded the years as t = years since 1900 then the best fit equation would be given by Population = -.558 t + 50.42. There are many ways to code the data but you must define the coding so that your work is clear.

   c) We want to use the best-fit equation to make some predictions. Using your equation of the best-fit line, predict the number of people living on farms in 1952. Based on the given table of data does your prediction seem reasonable? Justify your answer.

   d) Using your equation of the best-fit line, predict the number of people living on farms in 1974. Based on the given table of data does your prediction seem reasonable? Justify your answer.

   e) Using your equation of the best-fit line, predict the number of people living on farms in 1986. Based on the given table of data does your prediction seem reasonable? Justify your answer.

   f) Using your equation of the best-fit line, predict the number of people living on farms in 1995. Does your prediction seem reasonable? Justify your answer.

g) You made predictions for 1952, 1974, 1986, and 1995. One of these years is not like the others. Which one is it? Recall that one of the predictions based on these years was not reasonable. Can you explain why that year is different and why it resulted in an unreasonable prediction?

Special Note: <u>Extrapolation</u> is the use of a best-fit line for prediction outside the range of values of the independent variable. These predictions may not be very accurate far outside the known range of values since we do not know whether the linear pattern exhibited in the scatterplot continues outside of the given range.

---

2. The following data shows the grams of protein and grams of fat for various items at a fast food restaurant.

Protein (gm)	7	14	14	16	51	25	32	46	33	26	30	17	6
Fat (gm)	9	10	15	19	55	26	38	48	38	33	33	11	5

a) Draw a scatterplot in order to predict the grams of fat from the grams of protein. Make sure to label and scale your axes. Do you think that the data values need to be coded?

b) Based on the scatterplot, describe the relationship between the grams of protein and the grams of fat.

c) Using your calculator give the equation of the best-fit line that will predict grams of fat from grams of protein. Write your equation in the context of the problem.

d) Interpret the slope of the best-fit line in the context of this problem.

e) Predict the number of grams of fat in a food item that contains 40 grams of protein. Describe how you would use your scatterplot to determine if your prediction was reasonable.

f) Is it reasonable to predict the grams of fat in a food item if you know that the item contains 65 grams of protein? Justify your answer.

Using a Calculator to Determine a Fitted Line and to Extrapolate Beyond the Range of Data

Answers:

1. a)   Code the data as t = years since 1900.

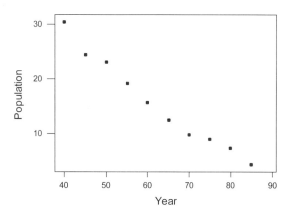

b)   As the years have increased, the number of people living on farms has decreased at a steady rate.

c)   Population = -.558 (year) +1110.96 if the years are not coded and
Population = -.558 t + 50.42 if the years are coded as t = years since 1900.

If the year is 1952 then t = 52 and Population = 21.404 million. The prediction seems reasonable since the number of people in 1950 is 23.1 million and in 1955 it was 19.2 million. The prediction fits between those values.

d)   For 1974, t = 74 and the predicted population is 9.128 million. Again this prediction fits between the two known values for 1970 and 1975 on the table.

c)   For 1986, then t = 86 and predicted population – 2.423. The same reasoning as the two previous parts applies here.

f)   For 1995, the predicted value is –2.59 million people. This is clearly an unreasonable prediction.

g)   The year 1995 is not like the other years. 1995 falls substantially beyond the range of the years for which you have data. It is not reasonable to assume that the linear relationship that exists for the given data on the scatterplot continues to be the same relationship that would exist for years substantially beyond 1985.

2.   a)   The data does not need to be coded. To predict grams of fats, fat goes on the y-axis and protein on the x-axis.

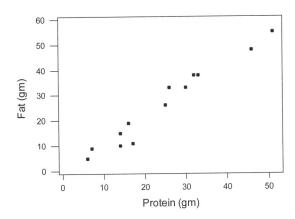

  b)   As the number of grams of protein increases the number of fat grams also increases.

  c)   Fat = 1.13 (protein) − 1.39

  d)   For every one gram increase in protein, there is an approximate increase of 1.13 grams of fat.

  e)   For 40 grams of protein, there will be 44.06 grams of fat. If you look at the scatterplot and draw a line on the graph you could give an estimate of the fat grams based on 40 protein grams. From the table we can see that 33 grams of protein has 38 grams of fat and 46 grams of protein has 48 grams of fats. If you were to average the fat values you get 43 grams which is pretty close to the predicted value of 44.06 grams.

  f)   It is not reasonable to predict the amount of fat from a food item with 65 grams of protein. The highest protein value is 51 grams, and most of the known values are below 34 grams, so 65 grams falls well outside the range of x-values.

Characteristics of Functions

Objective:
Students will be introduced to functions that are not linear and some of their characteristics.

Connections to Previous Learning:
Students should be able to graph functions from a table of values.

Connections to TEKS:
111.32   c2E, d1D, d3B, d3C

Connections to AP:
The AP Calculus objective of analysis of functions

Time Frame:
60 minutes

Materials:
Characteristics of Functions worksheet and graph paper

Teacher Notes:
This lesson could be taught early in the year after students have studied linear functions. It introduces functions, characteristics of functions, and terminology that students will use as they study functions during the remainder of the year. It emphasizes the relationship between equation, table, and graph. Some of the characteristics of functions to be emphasized are **x-intercept, y-intercept, increasing function, decreasing function, axis of symmetry, maximum value, minimum value, and average rate of change.**

Characteristics of Functions

1. Complete the following questions for the function below.

   $f(x) = 3x + 2$

x	$f(x)$
-2	
-1	
0	
1	
2	

   a) Copy the table of values to the right on your paper then complete the table of values.

   b) Graph the function on graph paper.

   c) Between which two integers does the graph cross the x-axis? Explain in a complete sentence how to find where the function crosses the x-axis by examining the table of values.

   d) State the y-intercept of the graph. Explain in a complete sentence how to find the y-intercept of the graph by examining the table of values and by looking at the equation.

   e) Is $f(x)$ an increasing or decreasing function? Explain in a complete sentence how you can determine if $f(x)$ is increasing or decreasing by examining the table and by looking at the graph.

2. Complete the following questions for the function below.

   $f(x) = x^2 - 3$

x	$f(x)$
-3	
-2	
-1	
0	
1	
2	
3	

   a) Copy the table of values to the right on your paper then complete the table of values.

   b) Graph the function on graph paper.

   c) Between which two negative integers does the graph cross the x-axis? Explain in a complete sentence how to find where the function crosses the x-axis by examining the table of values.

   d) State the y-intercept of the graph.

   e) Write the equation for the axis of symmetry for the graph of $f(x)$.

   f) Find the maximum or minimum value for $f(x)$.

   g) Find the values for the domain where $f(x)$ is increasing. Find the values for the domain where $f(x)$ is decreasing.

   h) Find the average rate of change between $x = 0$ and $x = 2$.

3. Complete the following questions for the function below.

    $f(x) = x^3$

x	$f(x)$
-2	
-1	
0	
1	
2	

    a) Copy the table of values to the right on your paper then complete the table of values.

    b) Graph the function on graph paper.

    c) For what values of x is $f(x)$ equal to 0?

    d) Find the y-intercept of the graph.

4. Complete the following questions for the function below.

    $f(x) = \dfrac{4}{x}$

x	$f(x)$
-8	
-4	
-2	
-1	
-0.5	
0	
0.5	
1	
2	
4	
8	

    a) Copy the table of values to the right on your paper then complete the table of values.

    b) Graph the function on graph paper.

    c) Find the value of x where $f(x) = 0$.

    d) Find the y-intercept of the graph.

    e) Does the graph have any symmetry? Explain.

5. Complete the following questions for the function below.

    $f(x) = 2^x$

x	$f(x)$
-3	
-2	
-1	
0	
1	
2	
3	

    a) Copy the table of values to the right on your paper then complete the table of values.

    b) Graph the function on graph paper.

    c) Find the value x where $f(x) = 0$.

    d) Determine the y-intercept of the graph.

    e) Is $f(x)$ an increasing or decreasing function?

    f) Find the average rate of change for the following intervals of x.

    $0 \le x \le 1$, $1 \le x \le 2$, $2 \le x \le 3$.

    As the value of x increases, what do you notice about the average rate of change?

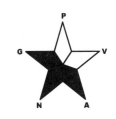

Characteristics of Functions

Answers:

1. a)

x	f(x)
-2	-4
-1	-1
0	2
1	5
2	8

b)

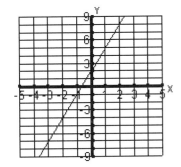

c) -1 < x < 0; The graph crosses the x-axis when the value of y changes from negative to positive.

d) 2; The graph crosses the y-axis when the value of x is 0.

e) $f(x)$ is increasing; On the table as the values of x increase the values of $f(x)$ increase and the graph slants upward to the right.

2) a)

x	f(x)
-3	6
-2	1
-1	-2
0	-3
1	-2
2	1
3	6

b)

c) -2 < x < -1; The function crosses the x-axis when the value of y changes from positive to negative, or from negative to positive.

d) -3

e) x = 0

f) Minimum value is -3; no maximum.

g) increasing $x \geq 0$; decreasing $x \leq 0$

h) 2

3. a)

x	f(x)
-2	-8
-1	-1
0	0
1	1
2	8

c) x = 0

d) y = 0

b)

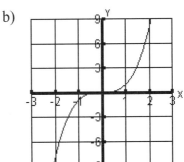

233

4. a)

x	f(x)
-8	-0.5
-4	-1
-2	-2
-1	-4
-0.5	-8
0	undefined
0.5	8
1	4
2	2
4	1
8	0.5

5. a)

x	f(x)
-3	0.125
-2	0.25
-1	0.5
0	1
1	2
2	4
3	8

b)

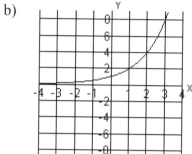

c) undefined or never

d) none

e) $y = x$ and $y = -x$

b)

c) undefined or never

d) $y = 1$

e) increasing

f) 1; 2; 4
The average rate of change is increasing.

Write Your Notes and Ideas Here!

Painting the House

Objective:
Students will determine a system of equations given a verbal description. They will then solve this system using a table of values, by graphing, and algebraically.

Connections to Previous Learning:
Students should be able to find area, make a table, graph, and solve a system of equations.

Connections to TEKS:
111.32 b1C, b1D, b1E, b2D, c3A, c3B, c4A, c4B, c4C

Connections to AP:
The AP calculus objectives of area and analysis of functions

Time Frame:
45 minutes

Materials:
A copy of the worksheet for each student, graphing calculator (recommended)

Teacher Notes:
This lesson should be used as a class exercise in groups to introduce writing a system of equations given a problem situation. Students should have already mastered at least one algebraic method of solving a system of equations. Although the student directions do not explicitly state this, the lesson is designed to make use of the table function on a graphing calculator. Without a calculator, the time frame will increase.

Painting the House

Mrs. Hamilton is one of the math coaches at Smedley Middle School. She is going to have the exterior of her house painted but does not want to do it herself. Her brother-in-law, Hank Hamilton, is a professional painter. He is willing to paint Mrs. Hamilton's home for $30 per hour, paint included. Mrs. Hamilton is always looking for ways for her math team members to raise money. Three students on her team have offered to paint her house for $7 an hour per person plus the cost of materials. Mrs. Hamilton has decided to make this decision a math project for her class. You can help her by answering the following questions.

1. Mrs. Hamilton's house is built of brick with wooden trim that will need to be painted. She is very frugal and does not want to buy extra paint. To carefully figure the amount of paint that she needs she makes the following list:

    - On the front and back there are 50 linear feet of trim, 3 feet wide.
    - The sides are 40 linear feet, also 3 feet wide.
    - The trim to be painted on the front porch is 4 feet by 8 feet.
    - The back porch area is 6 feet by 10 feet.
    - Two exterior doors are each 3 feet by 7 feet.
    - Her garage doors are 7 feet by 16 feet.
    - She has 18 square feet of trim (total) around her 9 windows.

    One gallon of paint will cover approximately 350 square feet and will cost $19 per gallon. It's been a while since Mrs. Hamilton had her house painted, so she plans to have two coats of paint put on each surface. How many gallons of paint will be required for Mrs. Hamilton's job? Be careful here. Can you buy fractional pieces of gallons of paint?

2. Write a function to represent what it will cost for Hank to paint the house as a function of time.

3. Write a function to represent what it will cost for Mrs. Hamilton's students to paint the house. Don't forget the fixed costs.

4. Make a table of values for the functions that you wrote in parts b and c. Use your table of values to estimate the number of hours when the cost of painting the house will be the same regardless of which she chooses.

5. On graph paper, sketch the graph of this situation. Use the graph to determine the number of hours at which the costs will be the same.

6. Use algebraic methods to determine number of hours at which the costs will be the same. What will that cost be?

7. Under what conditions should Mrs. Hamilton hire Hank?

8. Under what conditions should Mrs. Hamilton hire her students?

9. What other factors should Mrs. Hamilton use to determine which offer to accept?

Painting the House

Answers:

1. $50\text{ft}(3\text{ft})(2) + 40\text{ft}(3\text{ft})(2) + 4\text{ft}(8\text{ft}) + 6\text{ft}(10\text{ft}) + 2(3\text{ft})(7\text{ft}) + 7\text{ft}(16\text{ft}) + 18\text{ft}^2 = 804\ \text{ft}^2$;

   $804\ \text{ft}^2 \div \dfrac{350\,ft^2}{gal} = \dfrac{804\,ft^2}{1} \cdot \dfrac{1\,gal}{350\,ft^2} \approx 2.297$ gal. For two coats she will need 5 gal.

2. If x = hours, then $f(x) = 30x$

3. If x = hours, then $g(x) = 3(7)x + 5(19)$ or $g(x) = 21x + 95$

4. The table of values for the functions (below) shows that Hank's cost for painting the house is less through 10 hours; however at 11 hours, Hank's cost is more. I think that at almost 11 hours the cost for the two is the same. (Note: You can have students' change their table set up and get a more precise answer than "almost 11".)

x	$30x$	$21x + 95$
0	0	95
1	30	116
2	60	137
3	90	158
4	120	179
5	150	200
6	180	221
7	210	242
8	240	263
9	270	284
10	300	305
11	330	326
12	360	347

5. The graph below shows that the cost is the same when Hank has worked almost 11 hours and the students have worked almost 4 hours each.

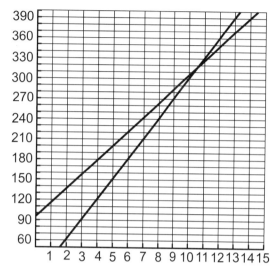

6. $y_1 = 30x$

    $y_2 = 21x + 95$, so $\quad 30x = 21x + 95$

    $\qquad\qquad\qquad\qquad 9x = 95$

    $\qquad\qquad\qquad\quad x = 10\dfrac{5}{9}$ hours   At this time she will owe about \$316.67.

    A question to think about: Should this problem have a discrete or a continuous domain?

7. Mathematically speaking, Mrs. Hamilton should hire Hank if he can do the job in less than $10\dfrac{5}{9}$ hours.

8. Mathematically speaking, Mrs. Hamilton should hire her students if it would take Hank more than $10\dfrac{5}{9}$ hours to complete the job.

9. Any reasonable answer should be accepted here. Some samples: Hire the students because they need the money more. Hire Hank because he's a professional and will do a better job.

Write Your Notes and Ideas Here!

Solving Systems of Linear Equations

Objective:
Students will solve systems of linear equations and find the area of a polygon.

Connections to Previous Learning:
Students should be able to solve systems of linear equations graphically and algebraically, write equations of a line given two points on a line, find the area of triangles, rectangles, and trapezoids.

Connections to TEKS:
111.32 b4A, c1C, c2D, c2E, c3A, c3B

Connections to AP:
The AP Calculus objectives of analysis of functions and area

Time Frame:
60 minutes

Materials:
Solving Systems of Linear Equations worksheet and graph paper

Teacher Notes:
This is a richer lesson if class time is given for discussion of how students determined areas. For problems 2, 4, and 8, students may find the area of the rectangle in which each trapezoid is enclosed and then subtract the non-shaded triangle. At a minimum, problem 5 should be examined. One possible solution is to subtract each of three non-shaded triangles from the 6 by 9 rectangle which encloses the shaded triangle, that is: $54 - [27 + 9 + 6]$.

The questions for these problems have been adapted from past AP Calculus exams.

Solving Systems of Linear Equations

For problems 1 - 8, graph and shade the region then find the area of the region. Carefully explain how you determined each area.

1. Find the area of the region below the graph of $f(x) = -2x + 6$ in the first quadrant.

2. Find the area of the region enclosed by the graphs of $y = 0$, $x = 0$, $x = 6$, and $y = \frac{1}{3}x + 3$.

3. Find the area of the region below the graph of $y = -5x + 9$ in the first quadrant.

4. Let R be the region in the first quadrant under the graph of $y = 2x$ for $4 \le x \le 9$. Find the area of R.

5. Find the area of the region bounded by the graphs of $y = \frac{1}{2}x + 6$, $y = \frac{7}{2}x$, and $y = \frac{3}{2}x$.

6. Find the area of the region enclosed by the graphs of $x = 0$, $y = \frac{1}{2}x + 1$, $y = -\frac{2}{3}x + 8$.

7. Find the area of the region in the first quadrant under the graph of $2x + 4y = 25$.

8. Find the area of the region enclosed by the graphs of $y = 0$, $y = -\frac{2}{3}x + 9$ for $0 \le x \le 5$.

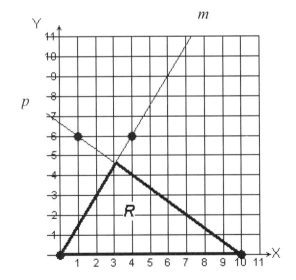

9. Find the area of the region R bounded by line m, line p, and the x-axis as shown in the graph to the left.

Solving Systems of Linear Equations

Answers:

1. 9 units^2

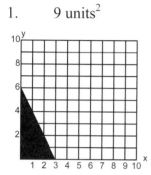

2. 24 units^2

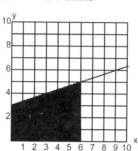

3. 8.1 units^2

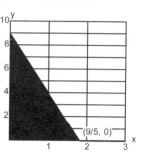

(9/5, 0)

4. 65 units^2

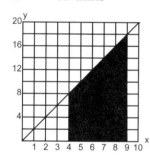

5. 12 units^2

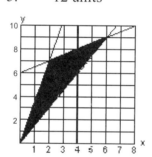

6. 21 units^2

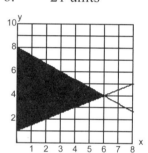

7. 39.0625 units^2

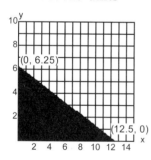

(0, 6.25)

(12.5, 0)

8. $36\frac{2}{3}$ units^2

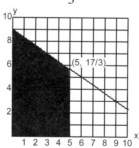

(5, 17/3)

9. $y = -\frac{2}{3}x + 6\frac{2}{3}$; intersects at $3\frac{1}{13}$, $4\frac{8}{13}$; area $= 23\frac{1}{13}$ units^2

Write Your Notes and Ideas Here!

Graphing and Finding Areas of Bounded Regions

Objective:
Students will review graphing lines and area formulas.

Connections to Previous Learning:
Students should know how to graph horizontal and vertical lines from their equations and should be able to transform a linear equation from standard to slope-intercept form in order to graph it. They should also know how to find the areas of simple geometric figures such as rectangles, triangles and trapezoids.

Connections to TEKS:
111.32 b4A, c1C, c2D, c2E, c4B

Connections to AP:
The AP Calculus topic of area

Time Frame:
45–60 minutes

Materials:
Worksheet, graph paper and colored pencils or crayons for each student

Teacher Notes:
Once all students have completed problem 2, the teacher may stop class and have them discuss the methods by which they found the area of the trapezoid. Some students might remember the formula from their previous classes. Others might add the area of the rectangle and the area of the triangle that is on top of it. (This will be the method most will use in problem 5, part c) Still others might have formed a 5 x 6 rectangle and then subtracted the area of the unnecessary triangle. All of these are valid methods. Encourage the various methods students use to find this area.

There can also be discussion regarding problem 6. Some students might have subtracted the area of region a from that of region b in order to determine the area of region c. Other students might have found the area of the triangle with its base on the *y*-axis and its height parallel to the *x*-axis.

Graphing and Finding Areas of Bounded Regions

Instructions: **Graph each of the regions described below. Problems with several parts can all be graphed on the same coordinate plane. Once the region is graphed, determine its area.**

1. Region bounded by: $x = -2, x = 3, y = 4$ and $y = 0$

2. Region bounded by: x-axis, y-axis, $x = 6$ and $x + 3y = 15$

3. Region bounded by: $x = 1, x = 3, y = -2,$ and $y = 4$

4. a) Region bounded by: $2x - y = 2, x + 2y = 14$ and $y = 0$

    b) Region bounded by: $2x - y = 2, x + 2y = 14$ and $x = 0$

5. a) Region bounded by: $3x - 2y = 0, x + 2y = 16$ and $x = 0$

    b) Region bounded by: $3x - 2y = 0, x = 2$ and $y = 0$

    c) Region bounded by: $3x - 2y = 0, x + 2y = 16, x = 2$ and $x = 10$

6. a) Region bounded by: $y = x, 3x + 2y = 15$ and $y = 0$

    b) Region bounded by: $x = 0, y = 0$ and $3x + 2y = 15$

    c) Region bounded by: $x = 0, y = x$ and $3x + 2y = 15$

7. a) Region bounded by: $3x + y = 7, x = 0$ and $2x - y = -2$

    b) Region bounded by: $3x + y = 7, y = 0$ and $2x - y = -2$

Connecting Algebra 1 to Advanced Placement Mathematics
A Resource and Strategy Guide

Graphing and Finding Areas of Bounded Regions

Answers:

1.

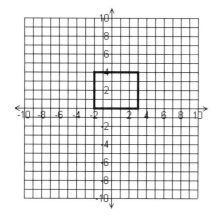

$$A = 20 \; units^2$$

2.

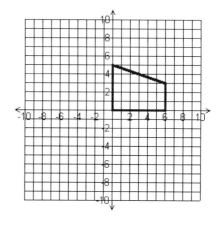

$$A = 24 \; units^2$$

3.

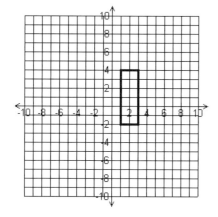

$$A = 12 \; units^2$$

4.

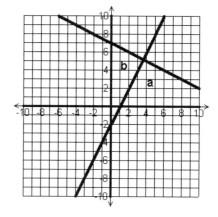

Region a : $33.8 \; units^2$

Region b : $16.2 \; units^2$

248

5.

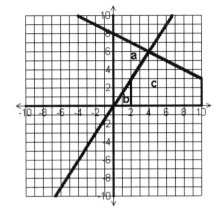

Region a: $16\,units^2$

Region b: $3\,units^2$

Region c: $36\,units^2$

6.

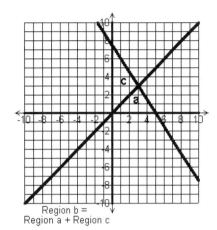

Region b =
Region a + Region c

Region a : $\dfrac{15}{2}units^2$

Region b : $\dfrac{75}{4}units^2$

Region c : $\dfrac{45}{4}units^2$

7.

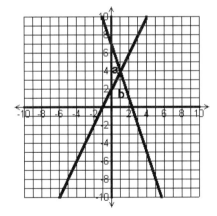

Region a : $\dfrac{5}{2}units^2$

Region b : $\dfrac{20}{3}units^2$

Investigation – Graphing Quadratic Functions

Objective:
Students will investigate transformations with a quadratic function.

Connections to Previous Learning:
Students should understand transformations with linear functions and be able to graph functions using a graphing calculator.

Connections to TEKS:
111.32 b2A, c2C, d1B, d1C

Connections to AP:
The AP Calculus objective of analysis of functions

Time Frame:
50 minutes

Materials:
Graphing Quadratic Functions worksheet and graphing calculator

Teacher Notes:
Students work with a partner to investigate transformations with the quadratic functions using a graphing calculator.

Investigation – Graphing Quadratic Functions

1. Complete a table of values and graph $y = x^2$.

2. Using a graphing calculator, graph each function. State which graph is the steepest.

   a) $y = x^2$ b) $y = 2x^2$ c) $y = 3x^2$ d) $y = 4x^2$

3. Using a graphing calculator, graph each function. State which graph is the steepest.

   a) $y = x^2$ b) $y = \dfrac{1}{2}x^2$ c) $y = \dfrac{1}{3}x^2$ d) $y = \dfrac{1}{4}x^2$

4. Determine which graph is the steepest without using a graphing calculator and without graphing.

   $y = 10x^2$ $y = 6x^2$ Explain your answer. Use a graphing calculator to check your predictions.

5. Using a graphing calculator, graph each function.

   a) $y = -x^2$ b) $y = -2x^2$ c) $y = -3x^2$ d) $y = -4x^2$

6. Using the graphing calculator, graph each function.

   a) $y = -x^2$ b) $-\dfrac{1}{2}x^2$ c) $y = -\dfrac{1}{3}x^2$ d) $y = -\dfrac{1}{4}x^2$

7. a) Sketch a graph for $y = ax^2$ if a > 0.   b) Sketch a graph for $y = ax^2$ if a < 0.

8. Using a graphing calculator, graph each function. Give the minimum value for y for each function.

   a) $y = x^2$ b) $y = x^2 + 1$ c) $y = x^2 - 1$ d) $y = x^2 + 3$

9. Using the graphing calculator, graph each function. Give the maximum value for y for each function.

   a) $y = -x^2$ b) $y = -x^2 + 1$ c) $y = -x^2 - 2$ d) $y = -x^2 + 4$

10. Without a calculator, determine the vertex for each graph and state if it gives a maximum or a minimum value for y. Use a graphing calculator to check your answers.

    a) $y = 4x^2$ b) $y = -x^2 + 3$ c) $y = x^2 - 5$ d) $y = -6x^2 + 8$

11. Match each function with its graph.

    i. $y = 8x^2$ ii. $y = 8x^2 + 3$ iii. $y = 8x^2 - 3$

  a) 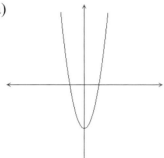   b) 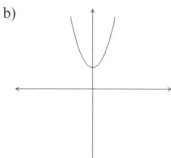   c)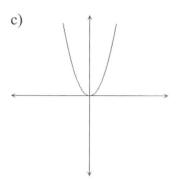

12. Match each function with its graph.

    i. $8x$ ii. $y = 8x + 3$ iii. $y = 8x - 3$

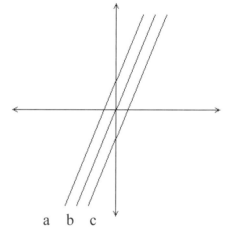

13. Match each function with its graph.

    i. $y = -2x^2$ ii. $y = -5x^2$

    iii. $-\dfrac{1}{4}x^2 - 2$ iv. $y = x^2 + 2$

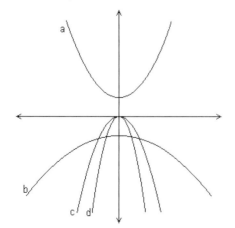

14. Match each function with its graph.

    i. $y = -x$ ii. $y = -5x$

    iii. $y = -\dfrac{1}{4}x - 2$ iv. $y = x + 4$

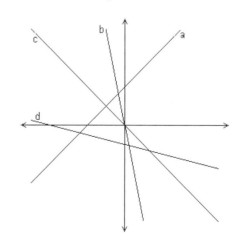

252

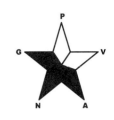

Investigation – Graphing Quadratic Functions

Answers:

1.

x	y
-3	9
-2	4
-1	1
0	0
1	1
2	4
3	9

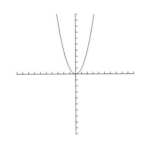

2. $y = 4x^2$ is the steepest.

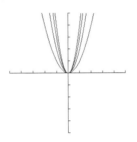

3. $y = x^2$ is the steepest.

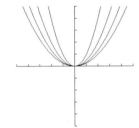

4. $y = 10x^2$ is the steepest.

5.

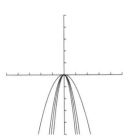

6.

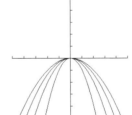

7. a) 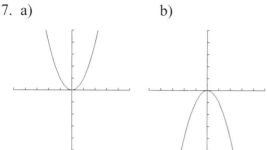   b)

8.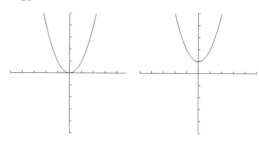

a) 0   b) 1

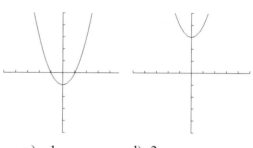

c) -1   d) 3

9.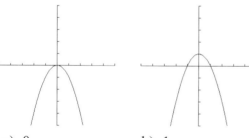

a) 0   b) 1

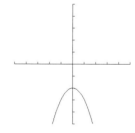   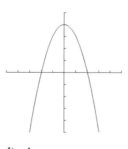

c) -2   d) 4

10.   a) (0,0) minimum value of y is 0
       b) (0,3) maximum value of y is 3
       c) (0,-5) minimum value of y is -5
       d) (0,8) maximum value of y is 8

11.   i. c   ii. b   iii. a

12.   i. b   ii. a   iii. c

13.   i. c   ii. d   iii. b   iv. a

14.   i. c   ii. b   iii. d   iv. a

Investigating Area Under a Curve

Objective:
Students will find the area under a graph of a linear function on a given interval and approximate the area under the graph of a non-linear function on a given interval.

Connections to Previous Learning:
Students should be familiar with the area of a rectangle and triangle formulas, reading a table of function values and relating its points on the coordinate plane, and graphing a function on a graphing calculator.

Connections to TEKS:
111.32 b.1B, b.2C

Connections to AP:
The AP Calculus objectives of area and accumulation.

Time Frame:
90 minutes

Materials:
Graphing calculator

Teacher Notes:
This lesson is designed to introduce the student to finding or approximating the area under the graph of a function on a given interval. In the first set of problems, the student can calculate the exact area under the graph because the functions are linear. The teacher should demonstrate to the students how to drop the vertical boundaries from the function to the x-axis at the endpoints of the interval. In the second set of problems, students are asked to approximate the area under the curve by inscribing and circumscribing rectangles. Again, the teacher should demonstrate to the students how to drop the vertical boundaries of the rectangles from the function to the x-axis at the values of x indicated in the table. A discussion of how to inscribe and circumscribe the rectangles would be appropriate, being sure that the student understands, for example, that the inscribed rectangle on 1(a) has width = 2 units and length = 2 units while the circumscribed rectangle has width = 2 units and length = 4 units.

Investigating Area Under a Curve

1. Find the area under the graph of the given function for the given interval:

    a) $y = x + 1$ for $1 \le x \le 3$

    b) $y = x + 1$ for $2 \le x \le 4$

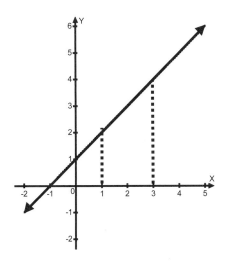
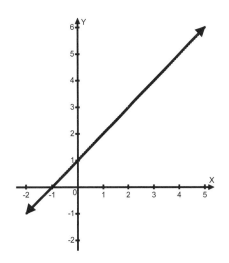

c) $y = -\dfrac{3}{4}x + 3$ for $1 \le x \le 4$

d) $y = -\dfrac{3}{4}x + 3$ for $-1 \le x \le 3$

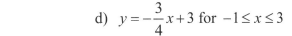

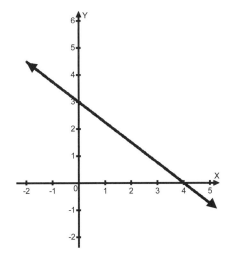
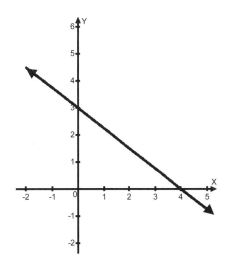

e) $f(x) = 1$ for $0 \le x < 3$ and
       $f(x) = x - 2$ for $3 \le x \le 5$

f) $f(x) = 1$ for $-2 \le x < 3$ and
       $f(x) = x - 2$ for $3 \le x \le 4$

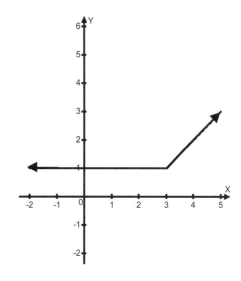

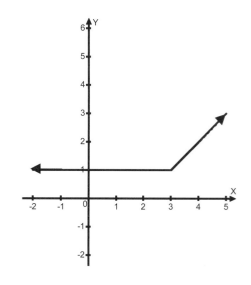

g) $f(x) = x + 2$ for $0 \le x < 2$ and
       $f(x) = 4$ for $2 \le x < 4$ and
       $f(x) = -x + 8$ for $4 \le x \le 6$

h) $f(x) = x + 2$ for $-2 \le x < 2$ and
       $f(x) = 4$ for $2 \le x < 4$ and
       $f(x) = -x + 8$ for $4 \le x \le 8$

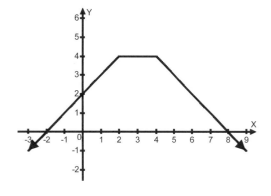

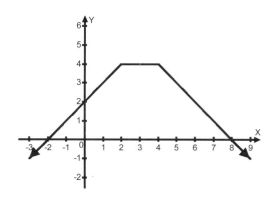

2. Appproximate the area under each curve for the interval given

    i.   by find the sum of inscribed rectangles with widths determined by the data in the table and

    ii.   by finding the sum of circumscribed rectangles with widths determined the the data in the table.

    iii. Find the average of your answers to *i*) and *ii*) and explain why this may be a better approximation to the actual area under the curve.

a)

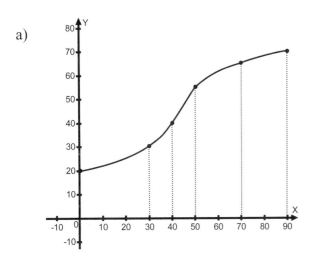

x	$f(x)$
0	20
30	30
40	40
50	55
70	65
90	70

b)

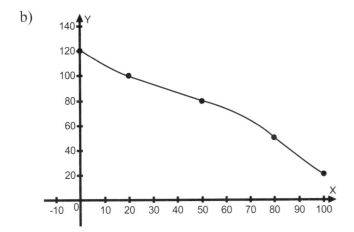

x	$f(x)$
0	120
20	100
50	80
80	50
100	20

c)

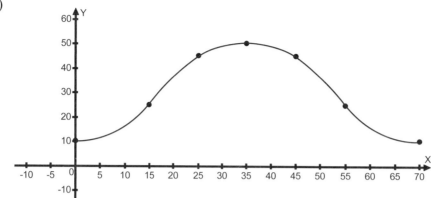

x	f(x)
0	10
15	25
25	45
35	50
45	45
55	25
70	10

3.   a)   Use a graphing calculator to sketch the graph of the function $y = x^2 + 5$ on the interval $0 \le x \le 5$.

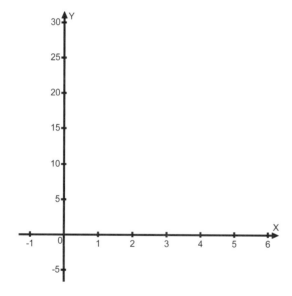

b)   Complete the table of values for the function.

x	f(x)
0	
2	
4	
5	

260

c)   Use the data in the table to approximate the area under the graph of the function by finding the sum of inscribed rectangles with widths indicated by the data table.

d)   Use the data in the table to approximate the area under the graph of the function by finding the sum of the circumscribed rectangles with widths indicated by the data table.

e)   Find the average of your answers to parts (c) and (d).

Investigating Area Under a Curve

Answers:

1. a) 6 sq. units

    b) 8 sq. units

    c) $\dfrac{27}{8}$ sq. units

    d) 9 sq. units

    e) 7 sq. units

    f) $6\dfrac{1}{2}$ sq. units

    g) 20 sq. units

    h) 24 sq. units

2. a) i.   3700 sq. units

        ii. 4550 sq. units

        iii. 4125 sq. units

    The average is a better approximation because the average gives the sum of areas of trapeziods whose upper edges are closer to the graph of f than the upper edges of the rectangles.

    b) i.   6300 sq. units

        ii. 8800 sq. units

        iii. 7550 sq. units

    c) i.   1700 sq. units

        ii. 2650 sq. units

        iii. 2175 sq. units

3   a)

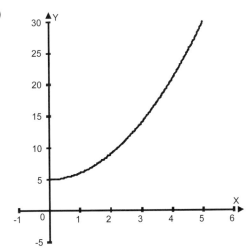

b)

x	$f(x)$
0	5
2	9
4	21
5	30

c)   49 sq. units

d)   90 sq. units

e)   69.5 sq. units

Quadratic Optimization

Objective:
Students will write quadratic equations for real world situations and find the maximum value of the functions.

Connections to Previous Learning:
Students should be able to find the maximum values of quadratic functions.

Connections to TEKS:
111.32 d1A, d1D, d2A

Connections to AP:
The AP Calculus objectives of analysis of functions and optimization

Time Frame:
60 minutes

Materials:
Quadratic Optimization worksheet and graph paper

Teacher Notes:
The four steps in this lesson are revised from calculus recommendations for optimization.

Quadratic Optimization

1. When Spot was a puppy, he had a rectangular puppy pen. The dimensions of his pen were 2 ft by 6 ft. Find the perimeter and area of his pen.

Steps for Modeling Optimization Problems

a) Define the problem: Determine the quantity or function that is to be optimized (maximized or minimized).

b) Gather the information: Make and label a sketch of the situation. Write any formula that you think you might need to solve this problem.

c) Write the function: Write a formula for the function to be optimized in terms of the variables. Next try to write the formula in terms of only one of the variables.

d) Solve the problem: Graph the function, determine the reasonable domain for the problem, and determine a strategy for finding the maximum or minimum value of the function, then find that value.

For problems 2 – 4, follow the steps for modeling optimization problems.

2. As Spot grew his owner needed to increase the size of Spot's pen without buying new boards for his pen. Find the largest pen that the owner can make using the boards from the existing fence.

3. When Spot was 2 years old, his master doubled the perimeter of his first pen. Find the pen with the largest area he can make and the dimensions that produce this area.

4. When Spot was 3 years old, the owner tripled the perimeter of his first pen. Find the pen with the largest area he can make and the dimensions that produce this area.

Quadratic Optimization

Answers:

1. perimeter: 16 feet, area: 12 square feet

2. a) Find the maximum area of the pen.

    b) $16 = 2L + 2W$
    $A = LW$

    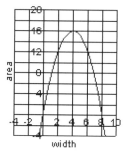

    c) $A(w) = w(8 - w)$

    d) domain $0 < w < 8$
    maximum area 16 ft^2
    dimensions 4 ft x 4 ft

3. a) Find the maximum area of the pen.

    b) $32 = 2L + 2W$
    $A = LW$

    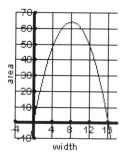

    c) $A(w) = w(16 - w)$

    d) domain $0 < w < 16$
    maximum area 64 ft^2
    dimensions 8 ft x 8 ft

4. a) Find the maximum area of the pen.

    b) $48 = 2L + 2W$
    $A = LW$

    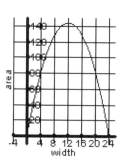

    c) $A(w) = w(24 - w)$

    d) domain $0 < w < 24$
    maximum area 144 ft^2
    dimensions 12 ft x 12 ft

Write Your Notes and Ideas Here!

Adaptation of AP Calculus 1997 AB-2

Objective:
Students will be introduced to the absolute maximum/minimum of a function and how to geometrically interpret $f(x) - g(x)$.

Connections to Previous Learning:
Students should be able to find rate of change or slope, characteristics of linear and quadratic functions, equation of a line, linear and quadratic transformations, function values, and the area of a triangle.

Connections to TEKS:
111.32   b1C-E, b2A-C, b3A, b4A, b4B, c1A, c1C, c2 A, c2C-E, d1A-C

Connections to AP:
The AP Calculus objectives of rate of change and area

Time Frame:
45 minutes

Materials:
One copy of the student activity for each student

Teacher Notes:
This lesson utilizes a variation of an AP Calculus free response exam question to recycle previously learned material. The absolute maximum/minimum is a straightforward concept for students to grasp. The absolute maximum/minimum is simply the y-coordinate of the single highest/lowest point in that specific *x*-interval. In fact, in some cases, the absolute maximum/minimum (or in some textbooks called the global maximum/minimum) may be the endpoint of an interval.

Some examples that are absolute maximums/minimums are:

a)   For $y = (x+2)^2 + 3$, abs. max is 3 at (-2, 3) and no abs. min.

b)   For $y = \dfrac{-1}{3}x + 2$ on the interval $-3 < x \le 9$, there is no abs. max and the abs. min is at -1.

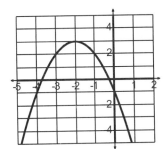

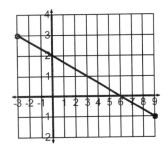

c)   For $f(x) = \dfrac{(x-1)^2(x+5)}{5}$, on the interval of $0 \le x \le \dfrac{1}{2}$ the abs. max is $f(0) = 1$ at (0, 1) & the abs. min is $f(\dfrac{1}{2}) = \dfrac{11}{40}$ at $(\dfrac{1}{2}, \dfrac{11}{40})$.

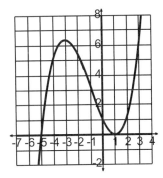

Two examples that do not have either an absolute maximum or an absolute minimum are:

d) $y = \dfrac{1}{6}x - 2$ on the whole line

e) $f(x) = \dfrac{(x-1)^2(x+5)}{5}$, for the interval $-6 < x < 4$

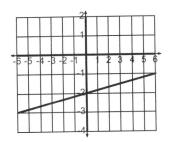

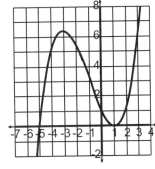

The absolute maximum or minimum value is just the *y*-value of the coordinate. In the coordinate the x-value tells where the maximum/minimum occurs, while the y-value tells the actual maximum/minimum value.

The function of $y = x$ is known as the identity function. It is helpful for the students to know the verbal name of this particular parent function, along with its graph and equation.

Adaptation of AP Calculus 1997 AB-2

Let f be the function given by $h(x) = -x^2 + 4$.

1. a) What is the difference between h and a linear function?

    b) From looking at the equation for h predict the changes the graph will have in comparison to the parent function.

    c) Fill in the table for h.

x	h(x)
-2	
-1	
0	
1	
2	

    d) Graph $h(x)$ on the coordinate plane below for $-2 \le x \le 2$. Label both axes.

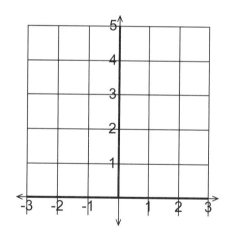

2. Identify:

    a) y-intercept _____   b) both coordinates of the x-intercepts _____

    c) domain _____   d) range _____

    e) absolute maximum value _____

    f) $h(-1/2)$ _____   g) $h(3a)$ _____

3. a) On the coordinate plane in #1, draw a line segment connecting the *y*-intercept and the positive *x*-intercept. Label this line segment *g*(*x*). Now draw another line segment connecting the *y*-intercept and the negative *x*-intercept. Label this line segment *f*(*x*).

   b) Find the rate of change, or slope, of *g*(*x*).

   c) Find the rate of change, or slope, of *f*(*x*).

   d) Find the two equations for *g*(*x*) and *f*(*x*), both in slope-intercept form.

4. a) Evaluate *h*(1).

   b) Evaluate g(1).

   c) Find $h(1) - g(1)$.

   d) What is the graphical significance of what you just found in part "c"?

5. a) What is the length of the graph of $g(x), < 0 \le x \le 2$?

   b) Determine the area of the triangle in the first quadrant bounded by the *x* and *y* axes and the graph of *g*(*x*).

6. a) State the absolute maximum, absolute minimum, and the corresponding coordinate(s) for $y = 7x^2 - 3$.

   b) Construct a quadratic equation with an absolute maximum value of -4.

Adaptation of AP Calculus 1997 AB-2

Answers:

1. a) The function h differs from a linear function in that its graph is not a straight line. The power or exponent of 2 makes its graph a parabola, not a line.

    b) The graph of $y = x^2$ is flipped over the x-axis and then shifted up 4 units to obtain the graph of h.

    c)

x	h(x)
-2	0
-1	3
0	4
1	3
2	0

    d)

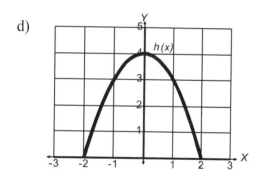

2. a) 4

    b) (2, 0) and (-2, 0)

    c) $-2 \leq x \leq 2$

    d) $0 \leq h(x) \leq 4$

    e) 4

    f) $3\dfrac{3}{4}$

    g) $-9a^2 + 4$

3. a)

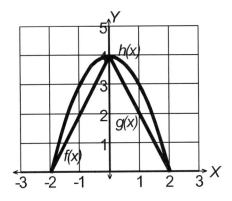

    b)   -2

    c)   2

    d) $g(x) = -2x + 4$ and $f(x) = 2x + 4$

4. a)   3

    b)   2

    c)   1

    d)   The distance from $h(x)$ to $g(x)$ at the one place where x is 1. Another way to say it is that is how far from the curved function to the linear function at x = 1.

5. a) $\sqrt{20}$ or 4.472

    b)   4

6. a)   There is no absolute maximum. There is an absolute minimum of -3.

    b)   In the general form of $y = a(x - h)^2 = k$, as long as "a" is any negative number and "k" is a negative 4, then the "h" can be any number. A few of the correct quadratic functions may include:

    $$y = -x^2 - 4, g(x) = -2(x - 5)^2 - 4, \text{ or } h(t) = \frac{-2}{3}(t + 4)^2 - 4$$

Graphing Quadratic Functions

Objective:
Students will graph a quadratic function.

Connections to Previous Learning:
Students should be able to solve a quadratic equation by factoring and graph a quadratic in the form $y = ax^2$ for $a > 0$ and $a < 0$.

Connections to TEKS:
111.32, b2C, b4A, d1A, d1D, d2A, d2B

Connections to AP:
The AP Calculus topic of analysis of functions

Time Frame:
50 minutes

Materials:
Graphing Quadratic Functions worksheet

Teacher Notes:
The class works example #1 and example #2 together with the teacher.

Example #1: As the class works this example it is important that the students notice the symmetry of the graph and that the x value that gives the maximum y-value is on the axis of symmetry for the parabola.

Example #2: The quadratic equations found in this worksheet can be solved easily by factoring and using the zero product property so that the students can practice this skill. The students will not use a graphing calculator on this worksheet.

a)   To help students become comfortable with function notation and to relate the question to the notation $h(t) = 528$. After the students solve the equation $528 = 224t - 16t^2$ by factoring, write the answer in the form $h(3) = 528$ and $h(11) = 528$. Ask the student why there are two times when the rocket's height is 528 feet.

b)   Again write $h(t) = 0$ and have the students solve the equation $0 = 224t - 16t^2$ by factoring. Write the answer in the form $h(0) = 0$ and $h(0) = 14$. Relate the answer to the zeros of the function $h(t)$.

c) To find the time when the rocket is at the maximum height, refer the students back to example 1 and the symmetry of the graph. The students can find the average of the times 0 and 14 or 3 and 11 in order to find that the *x* value of the maximum height is 7 feet. Have the students write the equation for the axis of symmetry, $t = 7$.

d) Now that the students know the *t* coordinate of the maximum height, they can find $h(7)$. Ask the students the meaning for $h(7)$ in the context of this problem.

e) The students now have enough points to graph the function. The students use the zeros of the function (when the ball is on the ground) to help them set the scale for the horizontal axis on their graph and the maximum height to help them set the scale for the vertical axis on their graph. This discussion helps students identify the reasonable domain and range for this situation in part f. After the students plot the points they found in parts a – d, ask them if they should connect the points.

f) The students can find the domain and range by looking at the graph.

Additional questions for discussion:

1. Find the average rate of change of the height for the interval of time $1 < t < 2$. What does this value represent? *(The average rate of change is 176 feet per second.)*

   a) Find the average rate of change of the height for the interval of time $3 < t < 4$. What does this value represent? *(The average rate of change is 112 feet per second.)*

   b) Compare the values for the average rate of change you found in parts 1 and 2. Explain the meaning of these values in the context of this problem. *The rate of change is decreasing because of gravity.)*

   c) Find average rate of change for the interval of time $9 < t < 10$. What does this value represent? *(The average rate of change is –80 feet per second.)* This value is negative. Explain the meaning of a positive rate of change and a negative rate of change in the context of this problem. *(A positive rate means that the rocket's height is greater at the end of the interval than at the beginning. A negative rate means that the rocket's height is less at the end of the interval than at the beginning.)*

Graphing Quadratic Functions

Example #1
Interpret the following situation.

Jan threw a ball straight up into the air. The graph to the right represents the height (h) of the ball at time (t).

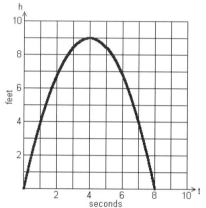

a)   When is the ball on the ground?

b)   What is the maximum height of the ball?

c)   When is the ball at its highest?

d)   When is the height of the ball 4 feet?

e)   Approximate the height of the ball at 5 seconds.

f)   Is the graph a function? If it is a function, find the domain and the range.

Example #2
A rocket is launched from ground level with an initial velocity of 224 ft/s. The height h in feet of the rocket at any given time t in seconds is $h(t) = 224t - 16t^2$.

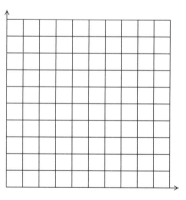

a)   When will the rocket reach a height of 528 feet?

b)   When will the rocket reach the ground?

c)   When will the rocket reach its maximum height?

d)   What is the maximum height of the rocket?

e)   Graph this situation.

f)   State the domain and range of the graph.

1. An object is hurled upward from the ground at an initial velocity of 128 ft/s. The height h in feet of the object at any given time t in seconds is $h(t) = 128t - 16t^2$.

   a) When will the object reach a height of 192 feet?

   b) When will the object reach the ground?

   c) When will the object reach its maximum height?

   d) What is the maximum height of the object?

   e) Graph this situation.

   f) State the domain and the range of the graph.

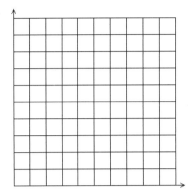

2. From ground level, an object travels upward with an initial velocity of 240 ft/s. The height h in feet of the object at any given time t in seconds is $h(t) = 240t - 16t^2$.

   a) Find $h(1)$. Explain the meaning of this question in the context of this problem.

   b) Find the value of t when $h(t) = 800$. Explain the meaning of this question in the context of this problem.

   c) Find the value of t when $h(t) = 0$. Explain the meaning of this question in the context of this problem.

   d) When will the object reach its maximum height?

   e) What is the maximum height of the object?

   f) Graph this situation.

   g) State the domain and the range of the graph.

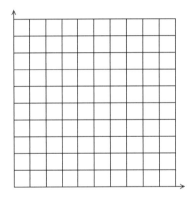

Graphing Quadratic Functions

Answers:

Example #1
 a) 0 seconds and 8 seconds
 b) 9 feet
 c) 4 seconds
 d) approximately 1 second and 7 seconds
 e) approximately 8.6 feet
 f) The graph is a function
   Domain: $0 \le t \le 8$, Range: $0 \le h \le 9$

Example #2
 a) 3 seconds and 11 seconds
 b) 14 seconds
 c) 7 seconds
 d) 784 feet
 e)

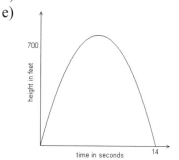

 f) Domain: $0 \le t \le 14$, Range: $0 \le h \le 784$

1. a) 2 and 6 seconds
 b) 8 seconds
 c) 4 seconds
 d) 256 feet
 e)

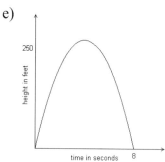

 f) Domain: $0 \le t \le 8$, Range: $0 \le h \le 256$

2. a) 224 feet (the height of the ball at 1 second)
 b) 5 and 10 seconds (the time when the ball is 800 feet in the air.)
 c) $t = 0$ and $t = 15$. $t = 0$ because the object starts at ground level; $t = 15$ means after 15 seconds, the object is back on the ground.
 d) 7.5 seconds
 e) 900 feet
 f)

 g) Domain: $0 \le t \le 15$, Range: $0 \le h \le 900$

278

Write Your Notes and Ideas Here!

Writing Equations Using Sequences

Objective:
Students will look at differences in terms of sequences to write a general description for the nth term of the sequence.

Connections to Previous Learning:
Students should be able to write an equation of a line, understanding that $y = mx + b$ has a y-intercept of b when $x = 0$.

Connections to TEKS:
111.32 b1A, b1B, b1C, 2B, 3A, B, c2A, c2B, c2D, c2E

Connections to AP:
The AP Calculus objective of analysis of functions

Time Frame:
50 minutes

Materials:
Worksheet

Teacher Notes:
All terms in the first two sequences of this activity have a common difference. This lesson relates a sequence of terms to the y values of a linear function when the x coordinates are counting numbers. For example, the sequence 2, 5, 8, 11 represents the points (1, 2) (2, 5) (3, 8) (4, 11). The students will not discover this until the end of the activity. They will realize that the common difference between the terms will be the slope and the y intercept will be the 0 term of the sequence. If you count back 3 units from 2 the 0 term would be -1. Since the common difference is 3, the nth term, T, of this sequence is $3n - 1$. After the activity is completed, ask the students to plot the position, n, and the term in the sequence as an ordered pair and to graph their equation. One will be a set of points and the other will be a line connecting the points. This activity helps the students understand that the difference between successive terms of the sequence is the slope of the line and that the y-intercept is the point on the y-axis.

The last few sequences do not have a common difference. The difference of the difference is a constant. Since this occurs on the 2nd difference, when the points are plotted, the students will see the graph is quadratic (2nd degree) equation. On a cubic equation, the difference is constant on the third difference. You are laying the foundation for 1st, 2nd and 3rd derivatives.

Writing Equations Using Sequences

Sequences can be described using a formula. If the position of the term in the sequence is represented by n, if $n = 1, 2, 3, 4 . . .$ the nth term in the sequence 2, 4, 6, 8. . . may be described as $2n$. Other sequences are more difficult to recognize. If $n = 1, 2, 3, 4…$ the nth term in the sequence 3, 5, 7, 9…may be described as $2n + 1$. We needed to add one to the first formula because each term in this 2nd sequence is one more than the corresponding term in the 1st sequence.

Given any sequence, how can an equation be written to describe the nth term?

In the examples above, find the difference between each term. Notice that the common difference of the terms is 2. It is not a coincidence that the coefficient of n is 2 (the common difference). Find the common difference in the sequences below.

3, 6, 9, 12, 15

5, 9, 13, 17, 21

9, 7, 5, 3, 1, -1

-3, 3, 9, 15, 21

The common difference is the multiplier of n.

To find out what should be added or subtracted, you can find the zero term.

We are now going to develop a formula. First, let us define our variables:

T = the nth term of the sequence d = the common difference
n = position in the sequence z = the zero term

The equation will be $T = dn + z$. How does this formula compare to $y = mx + b$?

Sequence	Difference of terms	Difference multiplied by position n	What is the zero term?*	Equation
3, 6, 9, 12, 15	3	$3n$	$3 - 3 = 0$	$T = 3n + 0$
5, 9, 13, 17, 21	4	$4n$	$5 - 4 = 1$	$T = 4n + 1$
9, 7, 5, 3, 1, -1	-2	$-2n$	$9 - -2 = 11$	$T = -2n + 11$
-3, 3, 9, 15, 21	6	$6n$	$-3 - 6 = -9$	$T = 6n - 9$

* subtract the difference from the first term

1. Write an equation to describe the sequences below.

    a) 9, 8, 7, 6, 5, . . .

    b) 13, 17, 21, 25, 29, . . .

    c) 6, 11, 16, 21, 26, . . .

    d) 112, 100, 88, 76 . . .

2. Describe two different methods to find the 100th term of the sequences in problem 1 b). Which will be easier. Calculate this 100th term.

3. Given the sequence 12, ___ , 20, _____28

    a) Find the missing terms of the sequence.

    b) Write an equation for the nth term T.

    c) What is the 20th term?

4. Given the sequence, 21, 20, 22, 19, 23, 18, 24, 17, 25, 16, 26, . . .

    a) What comes next in the sequence?

    b) How can you write an equation for this sequence?

    c) What is the 75th term?

    d) What is the 50th term?

5. Fill in the table below:

n	$n^2 + 1$	1st difference of terms	2nd difference of terms
1	2	-	-
2	5	3	-
3	10	5	2
4			
5			
6			
7			

6. Make a table like the one above for $3n^2 - 2$.

n	$3n^2 - 2$	1st difference	2nd difference

7. Make a table like the one above for x^3. (Use the table feature on your calculator.) Describe the pattern that you observe.

n	x^3	1st difference	2nd difference

8. The sequence -1, 2, 5, 8, 11 . . . can be described by the equation $T = 3n - 4$.

   a) Plot the points (1, -1) (2, 2) (3, 5) (4, 8) (5, 11).

   b) Plot the line on the same graph.

   c) How do these points relate to the sequence and the line?

Writing Equations Using Sequences

Answers:

1. Write an equation to describe the sequences below.

    a)   9, 8, 7, 6, 5, . . . $T = -n + 10$

    b)   13, 17, 21, 25, 29, . . . $T = 4n + 9$

    c)   6, 11, 16, 21, 26, . . . $T = 5n + 1$

    d)   112, 100, 88, 76 . . . $T = -12n + 124$

2. One method of calculating the 100th term is to continue to write out each term of the sequence until the 100th term is reach. The more efficient way is to utilize the formula.

    $T_{100} = 4(100) + 9 = 409$

3. Given the sequence 12, ___, 20, ____28

    a)   Find the missing terms of the sequence.

         Two differences equals 8 so one difference equals 4;   12, 16, 20, 24, 28

    b)   Write an equation the *n*th term *T*. $T = 4n + 8$

    c)   What is the 20th term? $T = 4(20) + 8 = 88$

4. Given the sequence, 21, 20, 22, 19, 23, 18, 24, 17, 25, 16, 26, . . .

    a)   What comes next in the sequence? **15, 27, 14, 28**

    b)   How can you write an equation for this sequence?

         This is a good place to discuss piecewise functions. The odd terms follow the sequence ½ n + 20 ½ and the even terms follow the sequence – ½ n + 21

    c)   What is the 75th term?   **Since 75 is an odd number, ½ (75) + 20 ½ = 58**

    d)   What is the 50th term?   **Since 50 is an even number, - ½ (50) + 21 = -4**

5. Fill in the table below:

n	$n^2 + 1$	1st difference of terms	2nd difference of terms
1	2		
2	5	3	
3	10	5	2
4	17	7	2
5	26	9	2
6	37	11	2
7	50	13	2

6. Make a table like the one above for $3n^2 - 2$.

n	$3n^2 - 2$	1st difference	2nd difference
1	1		
2	10	9	6
3	25	15	6
4	46	21	6
5	73	27	6
6	106	33	6
7	145	39	6

Ask the students to look at the differences from the two charts and predict what the 2nd difference will be for $4x^2 + 1$. The answer is 8. For extra credit have them develop a formula for the common difference for quadratics. The chart is below.

n	an^2	1st difference	2nd difference
1	a		
2	$4a$	$3a$	$2a$
3	$9a$	$5a$	$2a$
4	$16a$	$7a$	$2a$
5	$25a$	$9a$	$2a$
6	$36a$	$11a$	$2a$
7	$49a$	$13a$	$2a$

7. Make a table like the one above for x^3. Describe the pattern that you observe.

n	x^3	1st difference	2nd difference
1	1		
2	8	7	
3	27	19	12
4	64	37	18
5	125	61	24
6	216	91	30
7	343	127	36

Have the students notice that if they found the 3rd difference, it would be 6.

8. The sequence -1, 2, 5, 8, 11 . . . can be described by the equation $T = 3n - 4$.

Plot the points (1, -1) (2, 2) (3, 5) (4, 8) (5, 11).

How do these points relate to the sequence and the line?

The y values of the points are the terms of the sequence and the x values are the position. Connecting the points will graph the line $T = 3n - 4$.

This is a good place to discuss a discontinuous function. The sequence is not continuous because the n will always be a counting number. The line includes the values for n.

Write Your Notes and Ideas Here!

Adaptation of AP Calculus 1997 AB-1

Objectives:
Students will utilize the graph of a position function in order to find the position of a particle moving along the *x*-axis, and they will solve linear and quadratic equations in order to find the average rate of change in a position function. They will interpret the motion of a particle moving along the *x*-axis.

Connections to Previous Learning:
Students should be able to solve linear and quadratic equations, find slope, and understand position and velocity functions. They should be able to connect a graph to the physical situation that it illustrates.

Connections to TEKS:
111.32   1A, b1B, b1D, b1E, b2B, b2C, b2D, b3A, b4A, c2A, c2B, d1D, d2A, d2B

Connections to AP:
The AP Calculus topics of rate of change and position, velocity, and acceleration

Time Frame:
60 minutes

Materials:
Graphing calculator

Teacher Notes:
1. This AP Calculus problem is an excellent one to use in reviewing or assessing the students to check for their understanding of motion problems AFTER they have learned the concepts surrounding motion. Work with a motion detector can reinforce the concept of moving along a horizontal line while looking at an *xy*-graph with position on the *y*-axis and time on the *x*-axis.

2. Care must be taken with the vocabulary of motion problems. In this type of problem, the particles move on either horizontal lines or vertical lines. Do not try to extend this idea to motion in a plane since this complicates the physics of the problem. If the students are also taking the science course IPC, motion provides an excellent topic on which to collaborate with the science teachers.

3. The teacher will probably need to lead the students through this lesson providing plenty of guidance.

Teacher Lesson

4. The information given below may be helpful when answering student questions.

   If $x(t)$ represents the position of a particle along the x-axis at any time t, then the following statements are true.

   a) "Initially" means when time $t = 0$.

   b) "At the origin" means $x(t) = 0$.

   c) "At rest" means velocity $v(t) = 0$.

   d) "Magnitude" means the value of the function ignoring the sign or more formally the distance from the origin.

   e) If the velocity of the particle is positive, then the particle is moving to the right.

   f) If the velocity of the particle is negative, then the particle is moving to the left.

   g) If the acceleration of the particle is positive, then the velocity is increasing.

   h) If the acceleration of the particle is negative, then the velocity is decreasing.

   i) Speed is the absolute value of velocity.

   j) "Fastest" refers to the speed, so when asked when the particle is moving fastest, look at the absolute value of the velocity. In question 5c of this lesson, the students are asked to describe a situation in which the average rate of change over two intervals will be altered so that the slower interval will be the fastest interval. The magnitudes of the rates, not the signs, must be switched. The steepness of the slope, not the direction, is the critical factor.

   k) If the velocity and the acceleration at a particular time have the same sign (both are positive or both are negative), then the speed is increasing.

   l) If the velocity and the acceleration at a particular time have different signs (one is positive and the other is negative), then the speed is decreasing.

   m) To determine the total distance traveled over a time interval, you must find the sum of the absolute values of the differences in position between all resting points. This can also be done by find the area under the absolute value of the velocity curve.

5. This type of problem is designed to model the free response problems in the AP Calculus exam where students are graded according to their work and solutions. The assessment section of this guide gives suggestions as to how to "read with the student".

Adaptation of AP Calculus 1997 AB-1

A particle moves along the *x*-axis so that its velocity at any time $t \geq 0$ is given by the velocity function $v(t) = 3t^2 - 2t - 1$. The position function is given by $x(t) = t^3 - t^2 - t + C$, where the distance from the origin is measured in inches and time is measured in seconds.

1. If $x(2) = 5$, determine the value of C in the position function, and rewrite the function using the calculated value for C.

2. a) Using your graphing calculator, graph the new function $x(t)$ from question 1 for $0 \leq t \leq 3$.

    b) Find all values of t for which $x(t) = 2.207$.

    c) Interpret the meaning of the values of t that you found in part (b).

    d) Using the information from parts b and c, explain what you think the particle must do in order to be in the same place at two different times.

3. By analyzing the function from the table feature of your graphing calculator, describe the activity of the particle on the interval from $t = 0$ to $t = 5$ seconds.

4. a) Give the average rate of change for $x(t)$ on the interval from $t = 1$ to $t = 3$ seconds.

    b) Give the average rate of change for $x(t)$ on the interval from $t = 3$ to $t = 5$ seconds.

    c) Interpret the meaning of the average rate of change for this position function over each of the two time intervals. Be sure to include units.

5. a) Over which interval from 4a and 4b above is the particle moving the fastest?

    b) Explain your reasoning.

6. a) For $t \geq 0$, algebraically find when $v(t) = 0$.

    b) Describe the motion of the particle at the time calculated in part (a).

7. Interpret the meaning of $v(.36)$ and $v(1.276)$. Describe the motion of the particle at these times.

Adaptation of AP Calculus 1997 AB-1

Answers:

A particle moves along the x-axis so that its velocity at any time $t \geq 0$ is given by $v(t) = 3t^2 - 2t - 1$, which is the velocity function. The position function is represented by $x(t) = t^3 - t^2 - t + C$, where the distance from the origin is measured in inches and time is measured in seconds.

1. If $x(2) = 5$, determine the value of C in the position function, and rewrite the function using the calculated value for C.

   $C = 3$, $x(t) = t^3 - t^2 - t + 3$

2. a) Using your graphing calculator, graph the new function $x(t)$ from question 1 for $0 \leq t \leq 3$.

   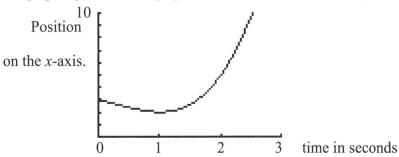

   b) Find t if $x(t) = 2.207$.

   $t = 0.645$ seconds and $t = 1.3$ seconds

   c) Interpret the meaning of the values of t that you found in part (b).

   At 0.645 seconds and 1.3 seconds, the particle is 2.207 inches to the right of the origin.

   d) Using the information from parts b and c, explain what you think the particle must do in order to be in the same place at two different times.

   The particle must change directions the time interval $.645 \leq t \leq 1.3$ at least once in order to be in the same place at two different times.

3. By analyzing the function from the table feature of your graphing calculator, describe the activity of the particle on the interval from $t = 0$ to $t = 5$ seconds.

   At 0 seconds, or when the particle starts being timed, the particle is 3 inches to the right of the origin. Since the position values get smaller for about 1 second, the particle moves to the left. After about 1 second, the particle's position values begin to get larger again, meaning that the particle is again traveling to the right. At 5 seconds when the timing is stopped, the particle is located at approximately 98 inches to the right of the origin.

4. a) Give the average rate of change for $x(t)$ on the interval from $t = 1$ to $t = 3$ seconds.

   $$\frac{x(3) - x(1)}{3 - 1} = \textbf{8 inches per second}$$

b)   Give the average rate of change for $x(t)$ on the interval from $t = 3$ to $t = 5$ seconds.

$$\frac{x(5) - x(3)}{5 - 3} = 40 \text{ inches per second}$$

c)   Interpret the meaning of the rate of change for this position function over each of the two time intervals. Be sure to include units.

The average rate of change tells how fast the particle is moving in inches per second over the two time intervals. For instance, in part "a", the particle covers a distance of 16 inches in 2 seconds while in part (b), the particle covers 80 inches in 2 seconds.

5.   a)   Over which interval from parts 4 "a" and "b" is the particle moving the fastest.

On the interval from $t = 3$ to $t = 5$.

b)   Explain your reasoning.

40 in/sec is faster than 8 in/sec. (During the interval for part (b) the particle is moving the fastest because the slope of the line connecting the two endpoint is steeper in that interval than it is in the interval in part (a). The absolute values of the slope in part (b) is greater than the absolute value of the slope in part (a).)

6.   a)   For $t \geq 0$, find when $v(t) = 0$ algebraically.

$v(t) = 3t^2 - 2t - 1 = 0$

$(3t + 1)(t - 1) = 0$

$(3t + 1) = 0$ and $(t - 1) = 0$

$3t = -1$ and $t = 1$

$t = \dfrac{-1}{3}$

Since $t \geq 0$, the velocity is zero when $t = 1$ second.

b)   Describe the motion of the particle at the time calculated in part (a)?

At this time, since the velocity is zero, the particle is not moving. The particle is at rest.

c)   This procedure of solving the quadratic equation is also called finding the **roots or zeros or x-intercepts** of the equation. In particle movement, a zero velocity often indicates a change of direction is about to occur. A change of sign in the velocity means a change in direction.

7.   Interpret the meaning of $v(.36)$ and $v(1.276)$. Describe the motion of the particle at these times.

At 0.36 seconds, the particle is moving to the left because the velocity is negative, at a speed of 1.331 inches per seconds, while at 1.276 seconds the particle is moving at about the same speed, 1.333 inches per second, but it is moving to the right, because the velocity is positive. The speed is the absolute value of the velocity.

Similar Triangles

Objective:
Students will simplify and add radicals.

Connections to Previous Learning:
Students should be able to use the Pythagorean Theorem and similar triangles.

Connections to TEKS:
111.32 b.4, 6.4A, 6.4B, 7.6D, 8.2C, 8.10A, 8.7C

Connections to AP:
The AP Calculus objective of area and volume

Time Frame:
50 minutes

Materials:
Worksheet and a protractor

Teacher Notes:
The teacher and students work the table for #1 part D and C together. First the students measure the angles of the triangles and find that the corresponding angles of the triangles are congruent. As the students find the lengths of the sides using the Pythagorean Theorem, on part C ask the students if they can write $\sqrt{45}$ differently. The students should notice that $\sqrt{45}$ is three times as long as the side in part D which has a measure of $\sqrt{5}$ leading them to conclude that $\sqrt{45} = 3\sqrt{5}$. The students should also make the connection when finding the perimeters that $\sqrt{5} + \sqrt{5} = 2\sqrt{5}$. The students complete the worksheet in groups. After completing the worksheet, the class discusses their findings.

Sample discussion topics:

If you double the length of all of the sides of the triangles, how does this affect the perimeter, the area, and the base to height ratio?

If you triple the length of all the sides of the triangles, how does this affect the perimeter, the area, and the base to height ratio?

The teacher might discuss the Pythagorean triples that are formed in the 2nd group of triangles (E-H) and have the students predict another set of triples and check their answer using the Pythagorean Theorem.

Additional question for problem #6:

What happened to the area of the triangular ends of the trough as the height and base of the triangle was multiplied by a scale factor of $\frac{1}{2}$. (The area is multiplied by $\left(\frac{1}{2}\right)^2$.)

What happened to the volume? (The volume is multiplied by $\left(\frac{1}{2}\right)^2$.)

The volume is a cubic measurement. Why is it not multiplied by $\left(\frac{1}{2}\right)^3$? (The length does not change.)

Similar Triangles

1. Your task is to investigate each of the three groups of triangles below. Complete the tables on the next page.

2. Compare the triangles in each group. Discuss all similarities, differences, or patterns you find in your table.

3. Each group of triangles below are classified as similar triangles. What conjectures can you make about similar triangles. Support your conjectures.

4. For each group draw at least one other similar triangle and explain why it is similar to the other triangles.

1 a)

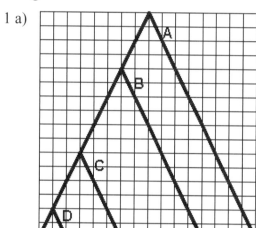

1 b)

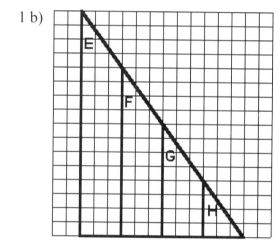

5. Draw two similar triangles. Explain how you drew them and how you know that they are similar.

1 c)

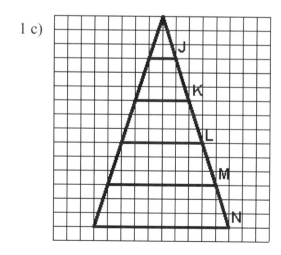

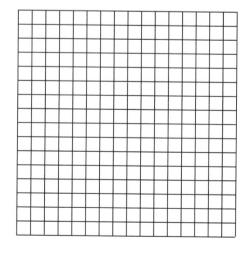

(1a)	side lengths(units)	perimeter (units)	base/height	area (square units)
D				
C				
B				
A				

(1b)	side lengths(units)	perimeter (units)	base/height	area (square units)
H				
G				
F				
E				

(1c)	side lengths(units)	perimeter (units)	base/height	area (square units)
J				
K				
L				
M				
N				

5. The trough shown is 6 feet long, and its ends are inverted isosceles triangles with base 2 feet and height 4 feet.

a) Find the area of the triangular ends of the trough.
   Find the volume of water in the trough when it is full.

b) If the depth of the water in the trough is 2 feet, find the area of the triangle formed by the water at the ends of the trough.
   Find the volume of the water in the trough.

c) If the depth of the water in the trough is 1 foot, find the area of the triangle formed by the water at the ends of the trough. Find the volume of the water in the trough.

d) Redesign the trough to hold the same volume of water as in part a), yet make the triangular ends an inverted right isosceles triangle. Keep the length the same.

Similar Triangles

Answers:

(1a)	side lengths(units)	perimeter (units)	base/height	area (square units)
D	$2,\sqrt{5},\sqrt{5}$	$2+2\sqrt{5}$	2/2	2
C	$6,3\sqrt{5},3\sqrt{5}$	$6+6\sqrt{5}$	6/6	18
B	$12,6\sqrt{5},6\sqrt{5}$	$12+12\sqrt{5}$	12/12	72
A	$16,8\sqrt{5},8\sqrt{5}$	$16+16\sqrt{5}$	16/16	128

(1b)	side lengths(units)	perimeter (units)	base/height	area (square units)
H	3,4,5	12	3/4	6
G	6,8,10	24	6/8	24
F	9,12,15	36	9/12	54
E	12,16,20	48	12/16	96

(1c)	side lengths(units)	perimeter (units)	base/height	area (square units)
J	$2,\sqrt{10},\sqrt{10}$	$2+2\sqrt{10}$	2/3	3
K	$4,2\sqrt{10},2\sqrt{10}$	$4+4\sqrt{10}$	4/6	12
L	$6,3\sqrt{10},3\sqrt{10}$	$6+6\sqrt{10}$	6/9	27
M	$8,4\sqrt{10},4\sqrt{10}$	$8+8\sqrt{10}$	8/12	48
N	$10,5\sqrt{10},5\sqrt{10}$	$10+10\sqrt{10}$	10/15	75

2. If you multiply the side lengths by a scale factor of x then the perimeter is multiplied by x and the area is multiplied by x^2. The base/height ratios for similar triangles are equal.

3. The lengths of the sides are proportional and the base/height ratios are equal. The corresponding angles in similar triangles are congruent.

4. Answers will vary. Students could draw their similar triangles on an overhead copy of the worksheet for classroom discussion.

5. Answers will vary. Students could draw their similar triangles on large grid boards so they can share them with the class.

6. a) The area of each triangular end is 4 square feet. The volume is 24 cubic feet.

   b) The area of each triangular end is 1 square foot. The volume is 6 cubic feet.

   c) The area of each triangular end is $\frac{1}{4}$ square foot. The volume is $\frac{3}{2}$ cubic feet.

   d) The height is 2 feet. The width is 4 feet.

Write Your Notes and Ideas Here!

Radical Probability – Simplifying Radical Expressions

Objective:
Students will combine compound probability and simplifying radical expressions.

Connections to Previous Learning:
Students should have had multiple experiences with simple and compound probability. Students should understand the Pythagorean Theorem, rational and irrational numbers, and simplifying radicals.

Connections to TEKS:
111.32 b1D, b4;   8.11A, 8.11C

Connections to AP:
The AP Statistics topic of probability

Time Frame:
10-50 minutes of class time

Materials:
Worksheet

Teacher Notes:
This lesson is intended to be done after students have reviewed the Pythagorean Theorem and after a first lesson on simplification of radicals. Spend enough time in class on this activity to be sure students understand why $\overline{AB}$ will not be on a slip in the container. This should take about 10 minutes. The teacher could review students' understanding of irrational numbers and simplifying radicals by doing the first two problems in class before having them construct the probability game. The sentences: *"Before you turn in these answers, you may go over them with your group. You may work as a group to make up your game."* were removed from this lesson so that it can be done as an independent lesson or project. Add them orally if you choose to let this be a group activity. If the lesson is done in class to this extent, it would take 50 minutes.

Note: It may be helpful to make a page of six grids for each student so that they could determine their line segments more easily.

Radical Probability – Simplifying Radical Expressions

For April Fools' Day your algebra teacher has had a (totally) radical idea. A container will have slips of paper that include all line segments that can be named using 2 of the endpoints on the grid below that are greater than or equal to four units. Your teacher is willing to give you extra credit for this six weeks if you can devise a two-person game where you will win more often than lose. The game must use the guidelines below.

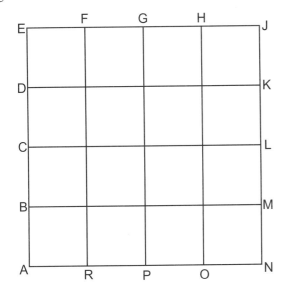

1. First make a simple sample space using the length of each segment.

   For example: $m\overline{AE}$ = 4 units

2. Tell which segments have rational and which have irrational lengths.

3. In your game, you must draw at least two segments from the container.

4. Your game must be based on compound probability.

You must turn in the answers for numbers 1 and 2 along with the rules for your game. If a length is a radical, it must be simplified. In order to receive extra credit, the rules for your game must be in written form and specific enough that your teacher can easily understand all of the rules for your game.

Radical Probability – Simplifying Radical Expressions

Answers:

1. The sample space your students make will depend on their prior knowledge and experience. The following is one possibility.

4 unit segments:	$\overline{AN}, \overline{BM}, \overline{CL}, \overline{DK}, \overline{EJ}, \overline{AE}, \overline{FR}, \overline{GP}, \overline{HO}, \overline{JN}$
$\sqrt{17}$ unit segments:	$\overline{AF}, \overline{GR}, \overline{HP}, \overline{OJ}, \overline{BN}, \overline{CM}, \overline{DL}, \overline{EK}, \overline{DJ}, \overline{CK}, \overline{BL}, \overline{AM}, \overline{ER}, \overline{FP}, \overline{GO}, \overline{HN}$
$2\sqrt{5}$ unit segments:	$\overline{EP}, \overline{FO}, \overline{GN}, \overline{AG}, \overline{HR}, \overline{JP}, \overline{AL}, \overline{BK}, \overline{CJ}, \overline{EL}, \overline{DM}, \overline{CN}$
5 unit segments:	$\overline{EO}, \overline{FN}, \overline{AH}, \overline{JR}, \overline{AK}, \overline{BJ}, \overline{EM}, \overline{DN}$
$4\sqrt{2}$ unit segments:	$\overline{EN}, \overline{AJ}$
$3\sqrt{2}$ unit segments:	$\overline{BH}, \overline{DO}, \overline{FM}, \overline{KR}$

2. There are 18 segments with rational lengths. There are 10 segments with lengths of 4 units and 8 with lengths of 5 units.

   There are 34 segments with irrational lengths. There are 16 segments with lengths of $\sqrt{17}$ units. There are 12 segments with lengths of $2\sqrt{5}$ units. There are 2 segments with lengths of $4\sqrt{2}$ units.

   There are 4 segments with lengths of $3\sqrt{2}$ units.

   Games will vary widely.

   Sample game:
   - Write each line segment on an index card, a piece of card stock, or on the face of a standard card.
   - The game maker is the dealer.
   - The game is for the dealer and one additional person.
   - The dealer gives each person two cards, face up.
   - The dealer gets all four cards if either player has one irrational card and one rational card.
   - The other player gets all four cards under any other circumstance.
   - The four cards dealt each round are not returned to the deck.
   - The player who has the most cards when ten are left wins.

Exponential Functions Exploration

Objective:
Students will be introduced to exponential functions and asymptotes.

Connections to Previous Learning:
Students should be able to complete and graph a table of values.

Connections to TEKS:
111.32   d3C

Connections to AP:
The AP Calculus objectives of analysis of functions and limits
The AP Statistics objective of non-linear bivariate data

Time Frame:
30 minutes

Materials:
Worksheet, 2 pieces of paper 8 inches x 10 inches, one pair of scissors and one calculator per group

Teacher Notes:
Students should complete this activity in groups of 2 or 3 students. After the activity, the teacher will need to discuss exponential functions, exponential decay and asymptotes with the class to connect these terms to this lesson. In both examples, the x-axis, that is the line $y = 0$, is the horizontal asymptote for the graph of A. Be sure the students understand the asymptote is a line, not a number.

Exponential Functions Exploration

1. Start with a piece of paper that is 8 inches x 10 inches. Find the area of the paper and record the area in the table below.

   Cut the paper in half. Find the area of one of the rectangles and record the area in the table below.

   Cut one of the halves in half; continue this process. For each cut, find the area of the new rectangle and record the area in the table.

Number of Cuts	process	Area (in^2)
0		
1		
2		
3		
4		
5		
6		
7		
8		
9		
10		
11		
n		

a) Graph the table of values (cuts, area).

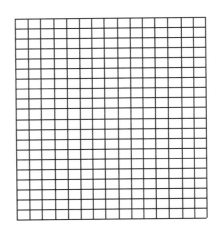

b) Write a function rule for the area of the rectangle $A(n)$ in terms of the number of cuts (n) you have made.

c) As the number of cuts gets larger, what number is the area is approaching?

2.   Start with a piece of paper that is 8 inches x 10 inches. Find the area of the paper and record the area in the table below.

   Form a new rectangle by cutting the length of the rectangle and the width of the rectangle in half. Find the area of this rectangle and record the area in the table.

   Continue to cut the length and the width of the rectangle in half. For each new rectangle, find the area and record the value in the table.

Number of Cuts	process	Area (in²)
0		
1		
2		
3		
4		
5		
6		
n		

a)   Graph the table of values (cuts, area).

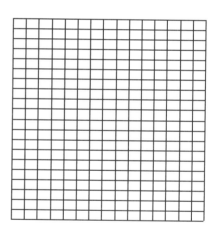

b)   Write a function rule for the area of the rectangle $A(n)$ in terms of the number of cuts (n) you have made.

c)   As the number of cuts gets larger, what number is the area is approaching?

Exponential Functions Exploration

Answers:

1.

Number of Cuts	process	Area (in²)
0	8X10	80
1	.5X80	40
2	.5X.5X80	20
3	.5X.5X.5X80	10
4	.5X.5X.5X.5X80	5
5	.5X.5X.5X.5X.5X80	2.5
6	.5X.5X.5X.5X.5X.5X80	1.25
7	(.5^7)X80	0.625
8	(.5^8)X80	0.3125
9	(.5^9)X80	0.15625
10	(.5^10)X80	0.078125
11	(.5^11)X80	0.0390625
n	(.5^n)X80	80(.5^n)

a)

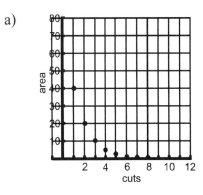

b) $A(n) = 80\left(\dfrac{1}{2}\right)^n$

c) As the number of cuts gets larger, the area approaches 0.

2.

Number of Cuts	process	Area (in²)
0	8X10	80
1	.5X8X.5X10	20
2	.5X.5X8X.5X.5X10	5
3	.5X.5X.5X8X.5X.5X.5X10	1.25
4	(.5^8)X80	0.3125
5	(.25^5)X80	0.078125
6	(.25^6)X80	0.01953125
n	(.25^n)X80	80(.25^n)

a)

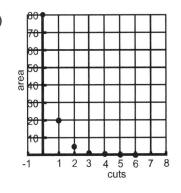

b) $A(n) = 80\left(\dfrac{1}{4}\right)^n$

c) As the number of cuts gets larger, the area approaches 0.

Exponential Growth

Objective:
Students will model a real world situation to develop the exponential growth function.

Connections to Previous Learning:
Students should understand and be able to write repeated multiplication as an exponential expression.

Connections to TEKS:
111.32 d3C

Connections to AP:
The AP Calculus objective of analysis of functions

Time Frame:
50 minutes

Materials:
One copy of the group activity and one of the choice activity for each student

Teacher Notes:
This lesson is written to be done in groups followed by a whole group discussion. Its secondary purpose is to acquaint students with invasive species. Other scenarios that can be used to exhibit exponential growth are compound interest, the cost of health care, growth of a colony of bacteria, population increase, increase in college tuition, etc.

Exponential Growth

An ecological system is vulnerable to destruction from the introduction of plants or animals outside that system. For example, when a non-native plant is introduced into a new area, it usually does not have its growth checked by the environment. With unlimited food and no predators, the non-native plant grows exponentially, quickly covering, killing, and replacing the endemic, native, plants. Such a plant is the water hyacinth which has been called the worst aquatic plant in the world! It is native to South America, but is now a part of the lakes, rivers and streams in most of the southern United States.

The water hyacinth is said to have been introduced into the United States in Louisiana at the World's Industrial and Cotton Centennial Exposition of 1884-1885. A Floridian went home with water hyacinth plants and later released them into the St. Johns River. From this beginning, water hyacinths now cause problems such as forming impenetrable mats of floating vegetation. These block boat traffic, prevent swimming and fishing, and prevent sunlight and oxygen from getting into the water. Perhaps the worst effect of the water hyacinth is a reduction of biological diversity in waters which it inhabits.

1. Water hyacinths double in 6 to 18 days. For the purposes of this investigation, consider that the number of water hyacinths will double in 12 days. Also assume that there is unlimited food and that there are no predators. Suppose 4 water hyacinths were put into the St. John's River. In question 5 you will make a table to figure out how many water hyacinths were produced from these 4 at a given time. Determine in your group the information in this problem that will be important in determining the number.

2. After 4 doubling periods, how many days will have elapsed? **Be sure to justify each answer in this investigation.**

3. After 96 days, there will have been how many doubling periods?

4. In 60 days, how many times will the water hyacinth population double? In 120 days?

5. Complete the following table to show the number of water hyacinths from these four at the given time intervals.

Days	Doubling Periods	Process Column	Exponential Version	Total Water Hyacinths
0	0 - Starting point	4	$4 \cdot 2^0$	4
12	1	$4 \cdot 2$	$4 \cdot 2^1$	8
24	2			
	3			
	4			
	5			
	6			
	10			

6. Develop a pattern which you can use to fill in the "days" and "total water hyacinths" columns below. The total water hyacinths will be a "formula" which includes the starting number of water hyacinths, the fact that the number is doubling, and the number of times that the number has doubled.

Days	Doubling Periods	Process Column	Exponential Version	Total Water Hyacinths
n				

7. About how many days would it take for there to be more than a billion from the original 4? How many years?

8. Using your formula, how many water hyacinths would there be after 3 years? (Ignore leap years.) Be sure to justify your answer in the space below.

9. Suppose growing conditions for water hyacinths were ideal and they doubled every 6 days. Rewrite your formula so that you start with the same four water hyacinths and double every 6 days.

10. Using the new formula, how many water hyacinths will there be after 3 years? (Still ignore leap years and justify your answer.)

11. Do you think that the formula will accurately predict the total water hyacinths indefinitely, or are there environmental conditions which might limit it? If you are the environmental scientist in charge of reducing the population, what will you try to keep the water hyacinths from completely clogging the waterways?

12. Non-native plants can destroy an ecosystem. Non-endemic animals can do the same. In 1859, 22 rabbits were imported to Australia from Europe. The rabbits found a land with plenty of food and no natural predators. Soon there were so many rabbits that they were destroying the island. In Australia, the rabbit population was doubling every 6 months. Determine in your group the information above that will be important in determining the number of rabbits at any given time.

13. Explain how to calculate the number of years elapsed after four doubling periods.

14. How many doubling periods will have elapsed after 18 months?

15. How many times has the rabbit population doubled after 4 years? After 7.5 years?

16. Complete the following table to show the number of rabbits from these 22 at the given time intervals.

Months	Growth Periods	Process Column	Exponential Version	Total Rabbits
0	0 - Starting point	22		
6	1			
	2			
	3			
	4			
	6			
	8			
	10			

17. In the table below, write an exponential function which can be used to determine the total number of rabbits after n growth periods in months.

Months	Growth Periods	Process Column	Exponential Version	Total Rabbits
n				

18. In 1887 there were so many rabbits that the government of Australia offered a reward for a way to control the population. How many growth periods had passed by 1887?

19. Approximately how many rabbits were there by 1887? Describe how you calculated your answer.

20. What population controls would you have offered?

21. Let a = the starting amount, b = the growth factor for a given amount of time, and n = number of doubling periods. Write an exponential function, in terms of n, which can be used for any exponential growth situation.

Choice Activity

The following are examples of invasive species which are now taking over areas of the United States. Some have exponential growth rates while some may model a different type of function. Choose one of the following situations, research it, determine its parent function, its growth rate, and use the information to

- write a poem,
- compose a song,
- write an essay,
- make a poster,
- design a billboard,
- make a brochure or flyer, or
- make a news bulletin.

1. CBS News 09-27-2002. The invasive fish **Asian carp** can launch like torpedoes when startled by motor noise. The carp were accidentally released during a flooding situation. Underwater electrical barriers are being used to jolt the carp away from a canal leading to the Great Lakes and an ecological nightmare.

2. The **zebra mussel** is native to the Balkans and was brought to the United States in ballast water which was discharged into Lake St. Clair, near Detroit, where the mussel was discovered in 1988. Since that time, they have spread rapidly to all of the Great Lakes and waterways in many states, as well as Ontario and Quebec. Note: a 9-09-2002 news release reports the discovery of a well established colony near Haymarket, Virginia.

3. **Purple loosestrife** was deliberately planted in gardens because of its beautiful flowers. The plants have naturalized in the wild and are crowding out native wetland plants and wildflowers.

4. *Chicago Tribune* 09-26-2002. Calling the invasive **snakehead fish** a serious threat to native fish and wildlife, the Illinois Department of Natural Resources has joined at least 13 other states in imposing an emergency ban on their importation, possession or release.

5. **Kudzu** was introduced in 1876 at the Philadelphia Centennial Exposition. It was promoted as a forage crop and an ornamental plant. In the first half of the 20th century, kudzu was widely planted in the south to reduce soil erosion.

6. Choose your own invasive species. There are many such as hydra, fire ants, etc. Go to a web site like http://www.nps.gov/plants/alien/common.htm or http://nas.er.usgs.gov/regionallinks.htm. Using a search engine, invasive species, and an area such as Texas or the United States, you will find multiple possibilities.

Exponential Growth

Answers:

1. Water hyacinths double in 6 to 18 days. For the purposes of this investigation, consider that the number of water hyacinths will double in 12 days. Also assume that there is unlimited food and that there are no predators. Suppose 4 water hyacinths were put into the St. John's River. You will make a table to help figure out how many water hyacinths were produced from these 4 at a given time. Determine in your group the information in this problem that will be important in determining the number.

   Various factors such as the following may be listed; however, all answers should include that there are 4 water hyacinths in the beginning, and that the number doubles in 12 days.

2. After 4 doubling periods, how many days will have elapsed? **Be sure to justify each answer in this investigation.**

   Since they double every 12 days, after 4 doubling periods $4 \times 12 = 48$ days will have elapsed.

3. After 96 days, there will have been how many doubling periods?

   $96 \div 12 = 8$ doubling periods

4. In 60 days, how many times will the water hyacinth population double? In 120 days?

   In 60 days the population will double $60 \div 12$ or 5 times. In 120 days it will double 10 times because 10 times 12 is 120.

5. Complete the following table to show the number of water hyacinths from these four at the given time intervals.

Days	Doubling Periods	Process Column	Exponential Version	Total Water Hyacinths
0	0 - Starting point	4	$4 \cdot 2^0$	4
12	1	$4 \cdot 2$	$4 \cdot 2^1$	8
24	2	$4 \cdot 2 \cdot 2$	$4 \cdot 2^2$	16
36	3	$4 \cdot 2 \cdot 2 \cdot 2$	$4 \cdot 2^3$	32
48	4	$4 \cdot 2 \cdot 2 \cdot 2 \cdot 2$	$4 \cdot 2^4$	64
60	5	$4 \cdot 2 \cdot 2 \cdot 2 \cdot 2 \cdot 2$	$4 \cdot 2^5$	128
72	6	$4 \cdot 2 \cdot 2 \cdot 2 \cdot 2 \cdot 2 \cdot 2$	$4 \cdot 2^6$	256
120	10	$4 \cdot 2 \cdot 2 \cdot 2 \cdot 2 \cdot 2 \cdot 2 \cdot 2 \cdot 2 \cdot 2 \cdot 2$	$4 \cdot 2^{10}$	4096

6. Develop a pattern which you can use to fill in the "days" and "total water hyacinths" columns below. See if you can come up with a "formula" which includes the starting number of water hyacinths, the fact that the number is doubling, and the number of times that the number has doubled.

Days	Doubling Periods	Process Column	Exponential Version	Total Water Hyacinths
n	$n \div 12$			$4 \cdot 2^{n \div 12}$

7. About how long would it take for there to be more than a billion from the original 4?

   This is a point to explore and celebrate the differences in students' answers. They may set up an equation and use the graphing calculator's table function. They may use trial and error to find that one billion water hyacinths occurs between 27 and 28 growth periods, so a reasonable answer would be 28 times 12 days. This is 336 days. Student answers may be more or less than this estimate; however, notice that the directions state "about how long" and "more than a billion". Any reasonable, justified answer which satisfies these conditions should be accepted.

8. Using your formula, how many water hyacinths would there be after 3 years? (Ignore leap years.) Be sure to justify your answer in the space below.

   $3 \cdot 365 = 1095$ *days.* 1095 *days* $\div 12$ *days per doubling period* ≈ 91 *doubling periods.* $4 \cdot 2^{91} \approx 9.904 \cdot 10^{27}$ *water hyacinths. NOTE: Be sure to discuss what this answer means.*

9. Suppose growing conditions for water hyacinths were ideal and they doubled every 6 days. Write a formula so that you start with the same four water hyacinths, but they double every 6 days.

   Total water hyacinths $= 4 \cdot 2^{n \div 6}$

10. Using the new formula, how many water hyacinths will there be after 3 years? (Still ignore leap years and justify your answer.)

    $3 \cdot 365 = 1095$ *days.* 1095 *days* $\div 6$ *days per growth period* ≈ 183 *growth periods.* $4 \cdot 2^{183} \approx 4.904 \cdot 10^{55}$ *water hyacinths.*

11. Do you think that the pattern above will extend indefinitely, or are there environmental conditions which might limit it? If you are the environmental scientist in charge of reducing the population, what will you try to keep the water hyacinths from completely clogging the waterways?

    Any reasonable well thought out answer should be accepted here.

12. Introduced plants can destroy an ecosystem. Non-endemic animals can do the same. In 1859, 22 rabbits were imported to Australia from Europe. The rabbits found a land with plenty of food and no natural predators. Soon there were so many rabbits that they were destroying the island. In Australia, the rabbit population was doubling every 6 months. Determine in your group the information above that will be important in determining the number of rabbits at any given time.

    Among the important information should be that there were 22 rabbits and that they doubled every 6 months.

13. After 4 doubling periods, how many years will have elapsed? Be sure to justify each answer in this investigation.

    Since the population doubles every 6 months, there are 2 doubling periods in one year and 4 doubling periods in 2 years; therefore, the answer is two years.

14. After 18 months, there will have been how many doubling periods?

    18 months $\div 6$ *months per doubling period = 3 doubling periods.*

15. After 4 years, how many times has the rabbit population doubled? In 7.5 years?

After 4 years it will have doubled 4 times 2 or 8 times. In 7.5 years it will have doubled 7.5 times 2 which is 15 times.

16. Complete the following table.

Months	Doubling Periods	Process Column	Exponential Version	Total Rabbits
0	0 - Starting point	22	$22 \cdot 2^0$	22
6	1	$22 \cdot 2$	$22 \cdot 2^1$	44
12	2	$22 \cdot 2 \cdot 2$	$22 \cdot 2^2$	88
18	3	$22 \cdot 2 \cdot 2 \cdot 2$	$22 \cdot 2^3$	176
24	4	$22 \cdot 2 \cdot 2 \cdot 2 \cdot 2$	$22 \cdot 2^4$	352
36	6	$22 \cdot 2 \cdot 2 \cdot 2 \cdot 2 \cdot 2 \cdot 2$	$22 \cdot 2^6$	1408
48	8	$22 \cdot 2 \cdot 2 \cdot 2 \cdot 2 \cdot 2 \cdot 2 \cdot 2 \cdot 2$	$22 \cdot 2^8$	5632
60	10	$22 \cdot 2 \cdot 2 \cdot 2 \cdot 2 \cdot 2 \cdot 2 \cdot 2 \cdot 2 \cdot 2 \cdot 2$	$22 \cdot 2^{10}$	22,528

17. In the table below, write an exponential function which can be used to determine the total number of rabbits after n doubling periods in months.

Months	Growth Periods	Process Column	Exponential Version	Total Rabbits
n	$n \div 6$			$22 \cdot 2^{n \div 6}$

18. In 1887 there were so many rabbits that the government of Australia offered a reward for a way to control the population. How many growth periods were there by 1887?

1887 − 1859 = 28 years. Since there are two growth periods a year, there were 28 times 2, or 56, growth periods by 1887.

19. Using your formula, approximately how many rabbits were there at that time?

There were $22 \cdot 2^{56}$ or approximately $1.585 \cdot 10^{18}$ rabbits by 1887.

20. What population controls would you have offered?

Again, any reasonable answer should be taken here. There is much historical data, including news reels, or controls that were tried which you could use if you have time to make those connections.

21. Let a = the starting amount, b = the growth factor for a given amount of time, and n = the number of growth periods. Write an exponential function, in terms on n, which can be used for any exponential growth situation.

Students should be able to come up with $f(n) = a(b)^n$.

Write Your Notes and Ideas Here!

A Study of Population Growth

Objective:
Students will graph data, recognize the parent function, and determine a function to fit data.

Connections to Previous Learning:
Students should be able to determine a line of best fit, recognize an exponential function, and know the exponential growth formula.

Connections to TEKS:
111.32 b1B, b1C, b1D, b1E, c1A, c2C, c2B, c2D, c2E, d3C

Connections to AP:
The AP Calculus objective of analysis of functions
The AP Statistics objective of non-linear bivariate data

Time Frame:
75 minutes

Materials:
One copy of the student page for each student, graph paper, graphing calculator (optional)

Teacher Notes:
Turn students loose with this data after they have studied exponential growth and internalized that formula. For maximum effect, it should be done in groups so that the workload as well as the observations can be shared. A web site is included where additional data can be found to vary the assignment. This web site gives data more often than every ten years. Students could explore the linearity within the populations of states that are obviously exponential, such as in Florida. The richness in this assignment will come in the discussion after students have finished. Graphs of each set of data and graphs with superimposed functions are provided in the solutions. This is be an ideal time to introduce students to the power of the graphing calculator so that they can check their functions against the ones that the calculator determines.

A Study of Population Growth

The following data is taken from an xls file provided by the US Bureau of Census. It can be found at www.window.state.tx.us. From this web site, click on Texas Economy, then under Population Data, go to Population and Economic Detail. The task of your group is as follows:

- Graph the populations of these ten states from 1900 through 2000 on separate graphs. Each state's data should be graphed by two different people to ensure the accuracy of your work. With your teacher's permission, you may consider looking at the data of different states as found on the web site above.
- Perform the following tasks for each graph:
  - Classify the graph according to the parent function that best presents the data. Provide justification for you choice.
  - Based on your choice of parent function, sketch a possible function on your graph lightly in pencil. Approximate the percent of data points that will be accurately represented by the function. Explain if a parent function is a good model for the data. Discuss if a piecewise function may provide a better representation.
  - Discuss if the model will provide an accurate prediction of the population in the 2010. Provide reasons why the model will or will not be accurate.
  - Identify any time periods in the graph that are significant or unusual. Explain what about the graph makes the time period significant. Provide possible causes in that state or in the nation as a whole during that time period that might be influencing the population.
- Identify at least one data set that is best represented by a linear function. Write the equation of the function that will represent the data. Identify and write the equation for at least one exponential and one piecewise function as well.

Year	Cal.	Con.	Del.	Florida	Maine	Mich.	N. Dk.	Ore.	Ten.	Texas
1900	1490	910	185	530	695	2423	321	415	2023	3055
1910	2406	1122	203	756	745	2832	580	677	2191	3922
1920	3554	1391	219	962	771	3723	646	788	2329	4300
1930	5711	1613	239	1471	800	4834	682	956	2619	5844
1940	6950	1708	269	1915	849	5315	640	1086	2935	6425
1950	10586	2007	318	2771	914	6372	620	1521	3292	7711
1960	15717	2535	446	4952	969	7823	632	1769	3567	9580
1970	19971	3032	548	6791	994	8882	618	2092	3926	11199
1980	23268	3108	594	9746	1125	9262	653	2633	4591	14229
1990	29760	3287	666	12938	1228	9295	639	2842	4877	16987
2000	33872	3406	784	15982	1275	9938	642	3421	5689	20852

A Study of Population Growth

Answers:

While graphs are given for each state, answers for each of the tasks will vary widely according to your students' expertise, whether they used a graphing calculator or analytical methods, and what portion of the lesson you assigned. Hopefully your students will make the following observations: North Dakota does not show a correlation. Several states are almost linear, such as Maine, Oregon, and Tennessee. An interesting extension of this lesson would be to take some graphs, such as Connecticut and Maine, and write their equations as piecewise linear functions. California, Delaware, Florida, and Texas are close to exponential functions. After the graphs of the data of the individual states, you will find additional data for the graphs of California, Florida, and Tennessee.

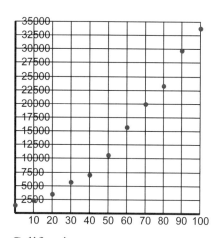

California

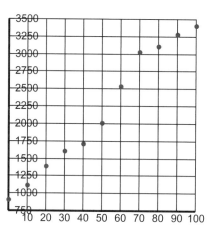

Connecticut

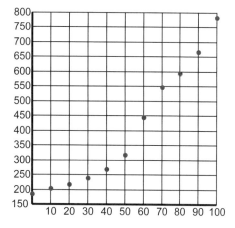

Delaware

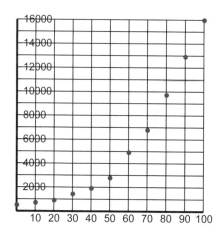

Florida

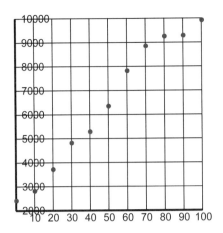

Michigan

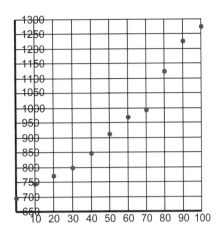

Maine

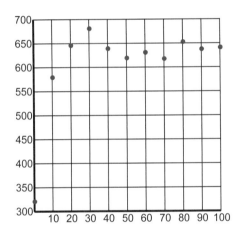

North Dakota

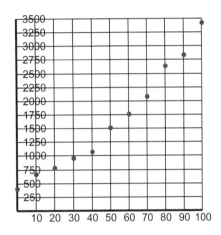

Oregon

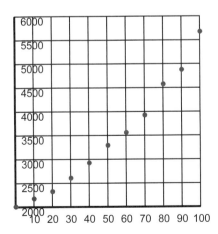

Tennessee

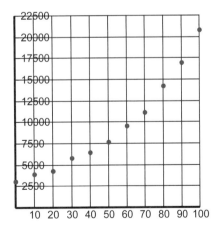

Texas

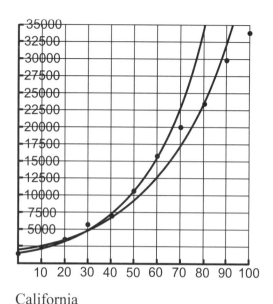

California

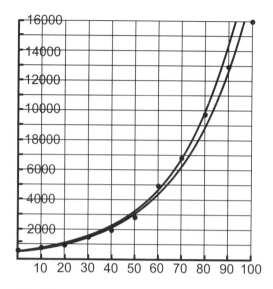

Florida

California's data, on the left, shows a student's prediction $y = 1490(1.04)^x$. This prediction works very well until 1970 when California's population started growing less rapidly than this function. The exponential regression function is $y = 1903.22(1.03199)^x$.

A student's prediction for Florida's exponential function is shown on the right as the top curve. This function is $y = 500(1.038)^x$. The exponential regression function is $y = 508.079(1.03642)^x$.

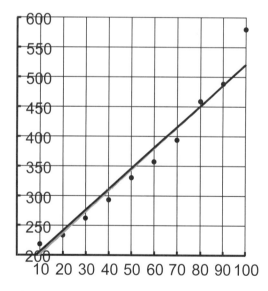

Tennessee

Tennessee's data is somewhat linear. Notice that the line of a student, $y = 35x + 1700$, and the median-median line, $y = 35.3429x + 1661.52$ are almost superimposed.

Another Way to Look at Factoring

Objective:
Students will use two methods to find the factors of simple quadratics; using a calculator to find the roots (zeros) and any previously learned technique for factoring quadratics symbolically.

Connections to Previous Learning:
Students should be able to multiply binomials, factor trinomials, find zeros of a function using a graphing calculator, convert decimal fractions to fractions using the calculator, find common denominators for algebraic expressions, and simplify algebraic expressions.

Connections to TEKS:
111.32 d2B

Connections to AP:
The AP Calculus topic of analysis of functions

Time Frame:
90 minutes

Materials:
Calculator

Teacher Notes:
The purpose of this assignment is to create a connection between a symbolic method of factoring and a graphical method. Students will be asked to factor using both procedures and to check to see that both produce the same results. Students who have been exposed to the quadratic formula can also use the results of the quadratic formula as a third method of factoring a quadratic expression.

The factoring of the quadratic expression $ax^2 + bx + c$ can always be written as $a(x - R_1)(x - R_2)$ where R_1 and R_2 are the roots (the zeros) of the quadratic and a is the leading coefficient (the coefficient of the squared term).

The leading coefficient can be particularly confusing, so be very careful to stress this part of the factoring process.

Work the first two examples with the students then assign the activity to be done either independently or in groups.

Example 1:

1. Algebraically factor: $y = 2x^2 - 7x + 6$ as $y = (2x-3)(x-1)$.

2. Graph $y1 = 2x^2 - 7x + 6$ and find the zeros (roots) 1.5 and 1. The linear factors are $x - \dfrac{3}{2}$ and $x - 1$.

3. Using the zeros found in part 2, write the function in factored form, $y1 = a(x - r_1)(x - r_2)$, where a is the coefficient of the x^2-term and r_1 and r_2 are the zeros of the function. (Using the zeros in fraction form rather than decimal form will make the comparison of the answers easier to do.)
$$y = 2\left(x - \frac{3}{2}\right)(x-1)$$

4. Manipulate the function in part 3 to verify that the factored expression in part 3 is equivalent to the factored expression in part 1.
$$y = 2\left(x - \frac{3}{2}\right)(x-1)$$
$$y = 2\left(\frac{2x-3}{2}\right)(x-1)$$
$$y = (2x-3)(x-1)$$

Example 2

1. Algebraically factor: $y = 18x^2 + 3x - 6$ as $y = 3(3x+2)(2x-1)$.

2. Graph $y1 = 18x^2 + 3x - 6$ and find the zeros (roots) in fraction form. $-\dfrac{2}{3}$ and $\dfrac{1}{2}$. The linear factors are $x + \dfrac{2}{3}$ and $x - \dfrac{1}{2}$.

3. Using the zeros found in part 2, write the function in factored form, $y1 = a(x - r_1)(x - r_2)$, where a is the coefficient of the x^2-term and r_1 and r_2 are the zeros of the function.
$$y = 18\left(x + \frac{2}{3}\right)\left(x - \frac{1}{2}\right)$$

4. Manipulate the expression in part 3 to verify that the factored expression in part 3 is equivalent to the factored expression in part 1.
$$y = 18\left(x + \frac{2}{3}\right)\left(x - \frac{1}{2}\right)$$
$$y = 18\left(\frac{3x+2}{3}\right)\left(\frac{2x-1}{2}\right)$$
$$y = 3(3x+2)(2x-1)$$

Another Way to Look at Factoring

Discussion:

1. Explain how to locate the roots given the graph of a quadratic function.
2. Explain how we can use the roots to then find the factors.
3. Describe a situation where the factors of a quadratic equation are useful.
4. Describe a situation where the roots of a quadratic equation are useful.

Activity: For each of the following quadratic functions

(a) Use a calculator to create the graph of the function. Sketch the graph on the paper; indicate the scale on the *x*-axis.

(b) Use a calculator to find the roots (zeros) of the function.

(c) List the linear factors for the function.

(d) Factor the function using the form $y = a(x - r_1)(x - r_2)$ then factor the function symbolically.

(e) Confirm that both procedures produce equivalent results.

1. $y = x^2 - 6x - 7$
2. $y = x^2 - 9x + 20$
3. $y = 2x^2 - 9x + 9$
4. $y = 3x^2 - 19x - 14$
5. $y = 3x^2 - 3x - 36$
6. $y = 6x^2 - 17x - 14$
7. $y = 4x^2 + 23x + 15$
8. $y = 10x^2 - 9x - 9$
9. $y = -x^2 + 3x - 2$
10. $y = 24x^2 - 20x + 4$
11. $y = 28x^2 + 51x - 27$
12. $y = 24x^2 + 26x - 28$

Another Way to Look at Factoring

Answers:

1.

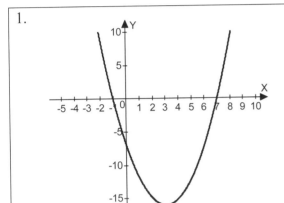

Zeros: -1 and 7

Linear factors: $x + 1$ and $x - 7$

$y = (x+1)(x-7)$

2.

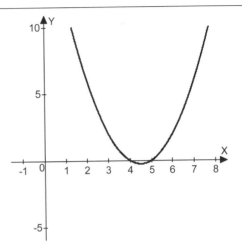

Zeros: 4 and 5

Linear factors: $x - 4$ and $x - 5$

$y = (x-4)(x-5)$

3.

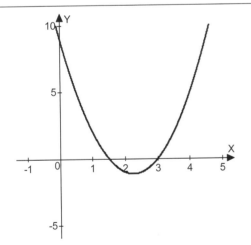

Zeros: $\dfrac{3}{2}$ and 3

Linear factors: $x - \dfrac{3}{2}$ and $x - 3$

$y = 2(x - \dfrac{3}{2})(x-3)$

$y = (2x-3)(x-3)$

4.

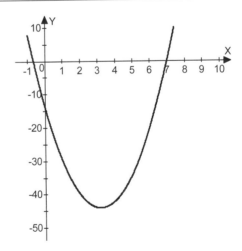

Zeros: $-\dfrac{2}{3}$ and 7

Linear factors: $x + \dfrac{2}{3}$ and $x - 7$

$y = 3(x + \dfrac{2}{3})(x-7)$

$y = (3x+2)(x-7)$

5.

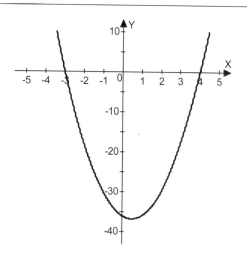

Zeros: -3 and 4

Linear factors: $x + 3$ and $x - 4$

$y = 3(x+3)(x-4)$

6.

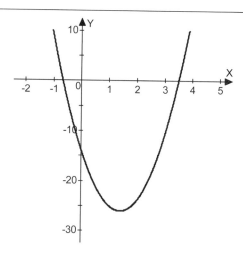

Zeros: $-\dfrac{2}{3}$ and $\dfrac{7}{2}$

Linear factors: $x + \dfrac{2}{3}$ and $x - \dfrac{7}{2}$

$y = 6\left(x + \dfrac{2}{3}\right)\left(x - \dfrac{7}{2}\right)$

$y = (3x+2)(2x-7)$

7.

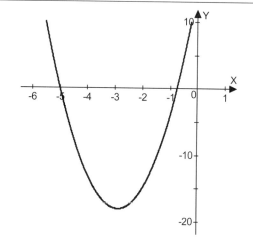

Zeros: -5 and $-\dfrac{3}{4}$

Linear factors: $x + 5$ and $x + \dfrac{3}{4}$

$y = 4(x+5)\left(x + \dfrac{3}{4}\right)$

$y = (x+5)(4x+3)$

8.

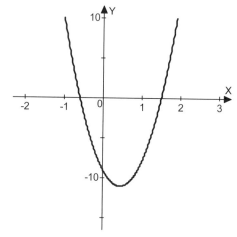

Zeros: $\dfrac{3}{2}$ and $-\dfrac{3}{5}$

Linear factors: $x - \dfrac{3}{2}$ and $x + \dfrac{3}{5}$

$y = 10\left(x - \dfrac{3}{2}\right)\left(x + \dfrac{3}{5}\right)$

$y = (2x-3)(5x+3)$

9.

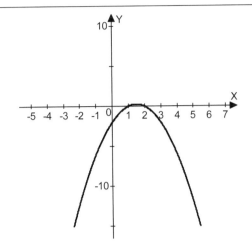

Zeros: 1 and 2

Linear factors: $x - 1$ and $x - 2$

$y = -1(x-1)(x-2)$

$y = (-x+1)(x-2)$

10.

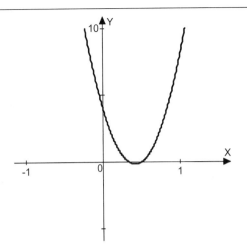

Zeros: $\dfrac{1}{3}$ and $\dfrac{1}{2}$

Linear factors: $x - \dfrac{1}{3}$ and $x - \dfrac{1}{2}$

$y = 24\left(x - \dfrac{1}{3}\right)\left(x - \dfrac{1}{2}\right)$

$y = 4(3x-1)(2x-1)$

11.

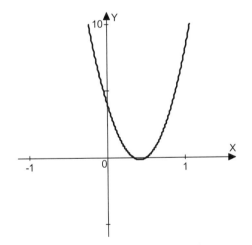

Zeros: $-\dfrac{9}{4}$ and $\dfrac{3}{7}$

Linear factors: $x + \dfrac{9}{4}$ and $x - \dfrac{3}{7}$

$y = 28\left(x + \dfrac{9}{4}\right)\left(x - \dfrac{3}{7}\right)$

$y = (4x+9)(7x-3)$

12.

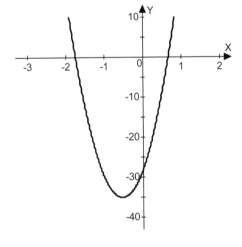

Zeros: $-\dfrac{7}{4}$ and $\dfrac{2}{3}$

Linear factors: $x + \dfrac{7}{4}$ and $x - \dfrac{2}{3}$

$y = 24\left(x + \dfrac{7}{4}\right)\left(x - \dfrac{2}{3}\right)$

$y = 2(4x+7)(3x-2)$

The Jury

Objective:
Students will use manipulatives to simulate binomial events.

Connections to Previous Learning:
Students should have experience with tables of frequencies, converting counts to relative frequencies (percents), calculating the probability of an event occurring, drawing circle graphs.

Connections to TEKS:
6.9, 6.10, 6.13, 7.4, 7.10, 7.11A, 8.11B, 8.11C, 8.12C, 8.16B

Connections to AP:
The AP Statistics topics of Probability and Simulations and Data Gathering

One of the 4 major themes in the AP statistics course is probability. Within this theme, this activity covers the topics of the "law of large numbers", simulation of probability distributions, and expected value.

Time Frame:
50 minutes

Materials:
Handouts, coins (pennies work well), dice (one per student), several decks of playing cards, calculator, and a paper clip for each student.

Teacher Notes:
Simulation is a procedure that uses experiments – which closely resemble real life problems – to answer questions about a real problem. This lesson provides an introduction to simulation techniques. Various physical manipulatives will be used to simulate random outcomes.

For a complete discussion of simulation refer to *The Art and Techniques of Simulation*, Quantitative Literacy Series, Gnanadeskan, Scheaffer, and Swift, Dale Seymour Publications.

For activities that involve simulations, students should work in pairs. This will enable students to discuss strategies and to collect data with a partner. In the data collection process, one student should simulate outcomes while the other student records the results. Half way through each simulation, the students should switch rolls.

The Jury

The Jury Question

In a certain city, 50% of the adult population are women and 50% are men. A jury was selected that contained nine men and three women. The defendant in a trial, a woman, claims bias in the jury selection. She thinks that the jury does not reflect the number of men and women in the city. The prosecutor claims that the jury was selected without regard to gender. Is the defendant's claim believable? In other words, if the population is 50% women, is selecting 3 or fewer women unlikely to happen by chance?

We are going to use a simulation to estimate the probability of selecting 3 or fewer women simply by chance and use the results to analyze the defendant's claim.

For this problem we are going to use a spinner as a randomization device. You can make a spinner by taking a paper clip and unbending the outside end to make it straight. Use you pencil to hold the spinner at the center of the diagram and flick it with your finger. You will use the value (gender) where the spinner lands as your random number. Use the spinner model on the next page.

a) Describe how you will conduct the simulation to answer the question above. Do not forget the 3 rules for a simulation.

b) Run 20 runs (trials) of your simulation. Create a table of your outcomes and frequencies.

c)   Estimate the probability of selecting three or fewer women for this jury.

d)   If you were the judge in this case, what would say to this defendant about bias in the jury selection? This answer should be several sentences long.

JURY PROBLEM SPINNER

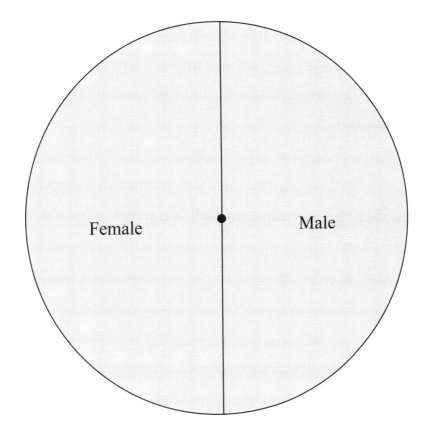

Practice Problems:

1. You have to take a ten-question quiz next period and you completely forgot to study for it. Not only that, but you have no idea about how to answer any of the questions. The teacher said the quiz was going to be all True/False. You decide to take your chances and are going to randomly guess on all the answers. What are your chances of getting at least six questions correct just by guessing?

   a) Use some randomization method to run a simulation to determine the probability that you get at least six questions correct — just by guessing. Describe how you would conduct 1 trial. (Do not forget your 3 rules.)

   b) Run 20 trials of your simulation and record your results in a table.

   c) What is the approximate probability that you will get at least six questions correct simply by guessing?

   d) Based on your simulation, explain to a classmate why guessing would not be a good method to use to pass his next quiz.

2. Today, you can not believe it, but as you walk into class, your teacher announces a Pop Quiz. The teacher says there are going to be ten questions with each question having five choices. Since you know nothing about the subject being tested, you again decide to randomly guess on all 10 questions.

a) Sketch a graph of the distribution of the number of correct answers for this 10 question quiz

b) Explain why your graph looks the way it does.

c) Would the distribution of correct answers for this 10-question quiz look different than the distribution for the 10 question True/False quiz? Explain why or why not.

d) Construct a spinner to use as your randomization device to run your simulation. You will have to use a protractor to correctly measure the angles in your spinner so one section of your spinner has a 1/5 chance of being selected and the other section has a 4/5 chance of being selected. Describe how you will calculate the degrees for the sections that you will use in your spinner.

e) Run a simulation to determine the probability that you get at least six questions correct, just by guessing. Describe how you would conduct 1 trial. (Do not forget your 3 rules.)

f) Run 20 trials of your simulation and record your results in a table.

g) What is the approximate probability that you will get at least six questions correct simply by guessing?

h) On average, how many questions should you expect to get right based purely on guessing for this quiz?

i) Based on your simulation, explain to a classmate why guessing would not be a good method to use to pass his next quiz.

SPINNER

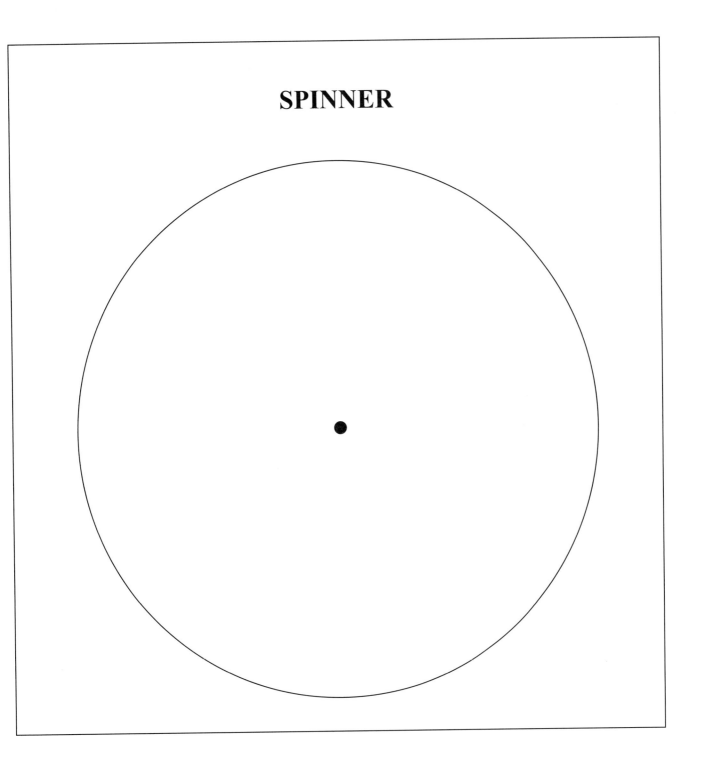

The Jury

Answers:
The Jury Question

a)   One trial in this simulation is 12 spins of the paperclip. This represents the 12 jurors in the jury selection process. I am assuming that the gender of people in the jury pool represent the percentage of women and men in the city and that there are not more women being excused from serving on a jury than men.

c)   The theoretical value of P(3 or fewer women out of 12) = P(0) + P(1) + P(2) + P(3) = .0723

d)   It seems to me that there is an indication that there might be bias. The case is not overwhelming, but, if the probability of selecting a woman juror is really 50%, then in only 7.23% of the juries would I expect to have 3 or fewer women. This is not very often and I would look very carefully at the jury selection process in the future.

Practice Problems.

1. a)   One needs to assume that the probability of getting each question correct is independent of getting another question correct and the probability of guessing and getting an answer correct is .5. One trial is one 10 question quiz, or rolling a die 10 times. The probability of getting a question correct, or being successful is rolling an even number and the probability of not getting a question correct is rolling an odd number. I would run many trials to estimate answers.

   c)   The theoretical answer to this question is P(6) + ... + P(10).

      The answer is .3770.

   d)   I do not think that this is a good way of trying to pass a quiz. There is less than a 40% chance of passing using the random method. It might just be easier to study and not worry about the small chance of guessing and passing the quiz.

2. c)   The distribution of successes for a quiz with 5 answer choices per question is much different than for a quiz with 2 answer choices per question. In the first, the distribution is skewed to the larger numbers and the graph peaks at the number 2. There is a long tail in the distribution. In the quiz with 2 answers per question, the distribution is symmetrical and peaks at the number 5. The graph looks "bell" shaped.

d)   To get the spinner to represent just a 20% probability of success, I would have to have a central angle of 360 degrees/5 or 72 degrees. Once I draw one angle of 72 degrees, the other portion of 360 – 72 degrees (288 degrees) will represent guessing an answer incorrectly.

g)   The theoretical answer to this question is P(6) + ... + P(10). This is 0.0064.

h)   The Expected Value or mean number of correct answers is 10 (.2) or 2 answers.

i)   The method of random guessing to pass this test would be a horrible idea. There is almost no possibility of guessing 6 or more answers correctly (.0064). For sure, a better idea to pass this test would be to study.

Assessment Foreword

The Pre-AP Mathematics experience introduces students to the skills, concepts and test-taking strategies that build students' confidence in their ability to solve problems they have never seen before, that are an extension of what has been taught, as they will encounter on the AP Calculus and AP Statistics exams. Questions that "push the envelope" and cover a broad range of difficulty levels can be introduced early in the Pre-AP sequence, and items such as these should be incorporated into each test and used daily in the Pre-AP classroom. These questions should challenge the students, not overwhelm them, and over time will prepare them for any testing situation they encounter.

In order to make students comfortable with higher-order thinking, challenging questions must be asked in a non-threatening environment. Initially students must be allowed the freedom to make mistakes, to learn from those mistakes without being penalized, and to develop understanding over a period of time. Teachers should encourage students to view assessment as a monitor of their achievement, as a guide to how they are progressing toward mastering the concepts. To promote this view of assessment, teachers could protect students' grades while they are in this learning process and not use tests as a device to weed students out of the Pre-AP sequence.

Shifting their view of assessment may require teachers to make significant changes in how they design, implement and use assessment in their mathematics classroom. By including a broader array of question types, checking for understanding rather than rote memorization, and scoring and modeling AP-type questions, teachers will better prepare students for AP classes and examinations. A study of the AP exam format and questioning techniques will help to generate these changes and lead to cohesiveness in a student's mathematical development.

Creating test questions that promote higher-level thinking is often difficult, but can be made easier by teaming horizontally and vertically with fellow teachers. Throughout this section, you will find vertical team activities that encourage you to collaborate with your colleagues. This collaboration will enhance the Pre-AP experience for teachers, as well as benefit the students.

Pre-AP assessment then will serve many different purposes, only one of which is assignment of grades. Assessment must play a role in the instructional process, solidifying and deepening the student's understanding of the skills and concepts being tested. Finally, teachers have an obligation to use the results of an assessment to drive future instructional decisions.

The assessment piece of this guide was designed to familiarize teachers with the format and scoring of the AP exams and to show how this information can impact Pre-AP assessment. Our ultimate goal is to promote higher-order thinking skills that will facilitate connecting Pre-AP Mathematics to Advanced Placement Calculus and Statistics.

I hope this section will provide you with much food for thought and a better understanding of the potential benefit of well-designed assessments in the Pre-AP classroom.

Wanda Savage

Overview of the AP Calculus and AP Statistics Exams

AP Calculus Exam	AP Statistics Exam
Free Response and Multiple Choice Sections each contributing 50% of the exam grade	Free Response and Multiple Choice Sections each contributing 50% of the exam grade
M C A: 28 items 55 min. no calculator	M C 40 questions 90 min
M C B: 17 items 50 min. calculator	F R 5 questions, 1 investigative task 90 min
F R A: 3 questions 45 min. calculator	
F R B: 3 questions 45 min. no calculator	Each student will be expected to bring a graphing calculator with statistical capabilities to both sections of the exam.
All Free Response questions are given equal weight of 9 points each. Multiple Choice is scored as the number right minus $\frac{1}{4}$ of the number wrong. Omitted answers are "ignored."	Multiple Choice is scored as the number right minus $\frac{1}{4}$ of the number wrong. Omitted answers are "ignored."

AP Exam Readers are given directives so that consistency in grading is achieved. The focus is on what the students know rather than penalizing for what they do not know. The reader "reads with the student" (takes a student's wrong answer and follows the student through the rest of the problem to ascertain if the student has mastered the concept). "Double jeopardy" is avoided by not deducting for the same mistake twice. Students must show steps to support their answers, or to explain, verify or justify why their answer is valid.

In the calculator portion of the Calculus Free Response Section, the students must show the mathematical set ups, not calculator keystrokes, then rely on the calculator's capabilities. On the Statistics Exam, students must be able to interpret and analyze computer-generated output that has been provided.

On the Calculus exam, answers must be shown correct to three decimal places, which means that, in a multi-step problem, early answers must be stored to retain all necessary digits. On the Statistics exam, students are expected to express probability to four decimal places. On both exams, it is important to label all charts, graphs or data clearly and to define all variables. In addition, students should make a habit of giving correct units for all answers.

The Free-Response Section of the AP Statistics Examination uses a holistic approach to grading on a zero to four scale: 4 – complete response, 3 – substantial response, 2 – developing response, 1 – minimal response.

To obtain full credit for a free-response question on both the Calculus and Statistics exams, students must analyze the situation completely and communicate their analyses and conclusions clearly. Answers should show enough work so that the reasoning process can be tracked throughout the analysis. This is particularly important for assessing partial credit. Good communication that demonstrates a deep understanding of the concept can often overcome weak arithmetic that might lead to an incorrect final answer.

Examples of AP Exam Questions – AP Calculus

Calculator active.

Starts specific - moves to general in part d.

Finding range of *f* is the synthesis of knowledge of limits in part a and the absolute minimum in part b.

AB–2 / BC–2

2. Let f be the function given by $f(x) = 2xe^{2x}$.

   (a) Find $\lim\limits_{x \to -\infty} f(x)$ and $\lim\limits_{x \to \infty} f(x)$.

   (b) Find the absolute minimum value of f. Justify that your answer is an absolute minimum.

   (c) What is the range of f?

   (d) Consider the family of functions defined by $y = bxe^{bx}$, where b is a nonzero constant. Show that the absolute minimum value of bxe^{bx} is the same for all nonzero values of b.

Complete analysis.

1998

Less rigorous than justify.

Family of functions and use of parameter.

(a) $\lim\limits_{x \to -\infty} 2xe^{2x} = 0$

$\lim\limits_{x \to \infty} 2xe^{2x} = \infty$ or DNE

$2 \begin{cases} 1: \ 0 \text{ as } x \to -\infty \\ 1: \ \infty \text{ or DNE as } x \to \infty \end{cases}$

Exact answer or correct to 3 decimal place.

(b) $f'(x) = 2e^{2x} + 2x \cdot 2 \cdot e^{2x} = 2e^{2x}(1+2x) = 0$

if $x = -1/2$ Location of minimum.

$f(-1/2) = -1/e$ or -0.368 or -0.367

$-1/e$ is an absolute minimum value because:

(i) $f'(x) < 0$ for all $x < -1/2$ and
$f'(x) > 0$ for all $x > -1/2$

–or–

(ii) $f'(x) \quad - \qquad +$
$\underline{\hspace{3cm}}$
$\qquad -1/2$

and $x = -1/2$ is the only critical number

$3 \begin{cases} 1: \ \text{solves } f'(x) = 0 \\ 1: \ \text{evaluates } f \text{ at student's critical point} \\ \quad 0/1 \text{ if not local minimum from} \\ \quad \text{student's derivative} \\ 1: \ \text{justifies absolute minimum value} \\ \quad 0/1 \text{ for a local argument} \\ \quad 0/1 \text{ without explicit symbolic} \\ \quad \text{derivative} \end{cases}$

Note: 0/3 if no absolute minimum based on student's derivative

Notice that the grader would deduct one point for incorrect solution, then read with the student throughout the question.

Open ended versus closed.

(c) Range of $f = [-1/e, \infty)$
or $[-0.367, \infty)$
or $[-0.368, \infty)$

Can be written in correct set notation or interval notation.

1: answer

Note: must include the left–hand endpoint; exclude the right–hand "endpoint"

(d) $y' = be^{bx} + b^2xe^{bx} = be^{bx}(1+bx) = 0$

if $x = -1/b$

At $x = -1/b$, $y = -1/e$

y has an absolute minimum value of $-1/e$ for all nonzero b

Recognize be^{bx} cannot equal zero.

$3 \begin{cases} 1: \ \text{sets } y' = be^{bx}(1+bx) = 0 \\ 1: \ \text{solves student's } y' = 0 \\ 1: \ \text{evaluates } y \text{ at a critical number} \\ \quad \text{and gets a value independent of } b \end{cases}$

Note: 0/3 if only considering specific values of b

Must show true for all values - rather than specific.

342

Examples of AP Exam Questions – AP Statistics

2002

5. At a school field day, 50 students and 50 faculty members each completed an obstacle course. Descriptive statistics for the completion times (in minutes) for the two groups are shown below.

	Students	Faculty Members
Mean	9.90	12.09
Median	9.25	11.00
Minimum	3.75	4.50
Maximum	16.50	25.00
Lower quartile	6.75	8.75
Upper quartile	13.75	15.75

a) Use the same scale to draw boxplots for the completion times for students and for faculty members.

b) Write a few sentences comparing the variability of the two distributions.

c) You have been asked to report on this event for the school newspaper. Write a few sentences describing student and faculty performances in this competition for the paper.

Scoring Guidelines for Question 5:

Solution

Part a)

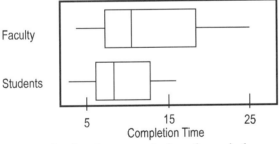

Part b) The range for faculty completion times is larger than for the students, but the IQR is the same for both groups. The spread is similar in the middle 50 percent of the data, but the smallest 25 percent and the largest 25 percent are more spread out for the faculty members than for the students.

Part c) Students should comment on at least two of center (mean, median, or general location), variation, or shape. The statements should be correct and clear and suitable for the school newspaper.

Example: Although some faculty members negotiated the obstacle course quickly, in general, students tended to have shorter completion times (This describes general location.).

The student completion times, ranging from 3.75 minutes to 16.5 minutes, were more consistent than the faculty times, which ranges from 4.5 minutes to 25 minutes (This describes variation). Many students and faculty finished relatively quickly, but the slower half of each group tended to spread out (This describes shape).

<u>**Scoring**</u>

Part a) is considered

Essentially correct if the boxplots are drawn correctly with labels and scale given.

Partially correct if boxplots have no more than one error such as these: missing labels, missing scales, not drawn to scale, or drawn showing outliers.

NOTES: • It is considered a minus if "time" label is omitted.
   • Any graphic that is not clearly a boxplot is incorrect.

Part b) is considered

Essentially correct if the response notes both that spread in the center is similar for the two groups and that spread in the tails is greater for faculty than for students.

Partially correct if response only comments that variability is greater for faculty than for the students.

NOTE: It is considered a minus if the 25 is called an outlier.

Part c) is considered

Essentially correct if there is a clear and coherent statement that comments on at least two of center (mean, median, or general location), variation, or shape. Both faculty and students must be mentioned in the response.

Partially correct if only comments on one aspect of the distribution or if communication is weak.

4   **Complete Response:** Essentially correct on all three parts.

3   **Substantial Response:** Essentially correct on two parts and partially correct on the other part.

2   **Developing Response:** Essentially correct on two parts and incorrect on the other
   or
   Essentially correct on one part and partially correct on the other two parts.
   or
   Partially correct on all three parts.
   or
   Essentially correct on one part, partially correct on one part, and incorrect on one part.

1   **Minimal Response:** Essentially correct on one part and incorrect on the other two parts.
   or
   Partially correct on one or two parts and incorrect on the other.

Characteristics of Pre-AP Test Items

Assessment that requires higher-level thinking skills should be a regular part of the teacher's instructional method and the student's learning experience. Checking for understanding a concept, rather than rote memorization, can be ascertained by using letters or symbols instead of numbers or by using **generic functions**, problems containing general, rather than specific, functions.

Example of using a generic function:

Given the graphs of $f(x)$ and $g(x)$, express $g(x)$ in terms of $f(x)$.

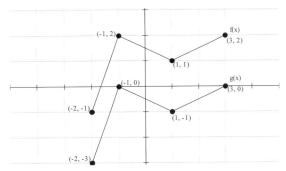

Example: In the chapter on exponentials in Algebra II, having reviewed $3^2 \cdot 3^4 = 3^6$, the following could be a multiple choice question.

Given $f(x) = 3^x$, find $f(a + 2)$

a) $6 \cdot 3^a$ b) 27^a c) 18^a d) $9 \cdot 3^a$ e) $2 + 3^a$

Assessment should include questions that review previously taught material.

Example: Having worked with factoring and solving equations in Algebra I, give the following test question combining those topics, reviewing finding area, and requiring multiple steps. Have the students show all work, but allow the use of the calculator.

Find the dimensions of the rectangle shown given "a" is 5 more than x and the area is 200 in^2.

$$x - 2 \boxed{}$$
$$x + a$$

$a = x + 5$
$[x + (x + 5)](x - 2) = 200$
$2x^2 + x - 10 - 200 = 0$
$(2x + 21)(x - 10) = 0$
x = 10 inches, so the dimensions are 25 in. by 8 in.

Assessment should include questions that introduce new material.

Example: Having taught finding the slope of a line in Algebra I, but before introducing the topic of slopes of perpendicular lines, a test on slope could include the following item:

The slopes of perpendicular lines have a product of -1. Find the slope of the line perpendicular to $3x - 5y = 15$.

Assessment should include questions which are open ended.

Example: Give an example of an event such that the probability of the event occurring is ½.

Questions that can be solved using multiple methods should be included in an assessment piece.

Example: Solve $4x^2 - 8x - 5 = 0$ showing all algebraic steps using the following methods.

    a)   Factoring

    b)   Completing the square

    c)   Using the Quadratic Formula

    d)   Graphing and finding the roots [show graph and label intercepts]

Questions should be included that encourage students to use multiple representations: analytical, verbal, graphical, and numerical.

Example: Verify that (3, -2) is the solution to the following system using at least three different methods.

$$y = x - 5$$
$$x + y = 1$$

Note: Students might create a table of values, substitute the values into both equations, solve algebraically by substitution or elimination, or graph the equations and find the point of intersection.

Questions that require students to verify, interpret and justify conclusions should be included in the assessment process.

Example: Practice in interpreting function notation should be introduced in Algebra 1.

The cost C of a road trip by car, in dollars, is a function of the distance traveled in miles. Interpret the meaning of C(300) = 25.

Note: The student's answer should be written as a complete sentence:

The cost of a 300-mile road trip by car is $25.

Assessment should include questions that require students to be familiar with and utilize the capabilities of their graphing calculator.

Example: Find all points of intersection of $f(x) = x^2$ and $g(x) = 2^x$.

Note: Two of the intersection points, (2, 4) and (4, 16), could be found by inspection. The third point should be found by using the intersect feature of the graphing calculator. Students should also be familiar with the method of setting the equations equal and finding the zeros of the new function with the root finder capability of the calculator.

Multiple Choice Format

Assessment should include multiple choice questions that encompass more than a single topic or skill.

Example: If $f(x) = \dfrac{4}{x-1}$ and $g(x) = 2x$ then the solution of $f(g(x)) = g(f(x))$ is

a) $\dfrac{1}{3}$ b) 2   c) 3   d) $-1, 2$ e) $\dfrac{1}{3}, 2$

Note: The student must perform the composition of functions, then solve the rational equations which result.

Multiple choice questions included in assessment should contain symbols, letters, or parameters.

Example: What are the values of k for which the graph of $y = x^3 - 3x^2 + k$ will have three distinct x-intercepts?

a) All $k > 0$ b) All $k < 4$ c) $k = 0, 4$ d) $0 < k < 4$ e) All k

Note: This would be a calculator-active question, but would still require careful analysis.

Assessment should help students recognize different forms of the same answer.

Example: Which of the following would be equivalent to $\dfrac{3}{2} \ln x$?

I) $\ln x^{\frac{3}{2}}$ II) $\dfrac{6 \ln x}{4}$ III) $\ln \dfrac{3x}{2}$ IV) $\ln\left(x\sqrt{x}\right)$ V) $\ln x + \ln \sqrt{x}$

a) I, II, V   b) II, IV   c) I, II, III   d) I, II, IV, V   e) II, III

Multiple choice questions, written so that all the answers must be investigated as possible choices, can test many concepts.

Example: Let f be a continuous function on the interval $(1, 10)$.
If $f(2) = -5, f(5) = 5$, and $f(9) = -5$, which of the following **must** be true?

I) f has at least two zeros

II)   the minimum value of f is -5

III) $f(x) = 0$ for some x, $5 < x < 9$

IV) $f(x) = 2$ for some x, $1 < x < 5$

a) None   b) I, II, III, IV   c) I, III, IV   d) I, III   e) II, IV

Scoring Student Work on Pre-AP Assessments

The scoring process used in Pre-AP assessments is an important component of a successful Pre-AP program. To be consistent with the grading standards of the AP exams the following are important considerations:

- Scoring should value student's work and reward what they know rather than penalize what they don't know.
- Students should not be penalized for the same mistake that appears in multiple problems on the same test.
- After points have been deducted for an error, read with the student to grade the following work, especially if of equal difficulty level.
- Consider the focus of the test and grade accordingly. Since the AP exams are focused on testing Calculus or Statistics concepts, arithmetic or even simple algebraic mistakes would not be penalized heavily.

Example: In Pre-Calculus, the following problem could be given after solving trigonometric equations. Find the zeros of $f(x) = 2e^{2\sin x} - 3e^{\sin x} + 1$ in $[0, 2\pi)$ by factoring and showing all algebraic steps. Give exact answers when possible and others correct to 3 decimal places. <u>Confirm</u> your findings by graphing.

$2e^{2\sin x} - 3e^{\sin x} + 1 = 0$

$(2e^{\sin x} - 1)(e^{\sin x} - 1) = 0$ [2 pts.]

$e^{\sin x} = 1$ or $e^{\sin x} = \frac{1}{2}$ [1 pt.]

$\ln e^{\sin x} = \ln 1$ or $\ln e^{\sin x} = \ln \frac{1}{2}$ [1 pt.]

$\sin x = 0$ or $\sin x = \ln (1/2) = -\ln 2$ [1 pt.]

For $[0, 2\pi)$, $x = 0, \pi, 3.907, 5.517$ [2 pts.]

Graph shown with 4 zeros in $[0, 2\pi)$ [1 pt.]

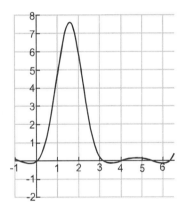

Note: The problem reviews factoring and solving exponential equations by using logarithms. It involves solving trigonometric equations both with and without the calculator, as well as solving by graphing.

In the example given, there are many concepts tested for which credit could be earned even if the final answers to the question are incorrect as demonstrated below.

If in solving $2e^{2\sin x} - 3e^{\sin x} + 1 = 0$ the student factored incorrectly, but the factors still contained $e^{\sin x}$, the work necessary to solve the equation is at the **same difficulty** level as if factored correctly. The teacher can read with the student and assign points as follows:

$(e^{\sin x} - 1)(2e^{\sin x} + 1) = 0$ **[1 out of the 2 poss. pts.]**

$e^{\sin x} = 1$ or $e^{\sin x} = -\frac{1}{2}$ [1 pt.]

$\ln e^{\sin x} = \ln 1$ or $\ln e^{\sin x} = \ln(-\frac{1}{2})$ [1 pt.]

$\sin x = 0$ or $\sin x = \ln(-\frac{1}{2})$,   [1 pt.]

$\ln(-\frac{1}{2})$ is not defined so $x = 0$ or π [2 pts.]

The student would lose the graph point, as the graph would show four solutions and the student only found two. This student would have justifiably earned 6 out of the 8 possible points, which is a reasonable score since the student has demonstrated mastery of the concept being tested. While being able to factor is important, it is not the focus of this test. Problems should be scored in such a way as to value what the student has learned.

Proficiency in tackling questions given in multiple choice format is essential if a student is to perform well on the AP Calculus and Statistics Exams. The multiple choice questions will range in difficulty level from the straightforward ones that can be answered without many steps to those requiring almost as much work as a free response question. No partial credit is awarded in the multiple choice section of the AP exams.

However, **grading the multiple choice questions and awarding partial credit** in Pre-AP classes confirms their importance and keeps the student from treating them as "multiple guess" questions. The students should approach them in the same manner as free response questions, the only difference being that the correct answer is given for them to find.

Example:

Solve $2e^{2x} - 7e^x + 3 = 0$. *Show steps to support your answer.*

a) $\ln 3, \ln 2$ b) $\ln 3, -\ln 2$ c) $-\ln 3, \ln 2$ d) $\ln \frac{1}{2}, -\ln 3$

$(2e^x - 1)(e^x - 3) = 0$ [1 pt.]

$e^x = \frac{1}{2}$ or $e^x = 3$ [1 pt.]

$x = \ln \frac{1}{2}$ or $\ln 3$ [1 pt.]

$x = -\ln 2, \ln 3$ [1 pt.]

We hope that the student will not carelessly choose **d** instead of the correct answer **b**, but will realize the need to simplify their answer to make it match those given. If **b** is not chosen, but the above work is shown, they have demonstrated mastery of the concept being tested and deserve the three points they will earn.

This should be a non-calculator question.

Sample Test: Algebra 1
Overview

Methods of assessing concepts in Pre-AP have been discussed in detail. The following test has been written to incorporate many of these methods. Depending on the length of class time available, the test might have to be given in two class sessions.

While a graphing calculator can be used on the test, all steps must be shown to gain credit for the problem.

Note: All tests need not be scored based on 100 points. A question that scores nicely at 5 points should not be given a value of 9 points because of the overall 100 test points requirement. Percentages (70 out of a possible 90) work just as well and do not over value some concepts being assessed. Additionally a test which is "pushing the envelope" can be more than 100 points giving the students the opportunity to try harder problems without jeopardy.

Concepts being tested on this sample test:
- Solving Systems of Linear Equations by

    Graphing
    Elimination
    Substitution
- Writing Systems of Linear Equations
- Solving Systems of Linear Equations containing Parameters

Methods of Assessment Covered:
- Testing on all levels of difficulty;
- Testing using problems that can be solved using multiple methods;
- Testing in free response and multiple choice modes;
- Testing problems that can have multiple answers;
- Multiple representations are explored;
- Testing in a format that is different from previously worked problems;
- Testing concepts not covered in classroom discussion, but which follow as an extension of taught material;
- Reading with the student and avoiding "double jeopardy";
- Testing previously taught material;
- Asking for verification of answers.

Point count and notes on scoring are included, as well as student samples.

Sample Test: Algebra 1
Solutions, Grading Standards, and Discussion

Calculator Active: Show All Work

Points   Problem

1. The table below shows coordinates of the linear
functions $f(x)$ and $g(x)$. Write the system of
equations $\begin{cases} f(x) = \\ g(x) = \end{cases}$ and give its solution.

> This question should be a review of
> writing equations of lines from data
> and give the student confidence at
> the beginning of the test.

x	-5	-4	-3	-2	-1	0	1	2	3	4	5
$f(x)$	11	9	7	5	3	1	-1	-3	-5	-7	-9
$g(x)$	-1	0	1	2	3	4	5	6	7	8	9

2 pts.   *$f(x) = -2x + 1$*

2 pts.   *$g(x) = x + 4$*

1 pt.   *solution is (–1 3)*

2. Using the following system of equations $\begin{cases} y = 2x - 4 \\ 3y + 2x = 12 \end{cases}$

3 pts.   a)   Explain the steps necessary to solve the system by graphing.

> *Graph the lines. Find the point where the lines intersect. Substitute the
> coordinates of the point into both equations to verify it is the solution to the
> system.*

3 pts.   b)   Explain the steps necessary to solve the system
using substitution.

> Simpler language stating the steps
> is acceptable.

> *Substitute 2x – 4 for y, so that the equation is in terms of a single variable, x.
> Solve the resulting equation for x. Substitute that value of x into y = 2x – 4 and
> solve for y. Substitute those x and y values into both equations to verify the
> solution.*

3 pts   c)   Explain the steps necessary to solve the system using elimination.

> *Put y = 2x – 4 into Ax + By = C form. Then the equations would be added to
> eliminate the x term and allow solving for y. Finally, substitute that value of y
> into either equation to solve for x. Substitute those x and y values into both
> equations to verify the solution.*

Points   Problem

d)   Solve the system using the method you consider most efficient.

$3(2x-4)+2x = 12$	*1 pt.*	$y - 2x = -4$	*1 pt.*	
$6x -12 + 2x = 12$	*1 pt.*	$3y + 2x = 12$		
$8x = 24$	*1 pt.*	$so\ 4y = 8$	*1 pt.*	
$x = 3$	*1 pt.*	$y = 2$	*1 pt.*	
$y = 2(3) - 4$	*or*	$2 = 2x - 4$	*1 pt.*	*or*
$y = 2$	*1 pt.*	$6 = 2x$		
$(3, 2)$	*1 pt.*	$x = 3$	*1 pt.*	
		$(3, 2)$	*1 pt.*	

1st line   1 pt slope
1 pt. y – int.
2nd line   2 pts x and y-int
or   1 pt slope,
1 pt y-int.
(3, 2)   2 pts.

(3, 2)

> Be sure to "read" with the student if there are mistakes made.

e)   Verify your answer.

1 pt.

$2 = 2(3) - 4$
$2 = 2$

2 pts.

$3(2) + 2(3) = 12$
$6 + 6 = 12$
$12 = 12$

> The question can be solved using multiple methods. Letting the student choose the method encourages higher-order thinking.

3.   Solve the following systems. Use the method you consider most efficient. Be sure to clearly show each step and verify your solution. A grid is given if you choose the graphing method.

9 pts.

a) $f(x) = 5x - 8$
$f(x) = -2x - 1$

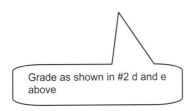

> Grade as shown in #2 d and e above

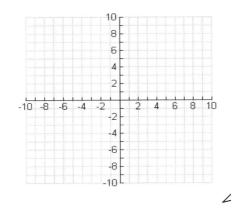

> To encourage using methods other than graphing, one system should have non-integral values.

Points   Problem

9 pts.   b) $x + y = 10$
              $x - y = 2$

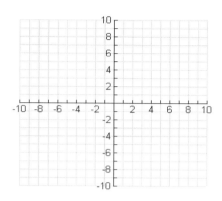

9 pts.   c) $6y = 3x - 4$
              $2x - 3y = 3$

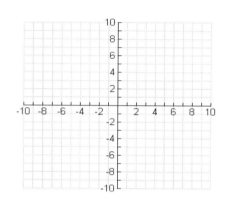

4 pts.   4.   If $g(x) = 2x + 3$ is the equation of one line in a system of two equations, write the equation of the other line so that the system will have no solution.
Explain your choice of equation.

> Asking the student to write the system is definitely encouraging higher-order thinking.

Any equation of the form f(x) = 2x + b, where b is not equal to 3. Lines that have the same slope, but different y-intercept would be parallel and thus have no solution.

4 pts.   5.   If $3x + 4y = 2$ is the equation of one line in a system of two equations, write the equation of the other line so that the system will have more than one solution (an infinite number of solutions).

> Problems 3, 4 and 5 all have multiple answers.

Any equation in the form of b(3x + 4y = 2), where b is not equal to 0. The lines must have the same slope and same y-intercept, be multiples of each other, be coincident and have an infinite number of solutions.

4 pts.   6.   Write a system of equations which has only the ordered pair $(2, -4)$ as its solution.
Verify your answer.

7. Using the graph find the following:

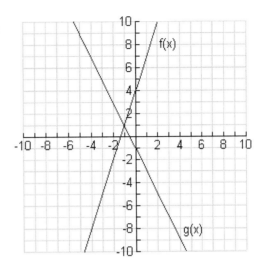

4 pts.

(2 pts. Slope
& 2 pts. Y-int.)

a) the equation of $f(x)$

$f(x) = 3x + 4$

4 pts.

(2 pts. Slope
& 2 pts. Y-int.)

b) the equation of $g(x)$

$g(x) = -2x - 1$

1 pt.

c) the point of intersection of $f(x)$ and $g(x)$

$(-1, 1)$

2 pts.

d) Show that your answer to part c satisfies both $f(x)$ and $g(x)$

8. Using the graph find the following:

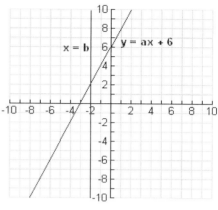

3 pts.   a)   The point of intersection of $y = ax + 6$ and the vertical line $x = b$

3 pts.   b)   The value of b

3 pts.   c)   The value of a

> Use of parameters **a** and **b**

9. The slopes of perpendicular lines have a product of (-1). The lines $g(x) = -\dfrac{3}{2}x + 4$ and $f(x)$, which is perpendicular to $g(x)$, intersect in the point (6, -5). Find the equation for $f(x)$ and write the system.

2 pts.   *Slope would be* $\dfrac{2}{3}$

2 pts. $y = \dfrac{2}{3}x + b$

> Reviewing slopes of perpendicular lines and incorporating the concept into systems.

2 pts. $-5 = \dfrac{2}{3}(6) + b$

              $-5 = 4 + b$

              $b = -9$

2 pts. $y = \dfrac{2}{3}x - 9$

1 pt. $\begin{cases} g(x) = -\dfrac{3}{2}x + 4 \\ f(x) = \dfrac{2}{3}x - 9 \end{cases}$

10. A fly lands on the left edge of a computer screen 4 inches up from the base and is crawling down the screen at the rate of one inch per second. A spider sees the fly and starts to chase it. The spider enters the computer screen also on the left side, 5 inches up from the base. The spider travels down the screen faster at the rate of 2 inches per second. Write the system of equations representing the path of the fly, $f(t)$, the fly's position in terms of time, and the path of the spider, $s(t)$, the spider's position in terms of time. Does the spider capture the fly? If so at what time?

2 pts. $f(t) = 4 - t$

> Looking at systems in a different format, as well as giving an application.

2 pts. $s(t) = 5 - 2t$

2 pts.   *Yes, at time t = 1 second.*
("Read" with the student using the solution of student's f and s functions.)

Multiple Choice Questions:
Show all work to gain credit for the answer.

Points   Problem

11. Find the value of the x coordinate of the solution to the system
$$2x - 5y = 31$$
$$-2x + 4y = -26$$

   a) 28   b) –5   c) 2   d) 1   e) 3

   Correct answer is e. The following steps, or comparable steps, must be shown. <u>*Partial credit should be awarded*</u>*.*

2 pts. $-y = 5 \rightarrow y = -5$

   $2x - 5(-5) = 31$

2 pts. $x = 3$

   > Requiring work to be shown, then awarding partial credit in multiple choice answers, confirms their importance and takes them out of the category of "multiple guess."

4 pts. 12. The point $(2, -3)$ is the solution of which system of equations?

   i) $\begin{array}{l} y = -3 \\ x = 2 \end{array}$ ii) $\begin{array}{l} 2x - 3y = 13 \\ x - 3y = -4 \end{array}$ iii) $\begin{array}{l} x - y = 4 \\ x + y = -1 \end{array}$ iv) $\begin{array}{l} y = 5x - 13 \\ 4x - 6y = 26 \end{array}$

   a) i only   b) ii, iii only   c) iii only   d) i, iv only   e) i, iii, iv only

   > The student must test all systems to get the correct answer.

   Correct answer is d. Student should show substitution and indicate which systems have $(2, -3)$ *as the correct answer.*

4 pts. 13. Find b if the system $\begin{cases} bx + 3y = 4 \\ y = 6x + 3 \end{cases}$ has no solution.

   a) 9   b) –18   c) 6   d) –6   e) 3

   Correct answer is b. Student should show that the lines need to have the same slope.

A Vertical Team Activity: Modifying AP Exam Questions

In order to help students to develop the skills necessary for success on the AP Calculus and Statistics examinations, teachers of Pre-AP classes should regularly meet together in order to examine recently released AP questions and see how they might adapt those questions for use in their own classes. The AP teacher can review the questions with the group and explain what skills and concepts are being tested. Valuable information can be gleaned by examining the grading standards as well.

After examining the AP questions, teachers can work in groups to create modified versions of those questions for use in their own classes. On the next pages, you will see an AP exam question followed by the modified versions for various grade levels or subjects.

Creating modified questions will allow Pre-AP teachers to increase their familiarity with the format and requirements for the AP exams. If teachers then use the questions in their classes, students will have a greater awareness of the AP program and will begin developing the skills and habits that will serve them well throughout their Pre-AP and AP experience.

AP Calculus 1999 AB-6

AB–6

1999

6. In the figure above, line ℓ is tangent to the graph of $y = \dfrac{1}{x^2}$ at point P, with coordinates $\left(w, \dfrac{1}{w^2}\right)$, where $w > 0$. Point Q has coordinates $(w, 0)$. Line ℓ crosses the x-axis at the point R, with coordinates $(k, 0)$.

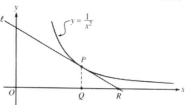

(a) Find the value of k when $w = 3$.

(b) For all $w > 0$, find k in terms of w.

(c) Suppose that w is increasing at the constant rate of 7 units per second. When $w = 5$, what is the rate of change of k with respect to time?

(d) Suppose that w is increasing at the constant rate of 7 units per second. When $w = 5$, what is the rate of change of the area of $\triangle PQR$ with respect to time? Determine whether the area is increasing or decreasing at this instant.

(a) $\dfrac{dy}{dx} = -\dfrac{2}{x^3}$; $\left.\dfrac{dy}{dx}\right|_{x=3} = -\dfrac{2}{27}$

Line ℓ through $\left(3, \dfrac{1}{9}\right)$ and $(k, 0)$ has slope $-\dfrac{2}{27}$.

Therefore, $\dfrac{0 - \dfrac{1}{9}}{k - 3} = -\dfrac{2}{27}$ or $0 - \dfrac{1}{9} = -\dfrac{2}{27}(k - 3)$

$k = \dfrac{9}{2}$

$$2 \begin{cases} 1: \left.\dfrac{dy}{dx}\right|_{x=3} \\[2mm] 1: \text{answer} \end{cases}$$

(b) Line ℓ through $\left(w, \dfrac{1}{w^2}\right)$ and $(k, 0)$ has slope $-\dfrac{2}{w^3}$.

Therefore, $\dfrac{0 - \dfrac{1}{w^2}}{k - w} = -\dfrac{2}{w^3}$ or $0 - \dfrac{1}{w^2} = -\dfrac{2}{w^3}(k - w)$

$k = \dfrac{3}{2}w$

$$2 \begin{cases} 1: \text{equation relating } w \text{ and } k, \\ \quad \text{using slopes} \\[2mm] 1: \text{answer} \end{cases}$$

(c) $\dfrac{dk}{dt} = \dfrac{3}{2}\dfrac{dw}{dt} = \dfrac{3}{2} \cdot 7 = \dfrac{21}{2}$; $\left.\dfrac{dk}{dt}\right|_{w=5} = \dfrac{21}{2}$

$1: \text{answer using } \dfrac{dw}{dt} = 7$

(d)

$P\left(w, 1/w^2\right)$

$Q(w, 0)$ $R(k, 0)$

$A = \dfrac{1}{2}(k - w)\dfrac{1}{w^2} = \dfrac{1}{2}\left(\dfrac{3}{2}w - w\right)\dfrac{1}{w^2} = \dfrac{1}{4w}$

$\dfrac{dA}{dt} = -\dfrac{1}{4w^2}\dfrac{dw}{dt}$

$\left.\dfrac{dA}{dt}\right|_{w=5} = -\dfrac{1}{100} \cdot 7 = -0.07$

Therefore, area is decreasing.

$$4 \begin{cases} 1: \text{area in terms of } w \text{ and/or } k \\[2mm] 1: \dfrac{dA}{dt} \text{ implicitly} \\[2mm] 1: \left.\dfrac{dA}{dt}\right|_{w=5} \text{ using } \dfrac{dw}{dt} = 7 \\[2mm] 1: \text{conclusion} \end{cases}$$

Note: 0/4 if A constant

Middle School Activity
Adaptation of AP Calculus 1999 AB-6

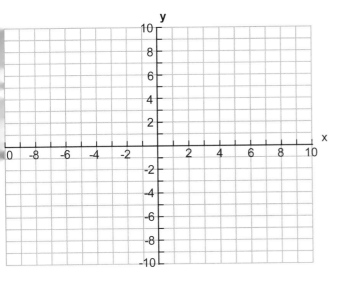

1. a)   Plot the points $(-2, 8)$, $(3, -2)$, and $(5, -6)$.

    b)   Draw the line that passes through the plotted points. Extend the line so that it covers the grid.

    c)   Name the coordinates of two other points that are on the line.

    d)   Give the coordinates of the point where the line crosses the x-axis (the x-intercept).

    e)   Give the coordinates of the point where the line crosses the y-axis (the y-intercept).

    f)   Find the area of the triangle formed in the first quadrant by the line, the x-axis and the y-axis.

Grading Standard: 10 points

1. a)   3 points
    b)   1 points
    c)   2 points – multiple answers are possible
    d) $(2, 0)$ 1 point
    e) $(0, 4)$ 1 point
    f) $A = \dfrac{1}{2}(2)(4) = 4$ 2 pts; one for set up, one for answer.

Note: Find the area of the triangle using the student's x and y intercepts to avoid "double jeopardy."

Algebra 1 Activity
Adaptation of AP Calculus 1999 AB-6

1. a) Use a table of values to draw the graph of the parabola $y = x^2 + 2x + 2$.

b) The slope of the line tangent to the parabola at the point (1,5) is 4. Draw this line and label its x-intercept as $(\mathbf{k}, 0)$.

c) Show the algebraic steps to find $\mathbf{k}$, the x-intercept, of this line.

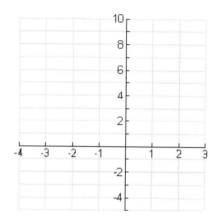

Grading Standard: 6 points

1. a) 1 point   Correct graph

b) 1 point   Line tangent to curve at (1,5) and showing its x-intercept as $(\mathbf{k},0)$

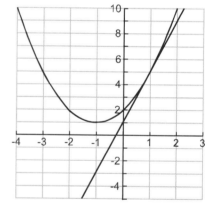

2 points $\dfrac{5-0}{1-k} = 4$

1 point $5 = 4 - 4k$

1 point $k = -\dfrac{1}{4}$

Another method would be to write the equation of the tangent line, then find its x-intercept:

2 points $y - 5 = 4(x - 1)$

1 point $0 - 5 = 4(x - 1)$

1 point $x = -\dfrac{1}{4}$, so the x-intercept is $(-\dfrac{1}{4}, 0)$ and the value of $\mathbf{k}$ is $-\dfrac{1}{4}$.

Geometry Activity
Adaptation of AP Calculus 1999 AB-6

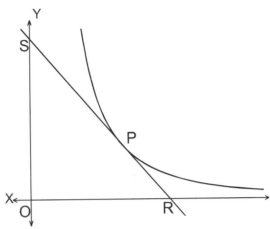

In the diagram, $\overleftrightarrow{SR}$ is tangent to the curve $y = \dfrac{1}{x^2}$ at an arbitrary point $P(w, \dfrac{1}{w^2})$ and intersects

the x-axis at $R(k, 0)$.

    a)   Draw the line perpendicular to the x-axis through point P.

    b)   Let Q be the point where the line in part *a* intersects the x-axis. Determine the coordinates
        of Q.

    c)   Write the equation of $\overleftrightarrow{PQ}$.

    d)   Determine the area of triangle PQR in terms of w and k.

Grading Standard: 7 points

1.   a)   Draw line   1 point

       b) Q: $(w, 0)$ 1 point

       c) $x = w$ 1 point [use student's response to part b]

       d) $A = \dfrac{1}{2}bh$ 1 point for formula

$$A = \frac{1}{2}(k - w)\left(\frac{1}{w^2}\right) \left.\begin{array}{l} \\ \\ \\ \\ \end{array}\right\}$$

            2 points $(k - w)$

            1 point h$= \dfrac{1}{w^2}$

            <-1 point> if not an equation.

Algebra 2 Activity
Adaptation of AP Calculus 1999 AB-6

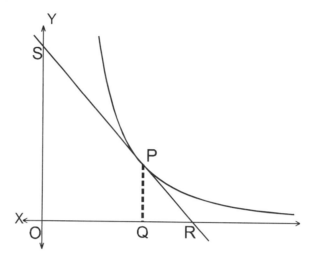

1. A line tangent to the graph of $y = \dfrac{1}{x^2}$ at point P intersects the x-axis at R. The coordinates of R are $(k, 0)$ and the coordinates of point Q are $(w, 0)$.

   a)   What are the coordinates of the point P?

   b)   Write the equation of the tangent line containing P and R in terms of k and w if the slope of the line is $\dfrac{-2}{w^3}$.

   c)   Solve the above equation for w in terms of k.

   d)   If the line intersects the x-axis at $(1.5, 0)$, find w.

   e)   Using the values of w and k, find the equation of this tangent line.

   f)   Find the area of triangle OSR.

Grading Standard: 8 points

1. a) $\left(w, \dfrac{1}{w^2} \right)$ 1 point

   b) $\dfrac{1}{w^2} - 0 = \dfrac{-2}{w^3}(w - k)$ 2 points

   c) $w = -2(w - k)$ 1 point

       $w = \dfrac{2k}{3}$ 1 point

   d) $w = 1$ 1 point

   e) $y = -2x + 3$ 1 point

   f) S has coordinates $(0, 3)$ so the Area $= 2.25$ 1 point

Pre-Calculus Activity
Adaptation of AP Calculus 1999 AB-6

Calculator Active   Be sure to show all steps.

Graph $y = \dfrac{1}{x^2}$ and the line tangent to the curve at the point $\left(w, \dfrac{1}{w^2}\right)$, where $w > 0$. This line will

intersect the x-axis at the point $(k, 0)$.

   a)   If the tangent line has a slope of $\dfrac{-2}{w^3}$, find k in terms of w.

   b)   Write the equation of the tangent line to the curve at the point $\left(4, \dfrac{1}{4^2}\right)$.

   c)   Find the x-intercept of this tangent line.

   d)   The line tangent to the curve at the point $\left(4, \dfrac{1}{4^2}\right)$ intersects the graph of $y = \dfrac{1}{x^2}$ at what

      other point? Show the analysis that leads to your conclusion.

Grading Standard: 7 points

   a) $\dfrac{\frac{1}{w^2} - 0}{w - k} = \dfrac{-2}{w^3}$ 1 point

      $\dfrac{1}{w^2} - 0 = \dfrac{-2}{w^3}(w - k)$

         $w = -2(w - k)$

         $k = \dfrac{3w}{2}$ 1 point

   b) $y - \dfrac{1}{16} = \dfrac{-1}{32}(x - 4)$ 2 points $\begin{cases} 1 \text{ pt. slope} \\ 1 \text{ pt. equation} \end{cases}$

c)   Since (k, 0) is the *x*-intercept

and $k = \dfrac{3w}{2}$; $k = 6$ when $w = 4$

or

$0 - \dfrac{1}{16} = \dfrac{-1}{32}(k - 4)$ 1 point

and $k = 6$

d)

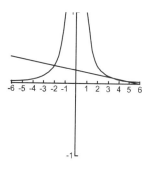

$y = -\dfrac{1}{32}x + \dfrac{3}{16}$

$\dfrac{1}{x^2} = -\dfrac{1}{32}x + \dfrac{3}{16}$ 1 point for setting $\dfrac{1}{x^2}$ equal to student's

$32 = -x^3 + 6x^2$ tangent line

$0 = -x^3 + 6x^2 - 32$

$x = -2$ and 4, so the tangent line   1 point
intersects the curve at $(-2, \frac{1}{4})$

**Note: In solving $-x^3 + 6x^2 - 32 = 0$, the graph
shows a solution at -2 and a double root
at x = 4. This verifies that the line intersects
at x = -2 and is tangent at x = 4.
See illustration at the right.**

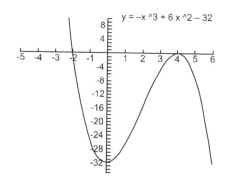

AP Statistics 1997 Problem 6

6. You are planning to sell a used 1988 automobile and want to establish an asking price that is competitive with that of other cars of the same make and model that are on the market. A review of newspaper advertisements for used cars yields the following data for 12 different cars of this make and model. You want to fit a least squares regression model to these data for use as a model in establishing the asking price for your car.

Production Year	1990	1991	1992	1987	1993	1991	1993	1985	1984	1982	1986	1979
Asking Price (in thousands of dollars	6.0	7.7	8.8	3.4	9.8	8.4	8.9	1.5	1.6	1.4	2.0	1.0

The computer printouts for three different linear regression models are shown below. Model 1 fits the asking price as a function of the production year. Model 2 fits the natural logarithm of the asking price as a function of the production year, and Model 3 fits the square root of the asking price as a function of the production year. Each printout also includes a plot of residuals from the linear model versus the fitted values, as well as additional descriptive data produced from the least squares procedure.

Model 1

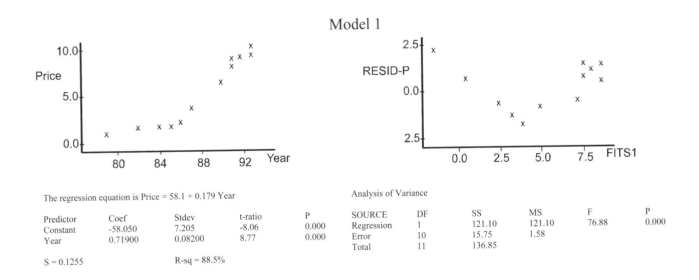

The regression equation is Price = 58.1 + 0.179 Year

Predictor	Coef	Stdev	t-ratio	P
Constant	-58.050	7.205	-8.06	0.000
Year	0.71900	0.08200	8.77	0.000

S = 0.1255   R-sq = 88.5%

Analysis of Variance

SOURCE	DF	SS	MS	F	P
Regression	1	121.10	121.10	76.88	0.000
Error	10	15.75	1.58		
Total	11	136.85			

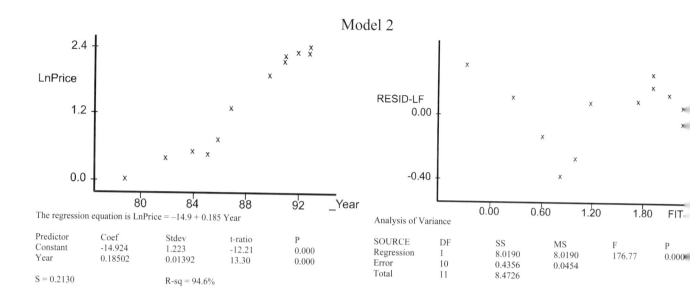

Model 2

The regression equation is LnPrice = −14.9 + 0.185 Year

Predictor	Coef	Stdev	t-ratio	P
Constant	-14.924	1.223	-12.21	0.000
Year	0.18502	0.01392	13.30	0.000

S = 0.2130   R-sq = 94.6%

Analysis of Variance

SOURCE	DF	SS	MS	F	P
Regression	1	8.0190	8.0190	176.77	0.000
Error	10	0.4356	0.0454		
Total	11	8.4726			

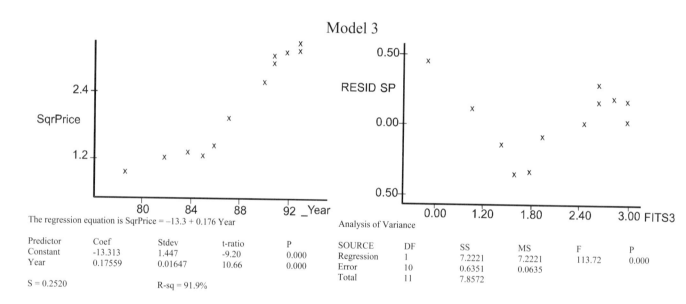

Model 3

The regression equation is SqrPrice = −13.3 + 0.176 Year

Predictor	Coef	Stdev	t-ratio	P
Constant	-13.313	1.447	-9.20	0.000
Year	0.17559	0.01647	10.66	0.000

S = 0.2520   R-sq = 91.9%

Analysis of Variance

SOURCE	DF	SS	MS	F	P
Regression	1	7.2221	7.2221	113.72	0.000
Error	10	0.6351	0.0635		
Total	11	7.8572			

a)   Use Model 1 to establish an asking price for your 1988 automobile.

b)   Use Model 2 to establish an asking price for your 1988 automobile.

c)   Use Model 3 to establish an asking price for your 1988 automobile.

d)   Describe any shortcomings you see in these three models.

e)   Use some or all of the given data to find a better model for establishing an asking price for your 1988 automobile. Explain why your model is better.

AP Statistics Question 6 (Investigative Task)
Scoring Guideline-1997

4   Complete Response

I.   Correctly estimates the asking price in dollars for at least two of the three models, including back transforming the predicted value for at least one of models b or c.

   a)   Price = -58.1 + 0.719(88) = 5.172 asking price is $5,172

   b)   Ln(price) = -14.9 + 0.185(88) = 1.380 exp(1.38) = 3.9749 asking price = $3975

   c)   Sqrt(Price) = -13.3 + 0.176(88) = 2.188 $(2.188)^2$ = 4.783 asking price = $4,787

II.   Describes the major shortcoming to be the non-linear pattern in the scatterplot or residual plot for all three models.

III. Suggests a new model that successfully deals with the non-linearity of the data. The prime Contenders for this model are:

Fit a simple linear model after the first two or three years are dropped. (R^2 = 0.978 with little pattern in the residuals after dropping 79, 82, and 84)

Fit separate linear models to the earlier and later years. (R^2 = 0.985 for the years 86 to 93, with little pattern in the residuals.)

Fit a model that attempts to model the curvature in the data. For example, fit a quadratic model to all of the data. (R^2 = 0.974 with little patter in the residuals for a quadratic model.)

IV.   Justifies why this model is better. For example, comments that there is no pattern in the residuals

as seen from looking at the fitted model on the scatterplot or from looking at the residual plot.

3   Substantial Response

Fails to do one of the following satisfactorily:

- Part I (for example, by failing to back transform the prediction)
- Describe the major shortcomings of the three models
- Justify why the new model is better (for example, by failing to comment on the residual plot)

2   **Developing Response**

Fails to do one of the following satisfactorily:

- Part I and describe the three major shortcomings of the three models
- Part I and justify why the new model is better
- Suggest a new model and justify it
- Describe the major shortcomings of the three models and justify why the new model is better.

1   **Minimal Response**

Gives correct response to one of the items I, II, or III above.

Note: Students cannot get IV correct without first specifying a new model.

Middle School Activity
Adaptation of AP Statistics 1997 Problem 6

You are planning to sell a used 1988 automobile and want to establish an asking price that is competitive with that of other cars of the same make and model that are on the market. A review of newspaper advertisements for used cars yields the following data for 12 different cars of this make and model.

Production Year	1990	1991	1992	1987	1993	1991	1993	1985	1984	1982	1986	1979
Asking Price (in thousands of dollars)	6.0	7.7	8.8	3.4	9.8	8.4	8.9	1.5	1.6	1.4	2.0	1.0

7th Grade TEKS 7.11A, 7.11B, 7.12B

a)   Use the information in the table above to construct a scatter plot.

b)   Estimate the asking price for your 1988 automobile. Give specific reasons how the information from the scatter plot helped you determine this price.

c)   You are planning on buying a used 1999 automobile. Use the scatter plot to determine a price for this automobile. Justify your answer.

d)   Would the price you determined in part (c) be reasonable? Why or why not?

Grading Standard: 4 points

a)

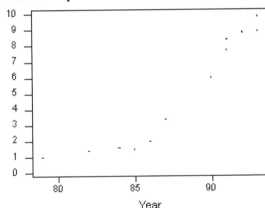

> 1 point
> Student is expected to draw a complete scatterplot including labeling and scaling the axes. Years can be coded in some way such as t = years since 1975, for example, or can use 91 for 1991.
>
> ½ point
> Student does a good job drawing the plot but neglects to include labels and/or scales.

b)   Student gives an estimate for a 1988 automobile. This estimate should be in the neighborhood of $4700 depending on student's justification.

> 1 point
> You should read with the student on this. Good communication is very important. For example, if a student justifies an answer of $4700 by explaining that the answer was found by averaging the prices for 1990 and 1987, ½ point for estimate and ½ point for justification. If the student provides a good justification, but gives an incorrect estimate then award ½ point for the justification. If the student provides an estimate (correct or not), but no justification is included, then award 0 points.

c.   Student gives an estimated asking price for a 1999 automobile. The estimate should be in the area of $15,900 depending on student's method.

> **1 point**
>
> **Reading with the student is very important. Before judging the student's estimate, read how the student justifies his or her answer. Good communication is critical.**
>
> If the justification is plausible then evaluate the student estimate in light of that plausibility. If the student has constructed a really good scatterplot on graph paper, he or she could draw a straight line through the data and make an estimate. The student may recognize that the later years (after 1990 for example) are more appropriate to the estimate and only draw a straight line through that part of the scatterplot to make an estimate.
>
> If a student has drawn a poor scatterplot in part (a) you read with the student. If the student uses that incorrect plot to make a plausible estimate (with justification) the student can get full credit in part (c).
>
> Award ½ point for estimate and ½ point for justification. If the student provides a good justification, but gives an incorrect estimate then award ½ point. If the student provides an estimate (correct or not) but no justification then award 0 points.

d)   The estimate made in part (c) would not be reasonable. The newest car in the data set is from 1993. It is not appropriate to estimate the asking price of a 1999 car since this year is well beyond the upper limit of the current data set. We would question the accuracy of this estimate.

> **1 point**
>
> ½ point for stating that estimate is not reasonable and ½ point for good justification.

Holistic Grading in Practice

What happens if a student has been awarded 3 ½ points? The reader must now step back and look at the whole solution. Should the score be rounded to a 3 or a 4? In AP Statistics the 4-point scale equates to 4 is a complete response, 3 is a substantial response, 2 developing, 1 minimal, and 0 barely started or off task.

As a reader looks at a 3 ½ score, he or she has to judge whether the overall paper represents a complete response or a substantial response. If the student communicates well, and it is only some arithmetic errors that mar the work, the score would be rounded up to a 4 – complete. If there is poor communication or it lacks clarity then the score would be rounded to a 3 – substantial.

The same holistic approach should be used if a half-score resulted on any question.

Algebra 1 Activity
Adaptation of AP Statistics 1997 Problem 6

You are planning to sell a used 1988 automobile and want to establish an asking price that is competitive with that of other cars of the same make and model that are on the market. A review of newspaper advertisements for used cars yields the following data for 9 different cars of this make and model.

Production Year	1990	1991	1992	1987	1993	1991	1993	1985	1986	1984	1982
Asking Price in $	6000	7700	8800	3400	9800	8400	8900	1500	2000	1600	1400

1. Often it is difficult to work with large or small data, such as $2,300,000,000. It is easier to work with coded data, that is, data that has been recalculated by a rule or transformation. In the above case, we would rewrite the number as $2.3 billion.

    a) Use this idea to code the data in the table above. For the data, Production Year, calculate the number of years since 1980. Using this rule, 1980 will be coded as 0 and 1990 will be coded as 10, and so forth.

    b) Code the asking price of the automobile in thousands of dollars. For example, $7700 will be written as $7.7 (thousands of dollars).

2. Complete the table of values below using your coded data.

Production Year	Asking Price ($ thousands)

3. Draw a scatterplot of the coded data. Be sure to label your axes with appropriate variables and scales.

4. Draw a trend line for the data.

    a) Write the equation for this line.

    b) What is the slope of this line?

    c) Interpret the meaning of the slope in the context of this problem.

5. Use your model to predict the selling price for your 1988 automobile. Do you think that this price is reasonable for this automobile? Use data in the problem to support your answer.

Grading Standard: 4 points

1. a) and b) See the table of values below for problem #2.

2.

Production Year	Asking Price ($ thousands)
10	6
11	7.7
12	8.8
7	3.4
13	9.8
11	8.4
13	8.9
5	1.5
6	2
4	1.6
2	1.4

1 point

Parts 1 and 2 are graded together: Award ½ point for each column. If a student makes one mistake it could still be judged as complete.

3.
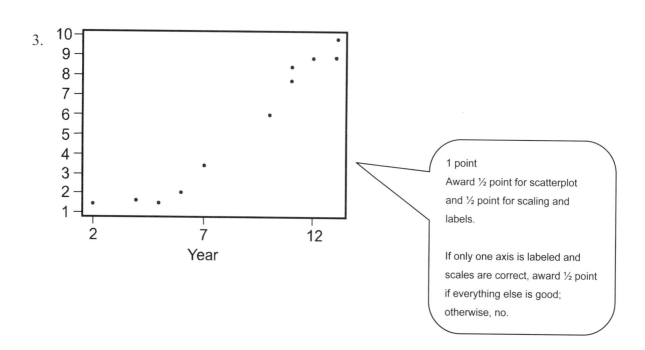

1 point

Award ½ point for scatterplot and ½ point for scaling and labels.

If only one axis is labeled and scales are correct, award ½ point if everything else is good; otherwise, no.

4. a) We will use Asking price = 0.9 (year since 1980) – 2.

(Answers will vary because the students are not using a graphing calculator to find the equation. The students will use their knowledge of linear functions and the graphs of linear functions to write a linear function that models this data. They will use their model to help them answer the remaining questions.)

b) The slope represents

$$\frac{the\ predicted\ change\ in\ asking\ price\,(in\,thousands\,)}{the\ change\ in\ years\,(after\ 1980)}$$

or a predicted change of $900 per year

or For every year after 1980, I would expect an increase in asking price of approximately one thousand dollars per year.

> 1 point
>
> Award ½ point for equation based on student's scatterplot and ½ point for interpretation of slope.

5. Using the model written in #4, we have Asking price = 0.9(8) – 2 = 5.2. This would mean that the predicted asking price for a 1988 automobile would be approximately $5200.

When I plotted the price (8, 5.2) on my scatter plot, the asking price appears to be somewhat high because year 7 is $3400 and year 10 is $6000. If I averaged the values for the two years 7 and 10, it would give me a value of $4700. I think the price should be closer to year 7 than to year 10.

> 1 point
>
> Read with the student's equation from part 4. Award ½ point for student's correct estimate based on their equation. If there is an arithmetic error reserve judgment until you look at the entire response.
>
> Assess student's response to reasonableness by looking at the scatterplot, trend line, predicted value and the strength of the communication. Minor arithmetic errors can be overcome with a well-written justification of reasonableness of their estimate. If this is good and the rest of the response is good then the minor arithmetic error would not be deducted. If there are several arithmetic errors than deducting an overall point is justified.

Algebra 2 Activity
Adaptation of AP Statistics 1997 Problem 6

Algebra 2 TEKS: a3, a5, b1A, f5

You are planning to sell a used 1988 automobile and want to establish an asking price that is competitive with that of other cars of the same make and model that are on the market. A review of newspaper advertisements for used cars yields the following data for 12 different cars of this make and model.

Production Year	1990	1991	1992	1987	1993	1991	1993	1985	1984	1982	1986	1979
Asking Price in Dollars	6000	7700	8800	3400	9800	8400	8900	1500	1600	1400	2000	1000

1. Draw a scatter plot of the data. Remember to scale and label both axes.
   Let t = years since 1979.

2. One model that would fit the data is given by Price $= 1.17^t$. Predict the selling price in thousands of your 1988 automobile using this exponential model.

3. Your friend thinks that the data would be better represented by using two line segments. Write a piecewise function for the data using two lines or segments of lines.

4. Use your piecewise defined function to determine a selling price for your 1988 automobile.

5. Which model do you think gives a better estimate of the selling price of your 1988 automobile? Justify your choice.

6. A friend bought a new car in 1996 and he decides to sell it now. Use your exponential model and your piecewise model to predict the price of this car. Which of the two prices would be the most accurate and why?

Grading Standard: 8 points

1.

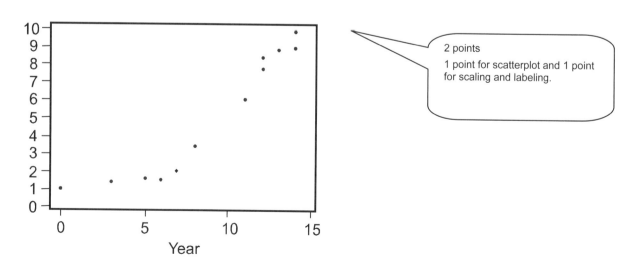

2 points
1 point for scatterplot and 1 point for scaling and labeling.

2. The predicted asking price would be about $4108.40 based on the exponential model. The asking price using this function is too low for $5 \le years \le 7$ and too high for $12 \le years \le 14$.

½ point

3. Price = $\begin{cases} 0.1t & for\ 0 \le t \le 7 \\ 1.15(t-7)+2 & for\ t \ge 7 \end{cases}$

1 point each piece
Answers will vary depending on domain choice.

4. The asking price for a 1988 automobile would be approximately $4300.

½ point

5. In you were to draw the two models on the scatterplot you would find that the piecewise model more closely fits the data than does the exponential model. In addition, the differences between the actual data and the predicted values would be smaller for the piecewise model.

1 point

6. Using the exponential model for the year **1996 (t=17)**, the asking price would be about **$14,426.16**. Using the piecewise model for the year **1996 (t=17)**, the asking price would be about $**13,500**.

The piecewise model would be more appropriate because the exponential model expected asking price is too high for the years between 12 and 14 so I think it would be to high for any year after the 14th year.

½ point each prediction

1 point for correct choice of piecewise model.

1 point for justification

I think the piecewise function better models the data because values of the data are closer to the piecewise function than to the exponential function. Also the rate of change in the exponential function continues to increase which does not seem to fit the context for the asking price of the automobiles. It appears from the scatter plot that the rate of change for the asking price of automobiles is a constant value and therefore linear.

Pre-Calculus Activity
Adaptation of AP Statistics 1997 Problem 6

Pre-Calculus TEKS: (c)3(A), (c)3(B), (c)3(C)
This is an example of what an investigative task might look like on the AP Statistics Examination. Students would be expected to allot approximately ½ hour for such a question.

You are planning to sell a used 1988 automobile and want to establish an asking price that is competitive with that of other cars of the same make and model that are on the market. A review of newspaper advertisements for used cars yields the following data for 12 different cars of this make and model. You want to fit a least squares regression model to these data for use as a model in establishing the asking price for your car.

Production Year	1990	1991	1992	1987	1993	1991	1993	1985	1984	1982	1986	1979
Asking Price in Dollars	6.0	7.7	8.8	3.4	9.8	8.4	8.9	1.5	1.6	1.4	2.0	1.0

Establish an asking price for the 1988 automobile using 4 models (linear, exponential, quadratic, and power). Let t = years since 1978 and p = price in thousands of dollars. Use your calculator's linear regression feature to determine a linear function in the form of …

1. $\ln p = mt + b$ using the transformed data $(t, \ln p)$. Using exponential/logarithmic properties, re-express the equation as an exponential function in the form of $p = ae^{kt}$ to determine the asking price of the automobile.

2. $\sqrt{p} = mt + b$ using the transformed data $(t, \sqrt{p})$. Using algebraic properties, re-express the equation in quadratic form, $p = at^2 + bt + c$, to determine the asking price of the automobile.

3. $\ln p = m \cdot \ln t + b$ using the transformed data $(\ln t, \ln p)$. Using exponential/logarithmic properties, re-express the equation as a power function, $p = at^b$, to determine the asking price of the automobile.

4. Graph the 3 models with the data points and their accompanying residual plots. Which appears to be the best model? Explain why.

Grading Standard: 15 points

1. $\ln p = .185021t - .492845$

   $e^{\ln p} = e^{.185021t - .492845}$

   $p = e^{.185021t} \div e^{.492845}$

   $p = .610886\, e^{.185021t}$

   1 point for linearized form
   1 point for expression
   ½ point predicted price

   p(10) = 3.9. Therefore, using this exponential model, the predicted asking price for a 1988 automobile would be $3900.

2. $\sqrt{p} = .175587t + .382519$

   $\sqrt{p}^{2} = (.175587t + .382519)^2$

   $p = 030831t^2 + .134331t + .146321"$

   p(10) = 4.6

   1 point for linearized form
   1 point for expression
   ½ point predicted price

   Therefore, using this quadratic model, the predicted asking price for a 1988 automobile would be $4600.

3. $\ln p = .953034 \ln t - .679989$

   $e^{\ln p} = e^{.95034 \ln t - .679989}$

   $p = e^{.95034 \ln t} \div e^{.679989}$

   $p = 0.506623(t^{.953034})$

   1 point for linearized form
   1 point for expression
   ½ point predicted price

   p(10) = 4.5. Therefore, using this power model, the predicted asking price of a 1988 automobile would be $4500.

4.

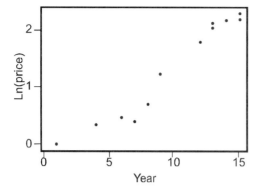

1 point each scatterplot

1 point each residual plot

½ point for choosing best model
(ln price versus year)

1 point for justification for that
model, that is, there is less
pattern in the residual plot than
the others.

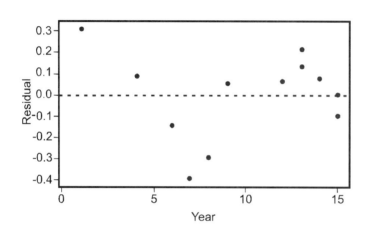

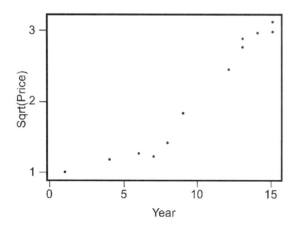

4. (cont.)

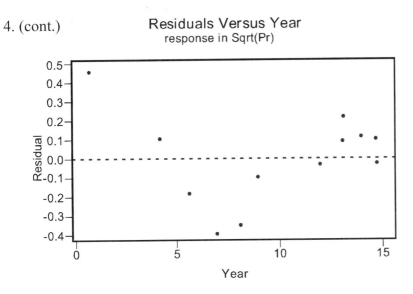

Residuals Versus Year
response in Sqrt(Pr)

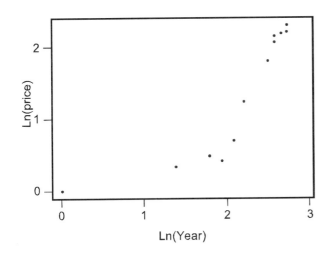

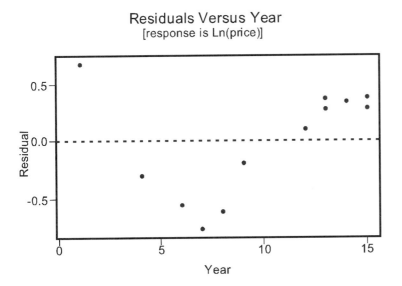

Residuals Versus Year
[response is Ln(price)]

Vertical Team Activity: Creating Pre-AP Questions Using Phrases from AP Exam Items

After examining various AP exam items, teachers should be challenged to write their own versions of questions that would be appropriate for their classes. The questions that they create should not just be used as test items, but should become an integral part of their teaching. These are questions that should be asked and answered as a part of classroom discussion, as part of homework assignments and as a part of formal assessments. Creating good questions is one of the most challenging tasks that Pre-AP teachers face.

In order to generate ideas and dialogue on this topic, we created a vertical team activity using phrases from released AP exam items. At one of our meetings, teachers were provided with the list of prompts, one for AP Calculus on page 383 and, at another meeting, one for AP Statistics on page 395. Working as a team with other teachers from their grade level or subject area, they were instructed to write as many Pre-AP style questions as they could based on the given prompts. We allowed approximately 45 minutes for this activity. Whichever team produced the most questions during the time period was declared the "winner." Recognition could also be given for particularly clever or unusual questions or for those most strongly connected to AP Calculus or Statistics.

This activity is probably most appropriate for a more experienced vertical team that has spent time examining released AP exam items. The statistics version was particularly difficult for us when we tried it, even though we had AP Statistics teachers as members of each team. We found that we had trouble developing questions that were statistics questions but still related to our particular subject areas. It became very clear to us that we needed to improve our familiarity with the statistics content and to better integrate it into what we were already teaching.

On the next few pages, you will see the list of prompts provided as well as the results of a group of teachers playing the game. As we put this guide together, we were not sure that we should include the results of the game. We feared that seeing what others had done might stifle other teachers' creativity or make you think that those are "the answers." We ultimately decided though that seeing someone else's responses might help you to generate your own ideas and that we wanted you to see that it was fine to leave some prompts blank. The emphasis should be on the quality of the questions rather than the quantity.

The goal of this activity is to further familiarize teachers with the types of questions that are asked on the AP examinations and to encourage them to produce their own assessment items that go beyond what they might normally use. This particular activity might be used on more than one occasion and could even be done as a take home assignment. When teachers bring their questions back, they could discuss what they have written in horizontal teams to see if teachers who are teaching the same course have similar expectations and are all asking questions at the same level of rigor. The results that we get from students are very closely related to what we ask of them. We hope that this activity helps you to ask more of them than you have in the past.

Template for Creating Pre-AP Questions Using Phrases from AP Calculus Exams

Consider the family of functions defined by…

Evaluate…

Find all points on the curve whose x coordinate is…

Find the area of the region enclosed by…

Find the domain and range of the function…

Find the domain of f…

Find the range of f…

Find the volume…

Find the volume of the solid generated when the region is revolved around the x-axis…

Find the x and y coordinates of the points of intersection of the graphs of f and g…

Find the x coordinate of each point on the curve where the slope is undefined…

For what values of the constant p does f have 2 distinct roots?

For what values of x does f have a maximum/minimum?

Given a velocity, for what values of t is the particle moving to the right?

In the viewing window provided, sketch the graph of f.

Is the velocity increasing? Why or why not?

Is there sufficient information to determine whether or not the graph of f…

Justify your answer…

Show that…

Show the analysis that leads to your equation…

Show the work that leads to your answer…

Using correct units, explain the meaning of…

Write an equation for each horizontal asymptote of f…

Write an equation for the line…

Write an expression for the volume…

Middle Grades

Consider the family of functions defined by:

For the picture shown describe the set of points ABC

Evaluate

Find all points on the triangle whose *x* coordinate is

Find all points on the triangle whose x coordinate is 5

Find the area of the region enclosed by

Find the area of the region enclosed by triangle ABC

Find the domain of *f* and find the range of *f*

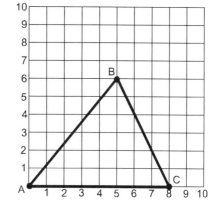

Write an inequality that gives all the values of x in the triangle.
Write an inequality that gives all values of y in the triangle.

Find the volume

What is the volume of the 10 foot tall triangular prism having triangle ABC as its base?

Find the *x* and *y* coordinates of the points of intersection of the graphs of *f* and g

Find the coordinates of the point where segment AB intersects segment BC.

For what values of the constant p does *f* have 2 distinct roots

What translation can be made so that triangle ABC has only one vertex on the x-axis?

For what values of *x* does *f* have a maximum/minimum

Find the maximum value of y on the triangle.
What is the x coordinate for this point?

In the viewing window provided, sketch the graph of *f*.

Graph the part of triangle ABC that you would see on the new viewing window.

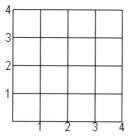

Is there sufficient information to determine whether or not the graph of *f*

Line segment EF divides triangle ABC into two figures. Do you have sufficient information to find the area of the 2 figures?

Justify your answer.

Give the coordinates of the midpoint D of line segment AB. Justify your answer.

Show the work that leads to your answer

Find the area of each of the two figures and show the work that leads to your answer.

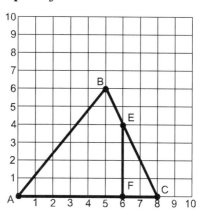

384

Algebra 1

Consider the family of functions defined by

Consider the family of functions defined by $Ax + 3y = 12$. What do the graphs of the functions have in common? How do they differ?

Evaluate

Evaluate $f(3)$ and $f(t)$ for $f(x) = 2x^2 - 5$

Find all points on the curve whose y coordinate is

Find all points on the curve $f(x) = 2x^2 + 7x - 1$ having y coordinate 3.

Find the area of the region enclosed by

Find the area of the region enclosed by the graphs of $y = 0$, $7x + 5y = 35$ and $2x - 3y = 0$.

Find the domain and range of the function

Find the domain and range of $f(x) = x^2 + 2x - 3$.

Find the domain of *f*

Find the range of *f*

Find the volume of the solid generated when the region is revolved around the *x*-axis

Find the volume of the solid generated when the region enclosed by $3x + 5y = 15, x = 0$, and $y = 0$ is revolved around the x-axis.

Find the *x* and *y* coordinates of the points of intersection of the graphs of *f* and g

Find the x and y coordinates of the points of intersection of the graphs of f and g given $f(x) = 4x - 7$ and $g(x) = x^2 - 4$.

Find the *x* coordinate of each point on the curve where the slope is undefined

Find the x coordinate of each point on the curve where the slope is undefined given the slope, m, where $m = \dfrac{x^2 - x - 6}{x^2 - 6x + 5}$.

For what values of the constant p does *f* have 2 distinct roots?

For what values of the constant p does $f(x) = x^2 - 6x + p$ have 2 distinct roots?

For what values of *x* does *f* have a maximum/minimum

Give the locations (x values) where $f(x) = 12x - 2x^2$ has a maximum or minimum.

Given a velocity, for what values of *t* is the particle moving right?

Given $v(t) = 3t - 6$, for what values of t is the particle moving right?

In the viewing window provided, sketch the graph of *f*.

Sketch the graph of f(x) = .25x² + x − 1.25
which would be contained in
the viewing window provided.

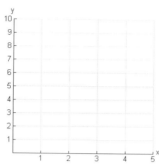

Is the velocity increasing? Why or why not.

In each of the four cases, is the velocity increasing? Why or why not?

$$v(t) = 3 \qquad v(t) = -2 \qquad v(t) = \frac{2}{3}t - 6 \qquad v(t) = -\frac{1}{4}t + 5$$

Is there sufficient information to determine whether or not the graph of *f* intersects the graph of *g*?

Is there sufficient information to determine whether the graph of f intersects the graph of g given
f(x) = 3x − 1 and g(x) is a linear function with a y-intercept of 2?

Justify your answer

Show that

Show that $\frac{1}{2}$ and −5 are roots of the equation $y = 2x^2 + 9x - 5$.

Show the analysis that leads to your equation

Find the equation of a line with the same y-intercept as 3x + 5y = 10 and parallel to 4x - 3y = 8.
Show the analysis that leads to your equation.

Show the work that leads to your answer

Show all steps necessary to find the average rate of change of $f(x) = x^2 + 2$ for $1 \le x \le 4$.

Using correct units, explain the meaning of

Using correct units, explain the meaning of p(5)=35 where the price, p, of a movie, in dollars,
is a function of the number of tickets bought.

Write an equation for each horizontal asymptote of *f*.

Write an equation for the horizontal asymptote of f and g given $f(x) = 2^x + 3$ and $g(x) = 3^{x-1}$.

Write an equation for the line

Write an equation for the line passing through the point (1, −5) and perpendicular to
2x + 3y = 6.

Write an expression

Write an expression for the area of a square as a function of its perimeter.

Geometry

Consider the family of functions defined by

Consider the family of functions defined by $y = (x - h)^2 + k$, where h and k are positive. As h increases, in which direction does the parabola move?

Evaluate

Evaluate $\dfrac{\sqrt{3}}{4} s^2$ if $s = 2\sqrt{2}$.

Find all points on the curve whose *y* coordinate is

Find all points on $\triangle ABC$ whose y coordinate is positive 1.

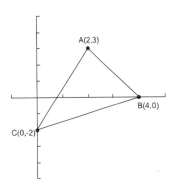

Find the area of the region enclosed by

Find the area of the region between the square and the inscribed circle.

Find the domain and range of the function

A(x) is the area of an isosceles triangle with legs 4 cm and base x cm. Find the domain and range of A(x).

Find the volume

Find the volume of the triangular trough when it is half full.

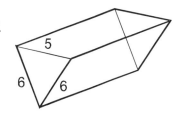

Find the volume of the solid generated when the region is revolved around the x – axis.

Find the volume of the solid generated when the region shown is revolved around the x-axis.

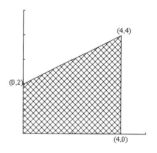

Find the x and y coordinates of the points of intersection of the graphs of

Find the x and y coordinates of the points of intersection of the graphs of $x^2 + y^2 = 9$, and $f(x) = x + 2$.

Find the x coordinate of each point on the curve where the slope is undefined.

Find the x coordinate of each point on $x^2 + y^2 = 16$ where the slope is undefined.

For what values of the constant p does f have 1 distinct root?

For what values of the constant p would the circle $x^2 + (y + p)^2 = 16$ be tangent to the x-axis?

Find the maximum area

Find the maximum area given a rectangle with perimeter 22 inches.

Given a velocity, for what values of t is the particle moving right?

Given a velocity $v(t) = t^2 - 5t + 4$ for what values of t is the particle moving right?

In the viewing window provided, sketch the graph of $f(x)$.

Sketch the graph of the portion of $x^2 + y^2 = 25$ which would be contained in the viewing window provided.

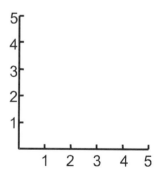

Is there sufficient information to determine

Is there sufficient information to determine if the circle with center (3,4) and radius 2 units intersects $y = 3x + 2$?

Justify your answer:

Find m∠A in terms of x if x is the measure of ∠B.

Justify.

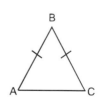

Show that

Show that the diagonals of a rectangle are equal.

Show the analysis that leads to your equation:

Given an equilateral triangle with side S, find A, the area, in terms of S.

Show the analysis that leads to your equation.

Show the work that leads to your answer:

The vertices of Rhombus ABCD are (1, 4), (10, 2), (3, –4) and (–6, –2) respectively. Show that the diagonals are perpendicular.

Using correct units, explain the meaning of

Using correct units, explain the meaning of the shaded region given:

y = 3 ft/sec and t = 8 sec

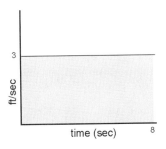

Write an equation

Write an equation for the points that make up the perpendicular bisector of segment AB if A & B have coordinates (0, 3) and (3, 0) respectively.

Write an expression

Write an expression for the volume of the water in the cone in terms of h.

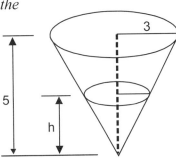

Algebra 2

Consider the family of functions defined by

Consider the family of functions defined by $y = (x - h)^2 - 4$ What do the graphs of the functions have in common? How do they differ?

Evaluate

Evaluate f(2) given $f(x) = \ln e^{2x-1}$.

Find all points on the curve whose y coordinate is

Find the area of the region enclosed by

Find the area of the region enclosed by $y = \sqrt{9 - x^2}$, $y = 0$, $2x - 3y = 6$ and $x = 5$.

Find the domain and range of the function

Find the domain and range of the function $f(x) = \frac{1}{2}\ln(2x^3 + e)$.

Find the domain of f

Find the domain of $\frac{(x+3)^2}{4} - \frac{(y-2)^2}{9} = 1$

Find the range of f

Find the range of $x^2 + 4y^2 + 4x - 24y + 24 = 0$

Find the volume

Find the volume of the solid generated when the region is revolved around the x-axis

Find the volume of the solid generated when the region enclosed by $5x + 3y = 15$, $x = 3$, and $y = 5$ is revolved around the x-axis

Find the x and y coordinates of the points of intersection of the graphs of f and g

Find the x and y coordinates of the points of intersection of the graphs f and g, given $f(x) = x^2$ and $g(x) = 2^x$.

Find the x coordinate of each point on the curve where the slope is undefined

For what values of p does f have 3 distinct roots?

For what values of p does $f(x) = x^3 - 6x^2 + p$ have 3 distinct roots?

For what values of x does f have a maximum/minimum

For what values of x does $f(x) = x^3 - 6x^2$ for $-1 \le x \le 8$ have a maximum/minimum?

Given a velocity, for what values of *t* is the particle moving right?

Given the velocity function $v(t) = t^2 - 5t + 4$, *for what value of t is the particle moving right?*

In the viewing window provided, sketch the graph of *f*.

In the viewing window provided, sketch the graph

of $f(x) = \dfrac{2x}{\sqrt{x^2 + x + 1}}$

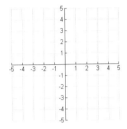

Is there sufficient information to determine whether or not the graph of *f*

Given $f(x) = (x - h)^2 + k$, *k< 0, is there sufficient information to determine whether or not the graph of f crosses the x-axis? Explain.*

Justify your answer

Show that

Show that the diagonals of a rhombus are perpendicular to one another.

Show the analysis that leads to your equation

Show the work that leads to your answer

Using correct units, explain the meaning of

Using correct units, explain the meaning of $\dfrac{s(3) - s(1)}{3 - 1}$ *for* $s(t) = t^2 - 2$ *where s is distance in*

feet and t is time in seconds.

Write an equation for each horizontal asymptote of *f*.

Write an equation for each horizontal asymptote of $f(x) = \dfrac{2x}{\sqrt{x^2 + x + 1}}$.

Write an equation for the line

Write an equation for a line passing through P(0,3) and $U(\dfrac{\pi}{2}, 0)$

Write an expression for the volume

Write an expression for the volume of a sphere in terms of its surface area.

Pre-Calculus

Consider the family of functions defined by

Consider the family of functions defined by $y = \ln(kx)$. What do the graphs of the functions have in common?

Evaluate

Evaluate $f\left(\dfrac{5\pi}{6}\right)$ given $f(x) = \ln(\sin x)$.

Find all points on the curve whose x coordinate is

Find all points on $\dfrac{(x-1)^2}{4} + \dfrac{(y+1)^2}{9} = 1$ whose x coordinate is 2.

Find the area of the region enclosed by

Find the area of the region enclosed by the x and y axes and the line $2x + 3y = 6$.

Find the domain and range of the function

Find the domain and range of $f^{-1}(x)$ if $f(x) = (x+2)^2 - 18$ for $x \le 2$.

Find the domain of

Find the domain of $f(g(x))$ if $g(x) = \sqrt{x-1}$ and $f(x) = \sqrt{5-x}$.

Find the range of

Find the range of $f(g(x))$ if $g(x) = \sqrt{x^2 - 1}$ and $f(x) = x - 1$.

Find the volume of

Find the volume of the cylinder formed by rotating the region enclosed by $y = A$, $x = 0$, $x = 4$, $y = 0$ around the x-axis.

Find the volume of the solid generated when the region is revolved around the x-axis

Find the volume of the solid generated when the region enclosed by $y = A$, $y = 1$, $x = 4$, $x = 0$ is rotated around the x-axis.

Find the x and y coordinates of the points of intersection of the graphs of f and g

Find the x and y coordinates of the points of intersection of the graphs of f and g, given $f(x) = \sqrt{x^2 - 4}$ and $g(x) = 2x$.

Find the x coordinate of each point on the curve where the slope is undefined

Find the x coordinate of each point on the given curve

$4x^2 - 8(y + \dfrac{3}{2})^2 = 18$ *where the slope is undefined.*

For what values of the constant p does *f* have 2 distinct roots?

For what values of the constant p does $f(x) = 2\sin x - p$ have 2 distinct roots

for $0 \leq x < 4$?

For what values of *x* does *f* have maximum/minimum?

For what values of x does $f(x) = x^3 - 3x^2 - 2x + 6$ have a relative maximum or minimum?

Given a velocity, for what values of *t* is the particle moving to the right?

Given $v(t) = e^{2t} - 6e^t + 8$, for what values of t is the particle moving to the right?

In the viewing window provided, sketch the graph of

In the viewing window provided, sketch the graph of

$f(x) = \dfrac{x^2 - 4}{x + 1}.$

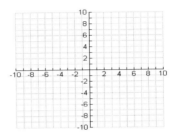

Is the velocity increasing? Why or why not?

Given the velocity $v(t) = t^2 - 4$ for t > 0, is the velocity increasing or decreasing?

Why or why not?

Is there sufficient information to determine whether or not the graph of *f*

Justify your answer.

Is there sufficient information to determine whether y has two distinct roots if $y = x^2 - 2x + b$ and $b < 0$? Justify your answer

Show that

Show the analysis that leads to your answer.

Show that the graph of $f(x) = \dfrac{(x+4)(x-1)}{(x-3)(x+2)}$ crosses its horizontal asymptote.

Show the analysis the leads to your answer.

Using correct units, explain the meaning of

Given v(t) in feet per second with maximum point A (2,10), explain the meaning of

A using correct units.

Write an equation for each horizontal asymptote of *f*.

Write an equation for each horizontal asymptote of $f(x) = \dfrac{2x - 2}{\sqrt{x^2 - 2x + 1}}$.

Write an equation for the line

Write an equation for the line joining the maximum and minimum point of f(x) if
$f(x) = x^3 + 4x^2 - 4x + 16.$

Template for Creating Pre-AP Questions Using Phrases from AP Statistics Exams

Describe a procedure to…

Explain the concept of …

Show the analysis that leads to your conclusion…

Explain how you would…

Use an appropriate graphical display to…

Describe your graph.

Explain how you found your answer…

What is the probability of …

Write a few sentences to …

Show that …

Justify your answer…

Show the work that leads to your answer…

Describe an appropriate model for the data…

Give a statistical justification to support your response…

Based on the graphical display…

Would it be reasonable to…

Describe an experiment that …

Predict …

Use the following set of data to …

Briefly describe a method you would use to …

Write an equation that models the following data… Explain why you chose this model.

What conclusions can be made from the graphical display?

What is the purpose of …

Middle Grades

Describe a procedure to

Describe a procedure to properly graph two sets of data.

Explain the concept of

Explain the concept of a probability sample space.

Show the analysis that leads to your conclusion

Explain how you would

Explain how to determine the number of bars in a bar graph.

Use an appropriate graphical display to... Describe your graph

Collect the heights of all the students in your class. Use an appropriate graph to display data. Describe the graph. (center, spread, shape)

Explain how you found your answer

Using data from the heights of all the students in your class, find the mean height, in inches. Explain how you found your answer.

What is the probability of

Given the students Alice, Bob, Carlos, Debra, and Eric, write the sample space of choosing two students. What is the probability that at least one girl is chosen?

Write a few sentences to

Write a few sentences to explain how you would determine outliers in a set of data.

Describe an appropriate model for the data

Draw a scatterplot for the following data. Does it appear that a line would be an appropriate model for the data? Explain.

Based on the graphical display

Based on the graphical display, would the mean or median be more appropriate measure of center?

Would it be reasonable to

The probability of rolling an even number on a fair die is 0.5. The probability of rolling a prime number is 0.5. Is it reasonable to conclude that the probability of rolling a prime or even number is 1? Explain.

Predict

Use the following scatterplot of husbands' heights to wives' heights to predict the height of a wife given the husband's height.

Use the following set of data to

What conclusions can be made from the graphical display?

What is the purpose of

What is the purpose of ordering the data when calculating the median?

Algebra 1

Describe a procedure to

Describe a procedure to properly graph two sets of data.

Explain the concept of

Explain the concept of the slope of a line.

Show the analysis that leads to your conclusion

Explain how you would

Explain how you would use a table of values to determine if a set of data can be modeled by a linear function.

Explain how you found your answer

What is the probability of

Write a few sentences to

Write a few sentences to explain how to determine the scale of the independent and dependent axes for a scatterplot.

Show that

For a symmetrical set of data, show that the median and mean are the same.

Justify your answer.

Show the work that leads to your answer

In a family of five children, what is the probability that there are at least 3 girls? Show the work that leads to your answer.

Describe an appropriate model for the data

Give a statistical justification to support your response

Given a reading passage, which of the vowels appears most often? Make a guess and give a statistical justification to support your response.

Based on the graphical display

Based on the graphical display what type of correlation do you observe?

Would it be reasonable to

Would it be reasonable to describe per capita income in a small town using mean, median, and/or mode?

Describe an experiment that

Describe an experiment that determines the relationship between the release point of a ball and the bounce height

Predict

Predict the value of stopping distance given a function in terms of car speed.

Use the following set of data to

Use the following set of data to determine the independent (explanatory), dependent (response) variables.

Briefly describe a method you would use to

Briefly describe a method you would use to obtain the equation that models height vs. arm span.

Write an equation that models the following data. Explain why you chose this model.

What conclusions can be made from the graphical display?

What is the purpose of

What is the purpose of a trend line?

Geometry

Describe a procedure to

Explain the concept of

Show the analysis that leads to your conclusion

Explain how you would

Given a circle of radius 2 inscribed in a square, what is the probability of randomly selecting a point in the region between the circle and the square?

Use an appropriate graphical display to... Describe your graph.

Use an appropriate graphical display to relate the diameter and circumference of various circular objects

Explain how you found your answer

On a certain bus route, a bus arrives every two minutes and waits two minutes for passengers to load and unload. Explain how you would determine the probability of randomly arriving while the bus is not there.

What is the probability of

The radius of the Earth is about 3960 miles. The area of the United Sates is about 3,679,240 square miles. What is the probability that a meteorite landing on Earth will land in the United States?

Write a few sentences to

Write a few sentences to explain how one should determine the probability of rolling a Pythagorean triple using 3 distinct die.

Show that

Justify your answer

Show the work that leads to your answer

The dimensions of a rectangle of area 72 are whole numbers. List the dimensions of all such rectangles. If two of these rectangles are chosen at random, what is the probability that each has a perimeter greater than 40. Show the work that leads to your answer.

Describe an appropriate model for the data

Give a statistical justification to support your response

Given a line, l, and a point, P, not on the line, many mathematicians would say the probability of randomly selecting a line through P parallel to the l is zero. Give a statistical justification to support this statement.

Based on the graphical display

Based on the graphical display relating diameter and circumference of various circular objects, draw a trend line (line of best fit).

Would it be reasonable to

Given a scatterplot of data of diameters of pizzas (6 inches to 18 inches) versus their price, would it be reasonable to predict the price of a 36-inch super-size pizza.

Describe an experiment that

Predict

Given a scatterplot of data of diameters of pizzas (6 inches to 18 inches) versus their price, predict the price of a 24-inch pizza.

Use the following set of data to

Given a set of data draw a scatterplot that relates the circumference to the diameter.

Briefly describe a method you would use to…

Write an equation that models the following data… Explain why you chose this model.

Given a rectangle with a set perimeter of 24, graph a scatterplot of the width of the rectangle versus its area. What conclusions can be made from this data?

What conclusions can be made from the graphical display

What is the purpose of

Algebra 2

Describe a procedure to

Describe a procedure to use the square root to linearize quadratic data.

Explain the concept of

Explain the concept of slope in terms of the context problem.

Show the analysis that leads to your conclusion

Explain how you would

Explain how you would use a permutation to find the number of ways to draw five cards from a deck of 52 cards.

Use an appropriate graphical display to... Describe your graph.

Explain how you found your answer

What is the probability of

What is the probability of rolling two die and getting a sum that is even.

Write a few sentences to

Write a few sentences to explain why the data is better modeled by an exponential function rather than a linear function.

Show that

Show that an exponential function can be used to model population growth.

Justify your answer

Show the work that leads to your answer

Describe an appropriate model for the data

Give a statistical justification to support your response

Based on the graphical display

Based on the graphical display of a cost function what is the value of the function at time 0 and explain its meaning in terms of the problem.

Would it be reasonable to

Given a function that represents population growth from 1900 to 1950, would it be reasonable to use that model to predict the population in 2010?

Predict

Given a function P(t) that represents population growth beginning in 1990, predict P(20). Explain the meaning of P(20) in the context of the problem.

Use the following set of data to

Briefly describe a method you would use to

Briefly describe a method you would use to find the equation of a line that models a set of data.

Write an equation that models the following data... Explain why you chose this model.

Write an equation that models the following data... Explain why you chose this model.

What conclusions can be made from the graphical display?

What is the purpose of

What is the purpose of matching data to graphs?

Pre-Calculus

Describe a procedure to

Explain the concept of

Show the analysis that leads to your conclusion

Explain how you would

Explain how you would transform a linearized best fit line of the form ln y = 2 + 4x.

Use an appropriate graphical display to… Describe your graph.

Explain how you found your answer

Given a logistic function representing the population of a deer on a small island, what is the upper limit of the herd size? Explain how you found your answer.

What is the probability of

The probability that a baseball team wins a game is 0.8. Using the binomial expansion, determine the probability that they will win exactly 3 of their next 5 games.

Write a few sentences to

Write a few sentences to explain the meaning of $_6C_3$.

Show that

Show the work that leads to your answer

Describe an appropriate model for the data

Given a set of data based on the phases of the moon over the last 3 months (percent of the moon's face showing), describe an appropriate function to model the data.

Give a statistical justification to support your response

Based on the graphical display

Would it be reasonable to

Given exponential data on cell phone sales from the years 1990 to 2000. Would it be reasonable to use this model to predict cell phone sales in 2010?

Describe an experiment that

Predict

As t goes to infinity on a given logistical model, predict the upper limit (carrying capacity) of the model.

Use the following set of data to

Given a set of data that is exponential in nature, describe a method to linearize the data.

Briefly describe a method you would use to

Briefly describe a method you would use to find the time when the point of diminishing return occurs.

Write an equation that models the following data… Explain why you chose this model.

Given data on cell phone sales over the last decade, determine an appropriate model for the data.

What conclusions can be made from the graphical display

What is the purpose of

A Vertical Team Activity: Enhancing Standard Questions

One of the most difficult tasks for Pre-AP teachers is changing their method of questioning. Questioning should be an integral part of every Pre-AP lesson and questioning techniques – whether for oral interaction, quizzing or testing – can be geared toward promoting higher-order thinking skills. While there will always be a place for simple recall and routine questions, in a Pre-AP classroom questions should take students to a different level. Questions should be posed that require students to apply what they have learned in a different context, that challenge them to justify their reasoning, or to demonstrate a creative approach to solving a problem.

On the next few pages, you will see examples of "standard" questions, similar to what most of us have in our textbooks and the types of questions many of us have asked for a long period of time. You will also see a corresponding "enhanced" version. These versions ask the student to take their knowledge to a whole new level. They often are asked using different representations (graphical, analytic, numerical, verbal, physical) or expect students to respond in that way. While teachers continue to ask students the "standard" questions, they should also try to integrate as many of the "enhanced" type into their daily instruction and assessments.

As a vertical team activity, teachers can bring standard questions from their textbooks or assessments and work with other teachers to create enhanced versions that they can then share with others who are teaching the same grade level or subject. As much as possible, these enhanced versions should be informed by what Pre-AP teachers have learned about assessment from examining and discussing AP examinations and their content. Teachers can even be asked to create questions in particular formats or over particular content. For example, each teacher could be asked to create three multiple choice and one multi-part free response question over the topic of linear functions. This activity can be repeated on numerous occasions. Just as students get better at answering challenging questions by having to do it often and over a long period of time, teachers get better at creating those questions and then by getting feedback on what they have written from other teachers.

	Standard	Enhanced
Middle Grades	Given the following metric and customary measurements, find the ratio of grams to ounces. Express your answer as a decimal. a) 453 grams 16 ounces b) 539 grams 19 ounces c) 227 grams 8 ounces	Using the data in the "standard" problem, graph grams to ounces. Write an equation that shows how many grams are in an ounce.
Algebra 1	Find the equation of the line passing through $(-1, 7)$ having a slope of $-\dfrac{2}{3}$.	Given the table of values a) Show that the function f is linear. b) Write the equation of the line passing through $(-1, 7)$ that is perpendicular to the linear function $f(t)$.

t	$f(t)$
-4	-2
-1	2.5
2	7
6	13

	Standard	**Enhanced**
Geometry	Find the area of a circle having a radius of 5 yards.	a) A circle is inscribed in a square as shown in the figure. Find the perimeter of the square, $P(r)$, in terms of the radius of the circle, r. 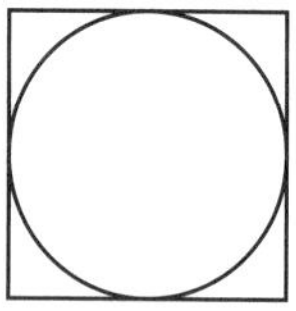 b) If the side of the square is k, find the area of the circle, $A(k)$, in terms of k.
Algebra 2	Find the equation of the axis of symmetry of $y = x^2 - 2x + 3$.	Find the equation of line k shown, if the slope of the line k is 4. 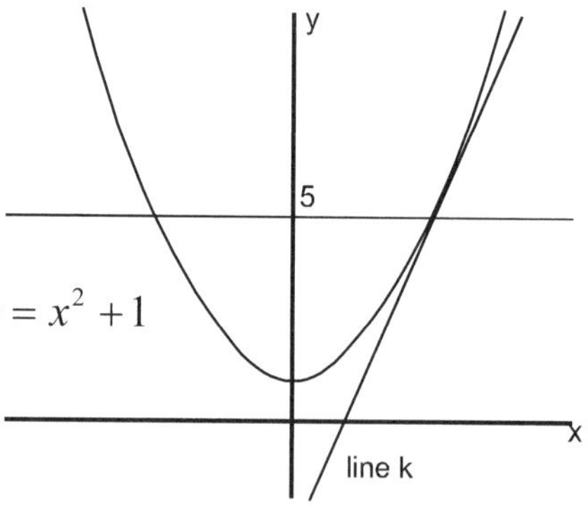 $y = x^2 + 1$ line k
Pre-Calculus	Find $g(-1)$ given $$g(t) = \begin{cases} \left\|\dfrac{t}{3}\right\| + 5, & -3 \le t \le 0 \\ 5 - t^2, & 0 < t \le 1 \\ \dfrac{2}{3}t + \dfrac{1}{2}, & t > 1 \end{cases}$$	Find k so that $g(t)$ is continuous $$g(t) = \begin{cases} \left\|\dfrac{t}{3}\right\| + 5, & -3 \le t \le 0 \\ 5 - t^2, & 0 < t \le 1 \\ \dfrac{2}{3}t + k, & t > 1 \end{cases}$$

Some Final Words from the Students

Since, ultimately, this guide is about helping students to be more successful in AP mathematics, we thought we should give the last word to them. We asked successful AP and Pre-AP students what advice they had to share with other Pre-AP students.

🖉 *Never think you're too smart to have to do the daily work. Being smart isn't all you need to get the A in any Pre-AP class—especially math. The more practice, the better.*

🖉 *I don't think my advice goes to just Pre-AP math students but rather to those who are thinking about moving up past their regular courses into Pre-AP or AP maths, or those who have made the change but aren't sure if it's worth it. I myself moved up from normal courses into the Pre-AP realm and I have done fine. I also would say for where I am going it is well worth it and just a wise choice.*

🖉 *Don't think anything you learn will go away. If you don't learn it early, it will come back to haunt you in later math classes.*

🖉 *Don't fall behind and bother not to learn something because it's difficult, because it doesn't get any easier as time passes and it will probably come back to haunt you as you see it again and are clueless once more.*

🖉 *Keep notes from classes from the past so you can look over them.*

🖉 *Don't just think about doing good on the next test so that you will make a good grade. Really strive to gain a deep understanding of the material because you will need to use it in AP math.*

🖉 *Students should always memorize their formulas and approach teachers or read their books to truly understand why/how each equation is used. If not truly understand, know when it needs to be used and where it is derived from (why the formula is the way it is.)*

🖉 *Learn to study, don't just do your homework. Specifically, use your homework assignments to study for quizzes, your quizzes for tests, and your tests for midterms and finals. You have to study!*

🖉 *Learn why you are doing things, don't just accept what you are being told; question everything so that you know you understand it.*

🖉 *Make sure you have a math class every year. Try to have science classes the semester you don't have math. This helps you remember everything better. If you don't understand something, ask. Everything builds on everything.*

🖉 *Don't just do enough to get by, be sure to develop good study habits.*

🖉 *Focus on learning and <u>understanding</u> more than just memorizing basic formulas. The understanding makes it all easier and it is then easier to learn new material which builds on previous knowledge.*

🖉 *Study things not for a test or quiz that happens to be given that week but study things for future knowledge. This concept is very important when taking AP tests that tests your knowledge over an entire year. Another thing that is important is to not just focus on getting the right answer but rather the process that accompanies the problem.*

🖉 *Be sure to read book along with taking notes. It's very helpful to read the book!!!*

🖉 *Don't forget anything.*

🖉 *To pay attention <u>all</u> the time. Do all your homework, it's good practice. Don't worry about failing a test, just learn from your mistakes. Don't ever give up, it will get easier at some point.*

🖉 *Memorize trig identities. Memorize the trig value of the major angles. Start using radians a lot. Get familiar with a graphing calculator.*

🖉 *If you don't understand something, ask in class. If you still don't get it, attend tutorials.*

🖉 *Practice a little bit every night.*

🖉 *Re-work the problems that you get wrong on your homework.*

🖉 *Do test corrections no matter what.*

🖉 *No matter how tired you are, how late it is, how smart you are--always do your homework. All of it! It all builds on top of itself. Do it all!!*

*"I advise my students to listen carefully the moment
they decide to take no more mathematics courses.*

They might be able to hear the sound of closing doors. "

James Caballero
CAIP Quarterly 2 (Fall, 1989)

*"It's time that we quit pretending
that all kids have equal access to AP classes
and get started in building a Pre-AP program
so strong and so supportive
that it gives students a real choice. "*

Evie Hiatt
Senior Director of Advanced Academic Services
Texas Education Agency

Write Your Notes and Ideas Here!